IN THE TRANSLATIONS OF

S. H. BUTCHER, ANDREW LANG,

WALTER LEAF AND ERNEST MYERS

Abridged

WITH SUMMARIES OF THE OMITTED BOOKS,

NOTES AND AN INTRODUCTION BY

MILDRED E. MARCETT

Illustrated with

REPRODUCTIONS OF GREEK VASE PAINTINGS

Barron's Educational Series, Inc.
Woodbury, New York

THE COMPACT HOMER

THE ILIAD

AND

THE ODYSSEY

*"All this the gods have fashioned, and have woven
the skein of death for men, that there might be
a song in the ears even of the folk of aftertime."*

Odyssey, Book VIII

All inquiries should be addressed to
Barron's Educational Series, Inc.
113 Crossways Park Drive
Woodbury, New York 11797

PRINTED IN THE UNITED STATES OF AMERICA

Library of Congress Catalog Card No. 62–18312

4 5 6 7 8 9 10 11 M 5 4 3 2

We wish to thank Vicomte de Roton (Notor) for permission to include some of the illustrations from his books *Homère L'Iliade, illustrée par la céramique grecque,* and *Homère L'Odyssey, illustrée par la céramique grecque,* Delmas, 1950.

CONTENTS

THE ILIAD

CONTENTS

THE ODYSSEY

CONTENTS

Introduction

THE *Odyssey* in translation is read in many schools and colleges; the *Iliad* in a smaller number, and both in a smaller number still. Whether the course in which Homer is studied is one devoted entirely to classical literature or whether he is part of a course covering a larger span—the literature of the West, or of the world, there is rarely time for both epics. If the *Odyssey* alone is read, because of the greater variety of its tone and subject matter, the reader has lost the beginning of the story on the doom-swept plains of Troy with its picture of heroic and human glory and grandeur and pain. And if the *Iliad* alone is studied, the reader is the poorer for the loss of some of the best stories in the world as the winds blow Odysseus across the "wine-dark sea."

Vivid and full of action as the poems are, there are still passages which are repetitious or which add little to the forward movement of the narrative or to the emotional effect. It has seemed possible by judicious cutting, sometimes of whole books and sometimes of sections of books, and by sufficient summary of the omitted portions to present the poems to the contemporary reader in a form which it is hoped does no disservice to Homer. And it is hoped that a substantial service may be performed for the reader—that, given a version of the two poems which is about half the length of the originals, he who runs may read something of both. He can be only the richer for the experience.

In any list of the greatest books of the Western world—whether a hundred or ten—the *Iliad* and the *Odyssey* of Homer would have a place. But these books do more than exist on a list; they are read by enormous numbers of people every year, by the so-called general audience, not just by the captive audience of students. The reasons are not far to seek.

The books are, first of all, rattling good stories. The reader watches characters of heroic mould performing deeds of a magnitude that sets them apart from the poor little half-men of modern fiction. Different their world may be from ours, but much of the time it seems extraordinarily real; the rest of the time it is fascinatingly fantastic. At any turn one may meet an enchantress or a monster, a god or a goddess very like a human being, or perhaps a human being not so very different from ourselves: there is little difference between the emotions of Thetis, the goddess mourning the approaching death of her son Achilles and Queen Hecabe mourning for the death of her son Hector; little difference between the grief of Andromache sending her husband off to battle and that of a woman today doing the same thing. But when a flaming hero falls, there is an empty place against the sky, and the world has changed.

To the Greeks, Homer was more than a storyteller. His poems contained solid history, and geography, and religion. He was in a sense the first of the dramatists, and the teacher of distinguished oratory. But particularly he was the teacher of the good life. Xenophon the Greek quotes Niceratus, the son of the general Nicias: "My father was anxious that I should be a good man, so he made me learn all the works of Homer; and I could recite you now by heart the whole of the *Iliad* and the *Odyssey*." And a little later he adds, "You know, I am sure, that Homer, the wisest of men, has written about practically everything pertaining to man." Plato called him the educator of Hellas, the best and most divine of poets. As clearly as the drama, he points out the great Greek lesson of *sophrosyne*, moderation, nothing in excess, and the results of *hubris* or arrogance. In the words of the

Roman Horace, "He tells us better than the philosophers . . . what is honorable and disgraceful, what is useful or vain."

The ancient Greeks had no doubt about the actuality of Homer or about his authorship of their two greatest poems. Not until the iconoclastic 19th century was there any doubt on the subject. But today everything about Homer is uncertain: where he lived (the old couplet says, "Seven Grecian cities fought for Homer dead/ Through which the living Homer begged his bread"); when he lived (the guesses range between the 12th and 7th centuries B.C.); whether he was blind, as one tradition says; whether he wrote both books, or one, or neither of them; whether he lived at all. A considerable body of contemporary scholarship, however, believes that Homer is the author of both poems, and that he lived in the 8th century B.C. in either Symrna or Chios, both in Asia Minor. For the average reader, further speculation is useless and unimportant, though he may derive amusement from the suggestion that the poems were written by King Solomon!

For a large part of the 19th century, Troy itself (also called Ilium), the scene of the *Iliad* and the remote background of the *Odyssey*, was as debatable as Homer. In the 70's and 80's of the last century, however, the excavations of Schliemann and Dorpfeld uncovered the real Troy. There proved to be nine Troys, one on top of the other, on the hill of Hissarlik not far from the Dardanelles, and the sixth from the bottom is generally thought to be Homer's Troy. There was a great outer wall with three main gates and two square towers for its defense. This city existed in the 13th and 12th centuries B.C. and was destroyed by fire. The traditional dates of the Trojan War being 1194–1184 B.C., it would seem that this is the scene of the *Iliad*.

Here for ten years the Achaeans (Homer does not use the term Greeks, but Achaeans, Danaans, or Argives) laid siege to the city for Helen's sake—or so the poet said. "The face that launched a thousand ships" cost unnumbered lives. A splendidly romantic conception indeed! Yet many solemn scholars conspire to spoil the story. There was a war, that they will agree to—but a war about trade rather than a war about a woman. The Trojans (whom Homer shows us as being very like the Greeks), sitting near the Dardanelles, controlled the trade routes to the rich Black Sea region; the Achaeans, who had assumed the sea power formerly wielded by Crete, found in the Trojans powerful opponents and were for a while stopped in their tracks. A great Eastern power and a great Western power and their allies joined in battle, and the West won.

After the war the Achaeans returned to their mainland homes. And there the bards, some of whom had perhaps accompanied the armies, made the lays which were the history of the war and which delighted men in the evening as they were sung to the accompaniment of the lyre in the great halls. As time passed, the stories grew more elaborate, no doubt; handed down by word of mouth as they were, details were inevitably changed. A war fought for trade routes is no fit subject for song, and so perhaps stern economics disappeared and Helen filled the poets' imaginations. (The suggestion has even been made that the stealing of Helen was a propaganda story made to inspire men to fight a war that would have been unpopular otherwise.) Into this body of material there were probably drawn fairy tales, myths, legends, and folk tales that had drifted around the world for long centuries. Material originally unconnected to the Troy story became part of it.

There came a day when the descendants of the Achaeans who had fought at Troy and their bards had to flee from their homeland before the iron weapons and iron spirit of the Dorian invaders (about 1100 B.C.); as the refugees found homes up and down the coast of Asia Minor, the lays of the bards returned to the scene that had given birth to so many of them. Several hundred years later, a poet named Homer, who knew the old lays well, chose some of them, arranged them according to carefully planned patterns, and produced the *Iliad* and the *Odyssey*. It was probably just about this time that writing came to the Western world; Homer may have written down his own poems, though it is equally possible that he may have dictated them or that they may have been written down not very many years after his death by his poetic heirs.

The *Iliad* means "the poem about Ilium," or Troy. The title is so general as to be misleading. It is not the whole life of the city that is the subject matter of the poem, but only fifty days in the last year of a ten-years' war. This period is filled by the wrath of Achilles, the chief Achaean hero—its beginning in his quarrel with Agamemnon, its duration as lesser Achaeans carry on the war without him and the Trojans make headway, its end after the death of Hector, the greatest of the Trojan heroes.

We are told little about the background of the war. We learn that it is being fought because Paris, son of King Priam of Troy, stole Helen from her husband, Menelaus, King of Sparta. Menelaus has come to regain his wife; with him are men from all the Greek lands, his brother Agamemnon, King of Argos, being leader because he has brought the most men.

There are many legends about the war that Homer does not use. One, which is referred to in a sentence or so, is the story of the golden apple which the goddess of Discord throws into the midst of the wedding feast of Peleus and Thetis; inscribed "For the Fairest," it is striven for by Hera, Zeus' queen, by Athene, goddess of Wisdom, and Aphrodite, goddess of Beauty and Love. Paris, chosen as judge, gives the apple to Aphrodite when she promises him the most beautiful woman in the world as his wife. (This story serves to explain, among other things, why Hera and Athene fight so strongly against the Trojans.) There is nothing in Homer of the sad story of Iphigenia, Agamemnon's daughter, who must be sacrificed before the Achaean ships can sail. There is nothing here of the invulnerability of Achilles. (If he were invulnerable, why would he need all the beautiful armor which Homer describes so carefully?) We are not told how the war ends nor how Achilles dies, though we know through prophecies that both Achilles and the Trojans are doomed.

The *Iliad* ends before Troy does, and it is in the *Odyssey* that we find the details of Achilles' funeral, though not his death, and the story of the Wooden Horse. Other poets after Homer wrote the poems he did not write and rounded out what is called the Trojan Cycle. Whether the legends he did not use developed after Homer's day, whether they existed in his day and he did not know them, or whether he knew them and chose not to use them, it is impossible to say. All we can say is that the wrath of Achilles has given the *Iliad* its unity, and that unity gives evidence of a carefully shaping hand.

The *Odyssey*, usually considered somewhat later in date than the *Iliad*, is "the poem about Odysseus" (called Ulysses by the Romans), one of the greatest heroes of the war. It deals with his adventures in returning home from the war and the vengeance he took on his wife Penelope's suitors. The events described in the tale cover the ten years after the close of the war, but the strict action of the poem covers only six weeks of the tenth year.

The form of the *Odyssey* is more complex than that of the *Iliad*. The story begins *in medias res*, in the middle of things, with Odysseus on the island of the nymph Calypso, where he has been held for seven years. He leaves with the help of the gods, finally arrives at the court of Alcinous, where he tells of his adventures since leaving Troy, and then makes his way back to his home in Ithaca and the end of the story. We know of Odysseus' later years and death only through the prophecy of Tiresias, whom he meets in Hades. In Homer's version his death is to come quietly from the sea, and not with the violence portrayed by later poets. Like counterpoint runs the story of Agamemnon, the hero who returns to the unfaithful wife in contrast to Odysseus, the hero who returns to a faithful one.

The return of the warrior must have been a favorite subject for the bards; the *Odyssey* gives us, besides the return of Odysseus and of Agamemnon, the return of Nestor and of Menelaus. The most fantastic part of Odysseus' wanderings, the adventures with enchantresses, sirens, giants, and the like, may well have been originally sailors' tales, old even in the heyday of Crete. Perhaps the giant Polyphemus once was a cliff dimly seen through the sea mist; perhaps the strange and strong currents between Italy and Sicily are responsible for those monsters, Scylla and Charybdis. The skill with which these varied materials have been assembled and organized points once more to a master's carefully shaping hand.

It must be re-emphasized, of course, that a considerable amount of the phraseology of the poems as well as the subject matter is derived from the centuries of bards who told one version or another of the old heroic tales. The hexameter rhythm was undoubtedly traditional; so certainly were the epithets, the repetition of which sounds so oddly uninventive to the modern reader. Achilles is, among other things, "fleet-footed" or "spear-famed;" Hera, "white-armed" or "ox-eyed;" Menelaus, "of the loud war-cry" or "of the fair hair." The epithets vary only because of the demands of the poetic line, not because variation is deemed desirable.

One of the glories of the poems, to the reader who will take the time to appreciate them, is the epic similes (prolonged similes to fit the epic, which is a prolonged poem). They are doubly interesting because they can be traced from Homer to Virgil to Dante to Milton. The assembly of the Achaeans meets: "Even as when the tribes of thronging bees issue from some hollow rock, ever in fresh procession, and fly clustering among the flowers of spring, and some on this hand and some on that fly thick; even so from ships and huts before the low beach marched forth their many tribes by companies to the place of assembly." The world of the warriors and the everyday world are brought together here as in a hundred other similes. The plain of Troy runs red with blood; gods and heroes lock in combat; Odysseus sails to the very gates of Hades. But life goes on normally somewhere in the world—the wind blows through a deep cornfield, the waves beat on the jutting rocks, the goatherds divide their sheep in the pasture, a man shapes a timber with an ax. Always the similes show us this normal world which ordinary men and women know and which affords a background for the great figures against the skyline. The reader will gain who savors the similes and does not hasten on through them to the story.

Inseparable from the stories is, of course, the picture of the life of the time (tinged, it is generally thought, with something of Homer's own day). It is a day when fighting seems to be a man's chief trade, when to be a hero is to be a member of a profession; a day when princes and heroes count for everything and when the footsoldier and the peasant are scarcely heard of, though the picture which Homer gives of the swineherd Eumaeus in the *Odyssey* is a refreshing exception to the general rule. It is a day when life is violent and dangerous, when the most sheltered princeling may find himself a slave overnight as a result of a raid. The only law is that of the strong hand. Yet the assemblies of the Achaeans in the *Iliad* and of the suitors and people of Ithaca in the *Odyssey* give us some foreshadowing of Greek democracy. There is beauty and graciousness in the homes of Nestor, Menelaus, and Alcinous which contrasts strongly with the violence of the poems. And if the openhanded generosity of princes is one way of acquiring fame, still there are many worse ways.

Sufficient has not yet been said about the presence of the gods in the poems. The writings of Homer became the Greek Bible; in his poems he gives us gods in the image and likeness of men, of the aristocrats of his day, who took pride in tracing their pedigrees back to the gods. Zeus preserves a degree of majesty with his undoubted power, but even he is not superior to Fate. The others, and even Zeus himself at times, mix in the battles before Troy; they can be wounded; they weep and wail.

They share too many of the weaknesses of human beings; they play favorites; they are capricious, cruel, jealous; they misuse their power. They may be good friends on occasion, as Odysseus and Telemachus know, but it will perhaps help us to understand their role in the poems a little better if we reflect that Athene, the goddess of Wisdom, gives help to a wise man and to the son who has inherited his wisdom; she does not waste her help on the stupid. By and large, the deities care little what human beings do so long as the smoke and savor of sacrifice rise to Mt. Olympus.

In the poems appear most of the twelve Olympians: Zeus, King of the gods and son of Cronos; Hera, his queen; Athene, goddess of Wisdom, who sprang full-armed from the head of her father Zeus; Ares, god of War and Hephaestus, the master smith, sons of Zeus and Hera; Apollo, god of Prophecy, of Poetry, of Medicine, and of Music (later, of the Sun) and his sister Artemis, goddess of the Chase, protectress of wild animals, children of Zeus and Leto; Aphrodite, goddess of Love, daughter of Zeus and Dione; Hermes, the ambassador of the gods, the son of Zeus and Maia; finally, Poseidon, like Zeus his brother, the son of Chronos and Rhea; the god of the sea, which he received as his domain when he, Zeus, and Hades divided the world among them. (Hades took the underworld and Zeus the sky; the three were to have equal rights on earth.) Demeter, goddess of the Corn, and Hades play no part in the poems. Important roles are played, however, by numerous lesser divinities, for to the Greeks, deity was everywhere. So vividly did Homer portray the gods that the pictures which he made were those which filled the mind of the so-called common man until the coming of Christianity, long after the more thoughtful Greeks had either turned the gods into symbols or spiritualized them.

Here is more than sufficient introduction. Turn to the poems. You will not, in the English, hear the roll of the Greek hexameters nor the music of Homer's voice, but you will hear the clang of spear on armor, and smell the salt of the "wine-dark sea;" you will feel the pathos of the brief lives of men and learn anew how courage crowns their little day with grandeur.

New York University   MILDRED E. MARCETT
February 1963

The Translation

No GREAT BOOK can ever be "perfectly" translated. The translation is always colored by the period in which it is done, and by the point of view of the translator. The number of translations of the *Iliad* and the *Odyssey* seems almost endless; even as this is being written, two new translations of the *Odyssey* are being reviewed in the papers. The two poems of Homer have been translated into almost every type of prose and almost every meter of poetry. When all is said, probably the prose versions come nearest to the original poem, since nothing of the meaning has to be sacrificed to the stern requirements of rhythm. The music of Homer must be forever lost to the reader who knows no Greek.

The translations used in this edition, that of the *Iliad* by Lang, Leaf, and Myers, that of the *Odyssey* by Butcher and Lang, were made at the end of the last century. They are generally regarded as highly accurate—perhaps the most accurate of any translations. The authors chose to use a somewhat antiquated prose, such as is used in the greatest translation of the Bible, the King James, feeling that Biblical English is as nearly analogous to the epic Greek as anything English has to offer. Homer himself used a somewhat artificial and archaic language.

When occasionally it has seemed that the meaning of an archaism would not be clear to a present-day reader, the editor has assumed the privilege of changing it without noting the fact. The editor is also responsible for a very occasional change in the paragraphing and for seeing that the usage of the two books is the same as regards quotation marks and the spelling of proper names.

THE ILIAD
OF HOMER

TRANSLATED BY

ANDREW LANG, WALTER LEAF AND ERNEST MYERS

I

Achilles and Agamemnon Quarrel

Sing, goddess, the wrath of Achilles Peleus' son, the ruinous wrath that brought on the Achaeans woes innumerable, and hurled down into Hades many strong souls of heroes, and gave their bodies to be a prey to dogs and all winged fowls; and so the counsel of Zeus wrought out its accomplishment from the day when first strife parted Atreides [1] king of men and noble Achilles.

---

[1] *Atreides* means "son of Atreus," a term used for the sake of variety. It is often used for Agamemnon in the poem, less frequently for Menelaus.

Who then among the gods set the twain at strife and variance? Even Apollo the son of Leto and of Zeus; for he in anger at the king sent a sore plague upon the host, that the folk began to perish, because Atreides had done dishonour to Chryses the priest. For he had come to the Achaeans' fleet ships to win his daughter's freedom, and brought a ransom beyond telling; and bare in his hands the fillet of Apollo the Far-darter upon a golden staff; and made his prayer unto all the Achaeans, and most of all to the two sons of Atreus, orderers of the host: "Ye sons of Atreus and all ye well-greaved Achaeans, now may the gods that dwell in the mansions of Olympus grant you to lay waste the city of Priam, and to fare happily homeward; only set ye my dear child free, and accept the ransom in reverence to the son of Zeus, far-darting Apollo."

Then all the other Achaeans cried assent, to reverence the priest and accept his goodly ransom; yet the thing pleased not the heart of Agamemnon son of Atreus, but he roughly sent him away, and laid stern charge upon him, saying: "Let me not find thee, old man, amid the hollow ships, whether tarrying now or returning again hereafter, lest the staff and fillet of the god avail thee naught. And her will I not set free; nay, ere that shall old age come on her in our house, in Argos, far from her native land, where she shall ply the loom and serve my couch. But depart, provoke me not, that thou mayest the rather go in peace."

So said he, and the old man was afraid and obeyed his word, and fared silently along the shore of the loud-sounding sea. Then went that aged man apart and prayed aloud to king Apollo, whom Leto of the fair locks bare: "Hear me, god of the silver bow, that standest over Chryse and holy Cilla, and rulest Tenedos [2] with might, O Smintheus! [3] If ever I built a temple gracious in thine eyes, or if ever I burnt to thee fat flesh of thighs of bulls or goats, fulfil thou this my desire; let the Danaans pay by thine arrows for my tears."

---

[2] All places in the region of Troy where Apollo was worshipped.

[3] So called possibly from *sminthos*, a mouse, as being the god who protected farmers by killing mice.

So spake he in prayer, and Phoebus Apollo [4] heard him, and came down from the peaks of Olympus wroth at heart, bearing on his shoulders his bow and covered quiver. And the arrows clanged upon his shoulders in his wrath, as the god moved; and he descended like to night. Then he sate him aloof from the ships, and let an arrow fly; and there was heard a dread clanging of the silver bow. First did he assail the mules and fleet dogs, but afterward, aiming at the men his piercing dart, he smote; and the pyres of the dead burnt continually in multitude.

Now for nine days ranged the god's shafts through the host; but on the tenth Achilles summoned the folk to assembly, for in his mind did goddess Hera of the white arms put the thought, because she had pity on the Danaans when she beheld them perishing. Now when they had gathered and were met in assembly, then Achilles fleet of foot stood up and spake among them: "Son of Atreus, now deem I that we shall be forced to return home again—if verily we escape death—if war at once and pestilence must indeed ravage the Achaeans. But come, let us now inquire of some soothsayer or priest, yea, or an interpreter of dreams—seeing that a dream too is of Zeus—who shall say wherefore Phoebus Apollo is so wroth, whether he blame us by reason of broken vow or some failure in our rites, if perchance he would accept the savour of lambs or unblemished goats, and so would take away the pestilence from us."

So spake he and sate him down; and there stood up before them Calchas son of Thestor, most excellent far of augurs, who knew both things that were and that would be and that had been before, and guided the ships of the Achaeans to Ilium by his soothsaying that Phoebus Apollo bestowed on him. He of good intent made harangue and spake amid them: "Achilles, dear to Zeus, thou biddest me tell the wrath of Apollo, the king that smiteth afar. Therefore will I speak; but do thou make covenant with me, and swear that verily with all thy heart thou wilt aid me both by word and deed.

---

[4] *Phoebus* means "the bright;" Apollo was god of Light.

For of a truth I deem that I shall provoke one that ruleth all the Argives with might, and whom the Achaeans obey. For a king is more of might when he is wroth with a meaner man; even though for the one day he swallow his anger, yet doth he still keep his displeasure thereafter in his breast till he accomplish it. Consider thou, then, if thou wilt hold me safe."

And Achilles fleet of foot made answer and spake to him: "Yea, be of good courage, speak whatever soothsaying thou knowest; for by Apollo dear to Zeus, him by whose worship thou, O Calchas, declarest thy soothsaying to the Danaans, no man while I live and behold light on earth shall lay violent hands upon thee amid the hollow ships; no man of all the Danaans, not even if thou mean Agamemnon, that now avoweth him to be greatest far of the Achaeans."

Then was the noble seer of good courage, and spake: "Neither by reason of a broken vow is he displeased, nor for any lack of hecatomb,[5] but for his priest's sake to whom Agamemnon did despite, and set not his daughter free and accepted not the ransom; therefore hath Apollo the Far-darter brought woes upon us, yea, and will bring. Nor will he ever remove the loathly pestilence from the Danaans till we have given the bright-eyed damsel to her father, unbought, unransomed, and carried a holy hecatomb to Chryse; then might we propitiate him to our prayer."

So said he and sate him down, and there stood up before them the hero son of Atreus, wide-ruling Agamemnon, sore displeased; and his dark heart within him was greatly filled with anger, and his eyes were like flashing fire. To Calchas first spake he with look of ill: "Thou seer of evil, never yet hast thou told me the thing that is pleasant. Evil is ever the joy of thy heart to prophesy, but never yet didst thou tell any good matter nor bring it to pass. And now with soothsaying thou makest harangue among the Danaans, how that the Far-darter bringeth woes upon them because, forsooth, I would not take the goodly ransom of the damsel

---

[5] A great public sacrifice, originally of a hundred oxen or cattle.

Chryseis, seeing I am the rather fain to keep her own self within mine house. Yea, I prefer her before Clytaemnestra my wedded wife; in no wise is she lacking beside her, neither in favour nor stature, nor wit nor skill. Yet for all this will I give her back, if that is better; rather would I see my folk whole than perishing. Only make ye me ready a prize of honour forthwith, lest I alone of all the Argives be disprized, which thing beseemeth not; for ye all behold how my prize is departing from me."

To him then made answer fleet-footed goodly Achilles: "Most noble son of Atreus, of all men most covetous, how shall the great-hearted Achaeans give thee a meed of honour? We know naught of any wealth of common store, but what spoil soe'er we took from captured cities hath been apportioned, and it beseemeth not to beg all this back from the folk. Nay, yield thou the damsel to the god, and we Achaeans will pay thee back threefold and fourfold, if ever Zeus grant us to sack some well-walled town of Troyland."

To him lord Agamemnon made answer and said: "Not in this wise, strong as thou art, O godlike Achilles, beguile thou me by craft; thou shalt not outwit me nor persuade me. Dost thou wish, that thou mayest keep thy meed of honour, for me to sit idle in bereavement, and biddest me give her back? Nay, if the great-hearted Achaeans will give me a meed suited to my mind, that the recompense be equal—but if they give it not, then I myself will go and take a meed of honour, thine be it or Aias', or Odysseus' that I will take unto me; wroth shall he be to whomsoever I come. But for this we will take counsel hereafter; now let us launch a black ship on the great sea, and gather picked oarsmen, and set therein a hecatomb, and embark Chryseis of the fair cheeks herself, and let one of our counsellors be captain, Aias or Idomeneus or goodly Odysseus, or thou, Achilles, son of Peleus, most redoubtable of men, to do sacrifice for us and propitiate the Far-darter."

Then Achilles fleet of foot looked at him scowling and said: "Ah me, thou clothed in shamelessness, thou of crafty mind, how shall any Achaean hearken to thy bidding with

Briseis of the Fair Cheeks.

PAINTING FROM AN AMPHORA OF EUXITHEUS FOUND AT VULCI.
(BRITISH MUSEUM)

all his heart, be it to go a journey or to fight the foe amain? Not by reason of the Trojan spearmen came I hither to fight, for they have not wronged me; never did they harry mine oxen nor my horses, nor ever waste my harvest in deep-soiled Phthia, the nurse of men; seeing there lieth between us long space of shadowy mountains and sounding sea; but thee, thou shameless one, followed we hither to make thee glad, by earning recompense at the Trojans' hands for Menelaus and for thee, thou dog-face! All this thou reckonest not nor takest thought thereof; and now thou threatenest thyself to take my meed of honour, wherefor I travailed much, and the sons of the Achaeans gave it me. Never win I meed like unto thine, when the Achaeans sack any populous citadel of Trojan men; my hands bear the brunt of furious war, but when the apportioning cometh then is thy meed far ampler, and I betake me to the ships with some small thing, yet mine own, when I have fought to weariness. Now will I depart to Phthia, seeing it is far better to return home on my beaked ships; nor am I minded here in dishonour to draw thee thy fill of riches and wealth."

Then Agamemnon king of men made answer to him: "Yea, flee, if thy soul be set thereon. It is not I that beseech thee to tarry for my sake; I have others by my side that shall do me honour, and above all Zeus, lord of counsel. Most hateful art thou to me of all kings, fosterlings of Zeus; thou ever lovest strife and wars and fightings. Though thou be very strong, yet that I ween is a gift to thee of God. Go home with thy ships and company and lord it among thy Myrmidons; I reck not aught of thee nor care I for thine indignation; and this shall be my threat to thee: seeing Phoebus Apollo bereaveth me of Chryseis, her with my ship and my company will I send back; and mine own self will I go to thy hut and take Briseis of the fair cheeks, even that thy meed of honour, that thou mayest well know how far greater I am than thou, and so shall another hereafter abhor to match his words with mine and rival me to my face."

So said he, and grief came upon Peleus' son, and his heart within his shaggy breast was divided in counsel, whether to

draw his keen blade from his thigh and set the company aside
and so slay Atreides, or to assuage his anger and curb his
soul. While yet he doubted thereof in heart and soul, and
was drawing his great sword from his sheath, Athene came
to him from heaven, sent forth of the white-armed goddess
Hera, whose heart loved both alike and had care for them.
She stood behind Peleus' son and caught him by his golden
hair, to him only visible, and of the rest no man beheld her.
Then Achilles marvelled, and turned him about, and straightway knew Pallas Athene; and terribly shone her eyes. He
spake to her winged words, and said: "Why now art thou
come hither, thou daughter of aegis-bearing [6] Zeus? Is it to
behold the insolence of Agamemnon son of Atreus? Yea, I
will tell thee that I deem shall even be brought to pass: by
his own haughtinesses shall he soon lose his life."

Then the bright-eyed goddess Athene spake to him again:
"I came from heaven to stay thine anger, if perchance thou
wilt hearken to me, being sent forth of the white-armed
goddess Hera, that loveth you twain alike and careth for
you. Go to now, cease from strife, and let not thine hand
draw the sword; yet with words indeed revile him, even as
it shall come to pass. For thus will I say to thee, and so it
shall be fulfilled; hereafter shall goodly gifts come to thee,
yea in threefold measure, by reason of this despite; hold thou
thine hand, and hearken to us."

And Achilles fleet of foot made answer and said to her:
"Goddess, needs must a man observe the saying of you twain,
even though he be very wroth at heart; for so is the better
way. Whosoever obeyeth the gods, to him they gladly
hearken."

He said, and stayed his heavy hand on the silver hilt, and
thrust the great sword back into the sheath, and was not disobedient to the saying of Athene; and she forthwith was departed to Olympus, to the other gods in the palace of aegis-
bearing Zeus.

---

[6] The *aegis* is a fringed goatskin or shield; when shaken, it is a source
of terror to the enemies of Zeus.

Then Peleus' son spake again with bitter words to Atreus' son, and in no wise ceased from anger: "Thou heavy with wine, thou with face of dog and heart of deer, never didst thou take courage to arm for battle among thy folk or to lay ambush with the princes of the Achaeans; that to thee were even as death. Far better availeth it, forsooth, to seize for thyself the meed of honour of every man through the wide host of the Achaeans that speaketh contrary to thee. Folk-devouring king! seeing thou rulest men of naught; else were this despite, thou son of Atreus, thy last. But I will speak my word to thee, and swear a mighty oath therewith: verily by this staff that shall no more put forth leaf or twig, seeing it hath for ever left its trunk among the hills, neither shall it grow green again, because the axe hath stripped it of leaves and bark; and now the sons of the Achaeans that exercise judgment bear it in their hands, even they that by Zeus' command watch over the traditions—so shall this be a mighty oath in thine eyes—verily shall longing for Achilles come hereafter upon the sons of the Achaeans one and all; and then wilt thou in no wise avail to save them, for all thy grief, when multitudes fall dying before manslaying Hector. Then shalt thou tear thy heart within thee for anger that thou didst in no wise honour the best of the Achaeans."

So said Peleides [7] and dashed to earth the staff studded with golden nails, and himself sat down; and over against him Atreides waxed furious. Then in their midst rose up Nestor, pleasant of speech, the clear-voiced orator of the Pylians, he from whose tongue flowed discourse sweeter than honey. Two generations of mortal men already had he seen perish, that had been of old time born and nurtured with him in goodly Pylos, and he was king among the third. He of good intent made harangue to them and said: "Alas, of a truth sore lamentation cometh upon the land of Achaea. Verily Priam would be glad and Priam's sons, and all the Trojans would have great joy of heart, were they to hear all this tale of strife between you twain that are chiefest of the

---

[7] *Peleides* means "son of Peleus."

Danaans in counsel and chiefest in battle. Nay, hearken to me; ye are younger both than I. Of old days held I converse with better men even than you, and never did they make light of me. Yea, I never beheld such warriors, nor shall behold, as were Peirithous and Dryas shepherd of the host and Caeneus and Exadius and godlike Polyphemus and Theseus son of Aigeus, like to the immortals. Mightiest of growth were they of all men upon the earth; mightiest they were and with the mightiest fought they, even the wild tribes of the mountain caves, and destroyed them utterly. And with these held I converse, being come from Pylos, from a distant land afar; for of themselves they summoned me. So I played my part in fight; and with them could none of men that are now on earth do battle. And they laid to heart my counsels and hearkened to my voice. Even so hearken ye also, for better is it to hearken. Neither do thou, though thou art very great, seize from him his damsel, but leave her as she was given at the first by the sons of the Achaeans to be a meed of honour; nor do thou, son of Peleus, think to strive with a king, might against might; seeing that no common honour pertaineth to a sceptred king to whom Zeus apportioneth glory. Though thou be strong, and a goddess mother bare thee, yet his is the greater place, for he is king over more. And thou, Atreides, abate thy fury; nay, it is even I that beseech thee to let go thine anger with Achilles, who is made unto all the Achaeans a mighty bulwark of evil war."

Then lord Agamemnon answered and said: "Yea verily, old man, all this thou sayest is according unto right. But this fellow would be above all others, he would be lord of all and king among all and captain to all; wherein I deem none will hearken to him. Though the immortal gods made him a spearman, do they therefore put revilings in his mouth for him to utter?"

Then goodly Achilles brake in on him and answered: "Yea, for I should be called coward and man of naught, if I yield to thee in every matter, howsoe'er thou bid. To others give now thine orders, not to me play master; for thee I deem that I shall no more obey. This, moreover, will I say to thee, and do thou lay it to thy heart. Know that not by violence will I strive for the damsel's sake, neither with thee nor any other; ye gave and ye have taken away. But of all else that is mine beside my fleet black ship, thereof shalt thou not take anything or bear it away against my will. Yea, go to now, make trial, that all these may see; forthwith thy dark blood shall gush about my spear."

Now when the twain had thus finished the battle of violent words, they stood up and dissolved the assembly beside the Achaean ships. Peleides went his way to his huts and trim ships with Patroclus and his company; and Atreides launched a fleet ship on the sea, and picked twenty oarsmen therefor, and embarked the hecatomb for the god, and brought Chryseis of the fair cheeks and set her therein; and Odysseus of many devices went to be their captain.

So these embarked and sailed over the wet ways; and Atreides bade the folk purify themselves. So they purified themselves, and cast the defilements into the sea and did sacrifice to Apollo, even unblemished hecatombs of bulls and goats, along the shore of the unharvested sea; and the sweet savour arose to heaven eddying amid the smoke.

Thus were they busied throughout the host; but Agamemnon ceased not from the strife wherewith he threatened Achilles at the first; he spake to Talthybius and Eurybates that were his heralds and nimble squires: "Go ye to the tent of Achilles Peleus' son, and take Briseis of the fair cheeks by the hand and lead her hither; and if he give her not, then will I myself go, and more with me, and seize her; and that will be yet more grievous for him."

So saying he sent them forth, and laid stern charge upon them. Unwillingly went they along the beach of the unvintaged sea, and came to the huts and ships of the Myrmidons. Him found they sitting beside his hut and black ship; nor when he saw them was Achilles glad. So they in dread and reverence of the king stood, and spake to him no word, nor questioned him. But he knew in his heart, and spake to them: "All hail, ye heralds, messengers of Zeus and men, come near; ye are not guilty in my sight, but Agamemnon that sent you for the sake of the damsel Briseis. Go now, heaven-sprung Patroclus, bring forth the damsel, and give them her to lead away. Moreover, let the twain themselves be my witness before the face of the blessed gods and mortal men, yea and of him, that king untoward, against the day when there cometh need of me hereafter to save them all from shameful wreck. Of a truth he raveth with baleful mind, and hath not knowledge to look before and after, that so his Achaeans might battle in safety beside their ships."

So said he, and Patroclus hearkened to his dear comrade, and led forth from the hut Briseis of the fair cheeks, and gave them her to lead away. So these twain took their way back along the Achaeans' ships, and with them went the woman all unwilling. Then Achilles wept anon, and sat him down apart, aloof from his comrades on the beach of the grey sea, gazing across the boundless main; he stretched forth his hands and prayed instantly to his dear mother: [8] "Mother, seeing thou didst of a truth bear me to so brief span of life, honour at the least ought the Olympian to have granted me, even Zeus that thundereth on high; but now doth he not honour me, no, not one whit. Verily Atreus' son, wide-ruling Agamemnon, hath done me dishonour; for he hath taken away my meed of honour and keepeth her of his own violent deed."

So spake he weeping, and his lady mother heard him as she sate in the sea-depths beside her aged sire. With speed arose she from the grey sea, like a mist, and sate her before the face of her weeping son, and stroked him with her hand, and spake and called on his name: "My child, why weepest thou? What sorrow hath entered into thy heart? Speak it forth, hide it not in thy mind, that both may know it."

Then with heavy moan Achilles fleet of foot spake to her: "Thou knowest it; why should I tell this to thee that knowest all! We had fared to Thebe, the holy city of Eëtion, and laid

---

[8] The goddess Thetis, one of the daughters of Nereus, the "Old Man of the Sea."

it waste and carried hither all the spoils. So the sons of the Achaeans divided among them all aright; and for Atreides they set apart Chryseis of the fair cheeks. But Chryses, priest of Apollo the Far-darter, came unto the fleet ships of the mail-clad Achaeans to win his daughter's freedom, and brought a ransom beyond telling, and bare in his hands the fillet of Apollo the Far-darter upon a golden staff, and made his prayer unto all the Achaeans, and most of all to the two sons of Atreus, orderers of the host. Then all the other Achaeans cried assent, to reverence the priest and accept his goodly ransom; yet the thing pleased not the heart of Agamemnon son of Atreus, but he roughly sent him away and laid stern charge upon him. So the old man went back in anger; and Apollo heard his prayers, seeing he loved him greatly, and he aimed against the Argives his deadly darts. So the people began to perish in multitudes, and the god's shafts ranged everywhither throughout the wide host of the Achaeans. Then of full knowledge the seer declared to us the oracle of the Far-darter. Forthwith I first bade propitiate the god; but wrath gat hold upon Atreus' son thereat, and anon he stood up and spake a threatening word, that hath now been accomplished. Her the glancing-eyed Achaeans are bringing on their fleet ship to Chryse, and bear with them offerings to the king; and the other but now the heralds went and took from my hut, even the daughter of Briseus, whom the sons of the Achaeans gave me.

"Thou therefore, if indeed thou canst, guard thine own son; betake thee to Olympus and beseech Zeus by any deed or word whereby thou ever didst make glad his heart. For oft have I heard thee proclaiming in my father's halls and telling that thou alone amid the immortals didst save Zeus, lord of the storm-cloud, from shameful wreck, when all the other Olympians would have bound him, even Hera and Poseidon and Pallas Athene.[9] Then didst thou, O goddess,

---

[9] *Pallas* is part of the title of the goddess Pallas Athene. The meaning of the name is unknown. It is perhaps the name of a goddess of some other religion with whom the Greeks identified Athene.

enter in and loose him from his bonds, having with speed summoned to high Olympus him of the hundred arms whom gods call Briareus, but all men call Aegaeon; for he is mightier even than his father—so he sate him by the side of Zeus the son of Cronos rejoicing in his triumph, and the blessed gods feared him withal and bound not Zeus. This bring thou to his remembrance and sit by him and clasp his knees, if perchance he will give succour to the Trojans; and for the Achaeans, hem them among their ships' sterns about the bay, given over to slaughter; that they may make trial of their king, and that even Atreides, wide-ruling Agamemnon, may perceive his blindness, in that he honoured not at all the best of the Achaeans."

Then Thetis weeping made answer to him: "Ah me, my child, why reared I thee, cursed in my motherhood? Would thou hadst been left tearless and griefless amid the ships, seeing thy lot is very brief and endureth no long while; but now art thou made short-lived alike and lamentable beyond all men; in an evil hour I bare thee in our halls. But I will go myself to snow-clad Olympus to tell this thy saying to Zeus, whose joy is in the thunder, if perchance he may hearken to me. But tarry thou now amid thy fleet-faring ships, and continue wroth with the Achaeans, and refrain utterly from battle: for Zeus went yesterday to Oceanus, unto the noble Ethiopians for a feast, and all the gods followed with him; but on the twelfth day will he return to Olympus, and then will I fare to Zeus' palace of the bronze threshold, and will kneel to him and think to win him."

So saying she went her way and left him there, vexed in spirit for the fair-girdled woman's sake, whom they had taken perforce despite his will: and meanwhile Odysseus came to Chryse with the holy hecatomb. When they were now entered within the deep haven, they furled their sails and laid them in the black ship, and lowered the mast by the forestays and brought it to the crutch with speed, and rowed her with oars to the anchorage. Then they cast out the mooring stones and made fast the hawsers, and so themselves went forth on to the sea-beach, and forth they brought the hecatomb for the Far-darter Apollo, and forth came Chryseis withal from the seafaring ship. Then Odysseus of many counsels brought her to the altar and gave her into her father's arms, and spake unto him: "Chryses, Agamemnon king of men sent me hither to bring thee thy daughter, and to offer to Phoebus a holy hecatomb on the Danaans' behalf, wherewith to propitiate the king that hath now brought sorrow and lamentation on the Argives."

So saying he gave her to her father's arms, and he gladly took his dear child; and anon they set in order for the god the holy hecatomb about his well-builded altar; next washed they their hands and took up the barley meal. Then Chryses lifted up his hands and prayed aloud for them: "Hearken to me, god of the silver bow that standest over Chryse and holy Cilla, and rulest Tenedos with might; even as erst thou heardest my prayer, and didst me honour, and mightily afflictedst the people of the Achaeans, even so now fulfil me this my desire; remove thou from the Danaans forthwith the loathly pestilence."

Sacrifice of Unblemished Hecatombs.

PAINTING FROM AN AMPHORA BY POLYGNOTOS.
(BRITISH MUSEUM)

So spake he in prayer, and Phoebus Apollo heard him. Now when they had prayed and sprinkled the barley meal, first they drew back the victims' heads and slaughtered them and flayed them, and cut slices from the thighs and wrapped them in fat, making a double fold, and laid raw collops thereon, and the old man burnt them on cleft wood and made libation over them of gleaming wine; and at his side the young men in their hands held five-pronged forks. Now when the thighs were burnt and they had tasted the vitals, then sliced they all the rest and pierced it through with spits, and roasted it carefully, and drew all off again. So when they had rest from the task and had made ready the banquet, they feasted, nor was their heart aught stinted of the fair banquet. But when they had put away from them the desire of meat and drink, the young men filled the bowls with wine to the brim, and gave each man his portion after the drink-offering had been poured into the cups. So all day long worshipped they the god with music, singing the beautiful paean, the sons of the Achaeans making music to the Far-darter; and his heart was glad to hear. And when the sun went down and darkness came on them, they laid them to sleep beside the ship's hawsers; and when rosy-fingered Dawn appeared, the child of morning, then set they sail for the wide camp of the Achaeans; and Apollo the Far-darter sent them a favouring gale. They set up their mast and spread the white sails forth, and the wind filled the sail's belly and the dark wave sang loud about the stem as the ship made way, and she sped across the wave, accomplishing her journey. So when they were now come to the wide camp of the Achaeans, they drew up their black ship to land high upon the sands, and set in line the long props beneath her; and themselves were scattered amid their huts and ships.

But he sat by his swift-faring ships, still wroth, even the heaven-sprung son of Peleus, Achilles fleet of foot; he betook him neither to the assembly that is the hero's glory, neither to war, but consumed his heart in tarrying in his place, and yearned for the war-cry and for battle.

Now when the twelfth morn thereafter was come, then the gods that are for ever fared to Olympus all in company, led of Zeus. And Thetis forgat not her son's charge, but rose up from the sea-wave, and at early morn mounted up to great heaven and Olympus. There found she Cronos' son of the far-sounding voice sitting apart from all on the top-most peak of many-ridged Olympus. So she sat before his face and with her left hand clasped his knees, and with her right touched him beneath his chin, and spake in prayer to king Zeus son of Cronos: "Father Zeus, if ever I gave thee aid amid the immortal gods, whether by word or deed, fulfil thou this my desire: do honour to my son, that is doomed to earliest death of all men: now hath Agamemnon king of men done him dishonour, for he hath taken away his meed of honour and keepeth her of his own violent deed. But honour thou him, Zeus of Olympus, lord of counsel; grant thou victory to the Trojans the while, until the Achaeans do my son honour and exalt him with recompense."

So spake she; but Zeus the cloud-gatherer said no word to her, and sat long time in silence. But even as Thetis had clasped his knees, so held she by him clinging, and questioned him yet a second time: "Promise me now this thing verily, and bow thy head thereto; or else deny me, seeing there is naught for thee to fear; that I may know full well how I among all gods am least in honour."

Then Zeus the cloud-gatherer, sore troubled, spake to her: "Verily it is a sorry matter, if thou wilt set me at variance with Hera, whene'er she provoketh me with taunting words. Even now she upbraideth me ever amid the immortal gods, and saith that I aid the Trojans in battle. But do thou now depart again, lest Hera mark aught; and I will take thought for these things to fulfil them. Come now, I will bow my head to thee, that thou mayest be of good courage; for that, of my part, is the surest token amid the immortals; no word of mine is revocable nor false nor unfulfilled when the bow-ing of my head hath pledged it."

Zeus spake, and bowed his dark brow, and the ambrosial locks waved from the king's immortal head; and he made great Olympus quake.

Thus the twain took counsel and parted; she leapt there-with into the deep sea from glittering Olympus, and Zeus fared to his own palace. All the gods in company arose from their seats before their father's face; neither ventured any to await his coming, but they stood up all before him. So he sate him there upon his throne; but Hera saw, and was not ignorant how that the daughter of the Ancient of the sea, Thetis the silver-footed, had devised counsel with him. Anon with taunting words spake she to Zeus the son of Cronos: "Now who among the gods, thou crafty of mind, hath devised counsel with thee? It is ever thy good pleasure to hold aloof from me and in secret meditation to give thy judgments, nor of thine own good will hast thou ever brought thyself to declare unto me the thing thou purposest."

Then the father of gods and men made answer to her: "Hera, think not thou to know all my sayings; hard they are for thee, even though thou art my wife. But whichsoever it is seemly for thee to hear, none sooner than thou shall know, be he god or man. Only when I will to take thought aloof from the gods, then do not thou ask of every matter nor make question."

Then Hera the ox-eyed queen made answer to him. "Most dread son of Cronos, what word is this thou hast spoken? Yea, surely of old I have not asked thee nor made question, but in every quietness thou devisest all thou wilt. But now is my heart sore afraid lest thou have been won over by silver-footed Thetis, daughter of the Ancient of the sea, for she at early morn sat by thee and clasped thy knees. To her I deem thou gavest a sure pledge that thou wilt do honour to Achilles, and lay many low beside the Achaeans' ships."

To her made answer Zeus the cloud-gatherer: "Lady, ever art thou imagining, nor can I escape thee; yet shalt thou in no wise have power to fulfil, but wilt be the further from my heart; that shall be even the worse for thee. And if it be so, then such must my good pleasure be. Abide thou in silence and hearken to my bidding, lest all the gods that are in Olympus keep not off from thee my visitation, when I put forth my unconquerable hands against thee."

He said, and Hera the ox-eyed queen was afraid, and sat in silence, curbing her heart; but throughout Zeus' palace the gods of heaven were troubled. Then Hephaestus the famed craftsman began to make harangue among them, to do kindness to his dear mother, white-armed Hera: "Verily this will be a sorry matter, neither any more endurable, if ye twain thus fight for mortals' sakes, and bring wrangling among the gods; neither will there any more be joy of the goodly feast, seeing that evil triumpheth. So I give counsel to my mother, though herself is wise, to do kindness to our dear father Zeus, that our father upbraid us not again and cast the banquet in confusion. What if the Olympian, the lord of the lightning, will to dash us from our seats! for he is strongest far. Nay, approach thou him with gentle words, then will the Olympian forthwith be gracious unto us."

So speaking he rose up and set in his dear mother's hand the two-handled cup, and spake to her: "Be of good courage, mother mine, and endure, though thou art vexed, lest I behold thee, that art so dear, chastised before mine eyes, and then shall I not be able for all my sorrow to save thee; for the Olympian is a hard foe to face. Yea, once ere this, when I was fain to save thee, he caught me by my foot and hurled me from the heavenly threshold; all day I flew, and at the set of sun I fell in Lemnos, and little life was in me. There did the Sintian folk forthwith tend me for my fall."

He spake, and the white-armed goddess Hera smiled, and smiling took the cup at her son's hand. Then he poured wine to all the other gods from right to left, ladling the sweet nectar from the bowl. And laughter unquenchable arose amid the blessed gods to see Hephaestus bustling through the palace.

So feasted they all day till the setting of the sun; nor was their soul aught stinted of the fair banquet, nor of the beauteous lyre that Apollo held, and the Muses singing alternately with sweet voice.

Now when the bright light of the sun was set, these went each to his own house to sleep, where each one had his palace made with cunning device by famed Hephaestus the lame god; and Zeus the Olympian, the lord of lightning, departed to his couch where he was wont of old to take his rest, whenever sweet sleep visited him. There went he up and slept, and beside him was Hera of the golden throne.

II

The Assembly of the Greeks.
PAINTING FROM A KYLIX (RESTITUTION).
(CORNETO MUSEUM)

The Roll Call of the Armies

❲ Zeus, pondering how he may honor Achilles by dishonoring Agamemnon, sends a false dream to Agamemnon bidding him attack Troy. Without Achilles, the Achaeans are bound to suffer many defeats, although ultimately the city will be destroyed because Hera has persuaded all the Olympians to agree to its downfall.

Agamemnon tells the elders of the council of the dream and of the test he desires to make of the Achaeans. When the assembly meets, Agamemnon tells the troops that he is convinced Troy can never be captured and suggests that they flee homewards. Shouting, they hasten towards the ships. Recalled, they are reminded by Odysseus and Nestor of the omens observed before they sailed foretelling that Troy would be taken in the tenth year of the war. These words inflame the host, which streams forth to battle.

There follows a long list of the captains of the ships, the number of the ships, and the lands from which they came.

The Trojans, being warned, hasten to meet the advancing host. There follows a list of the varied peoples on the Trojan side and their leaders.*

---

* The bridges summarizing the books or parts of books which are omitted are the work of the editor and are printed in italics.

III

Menelaus and Paris Fight a Duel

Now when they were arrayed, each company with their captains, the Trojans marched with clamour [1] and with shouting like unto birds, even as when there goeth up before heaven a clamour of cranes which flee from the coming of winter and sudden rain, and fly with clamour towards the streams of ocean, bearing slaughter and fate to the Pigmy [2] men, and in early morn offer cruel battle. But on the other side marched the Achaeans in silence breathing courage, eager at heart to give succour man to man.

Even as when the south wind sheddeth mist over the crests of a mountain, mist unwelcome to the shepherd, but to the robber better than night, and a man can see no further than he casteth a stone; even so thick arose the gathering dust-clouds at their tread as they went; and with all speed they advanced across the plain.

So when they were now come nigh in onset on each other, godlike Alexandros [3] played champion to the Trojans, wearing upon his shoulders panther-skin and curved bow and sword; and he brandished two bronze-headed spears and challenged all the chieftains of the Argives to fight him man to man in deadly combat. But when Menelaus dear to Ares

---

[1] The Trojan hosts contained both men from Troy and their allies, many of whom came from barbarian tribes.

[2] Dwarf inhabitants of Africa, with whom the cranes were supposed to carry on war.

[3] A name of Paris.

marked him coming in the forefront of the multitude with
long strides, then even as a lion is glad when he lighteth
upon a great carcase, a horned stag, or a wild goat that he
hath found, being an hungered; and so he devoureth it
amain, even though the fleet hounds and lusty youths set
upon him; even thus was Menelaus glad when his eyes beheld godlike Alexandros; for he thought to take vengeance
upon the sinner. So straightway he leapt in his armour from
his chariot to the ground.

But when godlike Alexandros marked him appear amid
the champions, his heart was smitten, and he shrank back
into the host of his comrades, avoiding death. And even as
a man that hath seen a serpent in a mountain glade starteth
backward and trembling seizeth his feet beneath him, and
he retreateth back again, and paleness hath hold of his
cheeks, even so did godlike Alexandros for fear of Atreus'
son shrink back into the throng of lordly Trojans. But Hector
beheld and upbraided him with scornful words: "Ill Paris,
most fair in semblance, thou deceiver woman-mad, would
thou hadst been unborn and died unwed. Yea, that were my
desire, and it were far better than thus to be our shame and
looked at askance of all men. I ween that the flowing-haired
Achaeans laugh, deeming that a prince is our champion only
because good looks are his; but in his heart is there no
strength nor any courage. Art thou indeed such an one that
in thy seafaring ships thou didst sail over the deep with the
company of thy trusty comrades, and in converse with strangers didst bring back a fair woman from a far country, one
that was by marriage daughter to warriors that bear the spear,
that she might be a sore mischief to thy father and city and
all the realm, but to our foes a rejoicing, and to thyself a
hanging of the head? And canst thou not indeed abide
Menelaus dear to Ares? Thou mightest see what sort of warrior is he whose lovely wife thou hast. Thy lyre will not
avail thee nor the gifts of Aphrodite, those thy locks and fair
favour, when thou grovellest in the dust. But the Trojans
are very cowards: else ere this hadst thou donned a robe of
stone for all the ill thou hast wrought."

And godlike Alexandros made answer to him again: "Hector, since justly thou chidest me and not unjustly—thy heart is ever keen, even as an axe that pierceth a beam at the hand of a man that shapeth a ship's timber with skill, and thereby is the man's blow strengthened; even such is thy heart undaunted in thy breast. Cast not in my teeth the lovely gifts of golden Aphrodite; not to be flung aside are the gods' glorious gifts that of their own good will they give; for by his desire can no man win them. But now if thou wilt have me do battle and fight, make the other Trojans sit down and all the Achaeans, and set ye me in the midst, and Menelaus dear to Ares, to fight for Helen and all her wealth. And whichsoever shall vanquish and gain the upper hand, let him take all the wealth aright, and the woman, and bear them home. And let the rest pledge friendship and sure oaths; so may ye dwell in deep-soiled Troy, and let them depart to Argos pasture-land of horses, and Achaea home of fair women."

So spake he, and Hector rejoiced greatly to hear his saying, and went into the midst and restrained the battalions of the Trojans, with his spear grasped by the middle; and they all sate them down. But the flowing-haired Achaeans kept shooting at him, aiming with arrows and casting stones. But Agamemnon king of men cried aloud: "Refrain, ye Argives; shoot not, ye sons of the Achaeans; for Hector of the glancing helm hath set himself to say somewhat."

So spake he, and they refrained from battle and made silence speedily. And Hector spake between the two hosts. "Hear of me, Trojans and well-greaved Achaeans, the saying of Alexandros, for whose sake strife hath come about. He biddeth the other Trojans and all the Achaeans to lay down their goodly armour on the bounteous earth, and himself in the midst and Menelaus dear to Ares to fight alone for Helen and all her wealth. And whichsoever shall vanquish and gain the upper hand, let him take all the wealth aright, and the woman, and bear them home; but let all of us pledge friendship and sure oaths."

So spake he, and they all kept silence and were still. Then

in their midst spake Menelaus of the loud war-cry: "Hearken ye now to me, too; for into my heart most of all is grief entered; and I deem that the parting of Argives and Trojans hath come at last; seeing ye have endured many ills because of my quarrel and the first sin of Alexandros. And for whichsoever of us death and fate are prepared, let him lie dead: and be ye all parted with speed. Bring ye two lambs, one white ram and one black ewe, for earth and sun; and let us bring one for Zeus. And call hither great Priam, that he may pledge the oath himself, seeing he hath sons that are overweening and faithless, lest any by transgression do violence to the oath of Zeus; for young men's hearts are ever unstable. But wheresoever an old man entereth in, he looketh both before and after, whereby the best issue shall come for either side."

So spake he, and Achaeans and Trojans were glad, deeming that they should have rest from grievous war. So they sent back their chariots to the ranks, and themselves alighted and doffed their arms. And these they laid upon the earth each close to each, and there was but small space between. And Hector sent two heralds to the city with all speed, to bring the lambs, and to call Priam. And lord Agamemnon sent forth Talthybius to go to the hollow ships, and bade him bring a ram; and he was not disobedient to noble Agamemnon.

Now Iris went with a message to white-armed Helen in the likeness of her husband's sister, the spouse of Antenor's son, even her that lord Helicaon Antenor's son had to wife, Laodice fairest favoured of Priam's daughters. And in the hall she found Helen weaving a great purple web of double fold, and embroidering thereon many battles of horse-taming Trojans and mail-clad Achaeans, that they had endured for her sake at the hands of Ares. So fleet-footed Iris stood by her side and said: "Come hither, dear sister, that thou mayest see the wondrous doings of horse-taming Trojans and mail-clad Achaeans. They that erst waged tearful war upon each other in the plain, eager for deadly battle, even they sit now in silence, and the battle is stayed, and they lean upon their shields, and the tall spears are planted by their sides. But Alexandros and Menelaus dear to Ares will fight with their tall spears for thee; and thou wilt be declared the dear wife of him that conquereth."

So spake the goddess, and put into her heart sweet longing for her former husband and her city and parents.

Forthwith she veiled her face in shining linen, and hastened from her chamber, letting fall a round tear; not unattended, for there followed with her two handmaidens, Aethre daughter of Pittheus and ox-eyed Clymene. Then came she straightway to the place of the Scaean gates.

And they that were with Priam and Panthous and Thymoetes and Lampus and Clytius and Hycetaon of the stock of Ares, Ucalegon withal and Antenor, twain sages, being elders of the people, sat at the Scaean gates. These had now ceased from battle for old age, yet were they right good orators, like grasshoppers that in a forest sit upon a tree and utter their delightful voice; even so sat the elders of the Trojans upon the tower. Now when they saw Helen coming to the tower they softly spake winged words one to the other: "Small blame is it that Trojans and well-greaved Achaeans should for such a woman long time suffer hardships; marvellously like is she to the immortal goddesses to look upon. Yet even so, though she be so goodly, let her go upon their ships and not stay to vex us and our children after us."

So said they, and Priam lifted up his voice and called to Helen: "Come hither, dear child, and sit before me, that thou mayest see thy former husband and thy kinsfolk and thy friends. I hold thee not to blame; nay, I hold the gods to blame who brought on me the dolorous war of the Achaeans—so mayest thou now tell me who is this huge hero, this Achaean warrior so goodly and great. Of a truth there are others even taller by a head; yet did mine eyes never behold a man so beautiful nor so royal; for he is like unto one that is a king."

And Helen, fair among women, spake and answered him: "Reverend art thou to me and dread, dear father of my lord; would that sore death had been my pleasure when I followed thy son hither, and left my home and my kinsfolk and my daughter in her girlhood and the lovely company of mine age-fellows. But that was not so, wherefore I pine with weeping. Now will I tell thee that whereof thou askest me and enquirest. This is Atreides, wide-ruling Agamemnon, one that is both a goodly king and mighty spearman. And he was husband's brother to me, ah shameless me; if ever such an one there was."

So said she, and the old man marvelled at him, and said: "Ah, happy Atreides, child of fortune, blest of heaven; now know I that many sons of the Achaeans are subject to thee. Erewhile fared I to Phrygia, the land of vines, and there saw I that the men of Phrygia, they of the nimble steeds, were very many, even the hosts of Otreus and godlike Mygdon, that were then encamped along the banks of Sangarius. For I too being their ally was numbered among them on the day that the Amazons came, the peers of men. Yet were not even they so many as are the flashing-eyed Achaeans."

And next the old man saw Odysseus, and asked: "Come now, tell me of this man too, dear child, who is he, shorter by a head than Agamemnon son of Atreus, but broader of shoulder and of chest to behold? His armour lieth upon the bounteous earth, and himself like a bell-wether rangeth the ranks of warriors. Yea, I liken him to a thick-fleeced ram ordering a great flock of white ewes."

Then Helen sprung of Zeus made answer to him: "Now this is Laertes' son, crafty Odysseus, that was reared in the realm of Ithaca, rugged though it be, and is skilled in all the ways of wile and cunning device."

Then sage Antenor made answer to her: "Lady, verily the thing thou sayest is true indeed, for erst came goodly Odysseus hither also on an embassage for thee, in the company of Menelaus dear to Ares; and I gave them entertainment and welcomed them in my halls, and learnt the aspect of both and their wise devices. Now when they mingled with the Trojans in the assembly, while all stood up Menelaus overpassed them all by the measure of his broad shoulders;

but when both sat down, Odysseus was the more stately. And when they began to weave the web of words and counsel in the face of all, then Menelaus harangued fluently, in few words, but very clearly, seeing he was not long of speech, neither random, though in years he was the younger. But whenever Odysseus full of wiles rose up, he stood and looked down, with eyes fixed upon the ground, and waved not his staff whether backwards or forwards, but held it stiff, like to a man of no understanding; one would deem him to be churlish, and naught but a fool. But when he uttered his great voice from his chest, and words like unto the snow-flakes of winter, then could no mortal man contend with Odysseus; then we were not misled by Odysseus' aspect."

And thirdly the old man saw Aias, and asked: "Who then is this other Achaean warrior, goodly and great, pre-eminent among the Argives by the measure of his head and broad shoulders?"

And long-robed Helen, fair among women, answered: "This is huge Aias, bulwark of the Achaeans. And on the other side amid the Cretans standeth Idomeneus like a god, and about him are gathered the captains of the Cretans. Oft did Menelaus dear to Ares entertain him in our house whene'er he came from Crete. And now behold I all the other glancing-eyed Achaeans, whom well I could discern and tell their names; but two captains of the host can I not see, even Castor tamer of horses and Polydeuces the skilful boxer, mine own brethren, whom the same mother bare. Either they came not in the company from lovely Lacedaemon; or they came hither indeed in their seafaring ships, but now will not enter into the battle of the warriors, for fear of the many scornings and revilings that are mine."

So said she; but them the life-giving earth held fast there in Lacedaemon, in their dear native land.

Meanwhile were the heralds bearing through the city the holy oath-offerings, two lambs and strong-hearted wine, the fruit of the earth, in a goat-skin bottle. And the herald Idaeus bare the shining bowl and golden cups; and came to the old man and summoned him and said: "Rise, thou son of Laomedon. The chieftains of the horse-taming Trojans and mail-clad Achaeans call on thee to go down into the plain, that ye may pledge a trusty oath. But Alexandros and Menelaus dear to Ares will fight with their long spears for the lady's sake; and let lady and treasure go with him that shall conquer. And may we that are left pledge friendship and trusty oaths and dwell in deep-soiled Troy, and they shall depart to Argos pasture-land of horses and Achaea home of fair women."

So said he, and the old man shuddered and bade his companions yoke the horses; and they with speed obeyed. Then Priam mounted and drew back the reins, and by his side Antenor mounted the splendid chariot. So the two drave the fleet horses through the Scaean gates to the plain. And when they had come even to the Trojans and Achaeans, they went down from the chariots upon the bounteous earth, and marched into the midst of Trojans and Achaeans. Then forthwith rose up Agamemnon king of men, and up rose Odysseus the man of wiles; and the lordly heralds gathered together the holy oath-offerings of the gods, and mingled the wine in a bowl, and poured water over the princes' hands. And Atreides put forth his hand and drew his knife that hung ever beside his sword's great sheath, and cut the hair from off the lambs' heads; and then the heralds portioned it among the chief of the Trojans and Achaeans. Then in their midst Atreus' son lifted up his hands and prayed aloud: "Father Zeus, that rulest from Ida,[4] most glorious, most great, and thou Sun that seest all things and hearest all things, and ye Rivers and thou Earth, and ye that in the underworld punish men outworn, whosoever sweareth falsely; be ye witnesses, and watch over the faithful oath. If Alexandros slay Menelaus, then let him have Helen to himself and all her possessions; and we will depart on our seafaring ships. But if golden-haired Menelaus slay Alexandros, then let the Trojans give back Helen and all her posses-

---

[4] A range of mountains in the southern part of the Troad; from its top Zeus watched the Trojan war.

sions and pay the Argives the recompense that is seemly, such as shall live among men that shall be hereafter. But if so be that Priam and Priam's sons will not pay the recompense unto me when Alexandros falleth, then will I fight on thereafter for the price of sin, and abide here till I compass the end of war."

So said he, and cut the lambs' throats with the pitiless knife. Them he laid gasping upon the ground, failing of breath, for the knife had taken their strength from them; and next they drew the wine from the bowl into the cups, and poured it forth and prayed to the gods that live for ever. And thus would say many an one of Achaeans and Trojans: "Zeus most glorious, most great, and all ye immortal gods, which folk soe'er be first to sin against the oaths, may their brains be so poured forth upon the earth even as wine, theirs and their children's and let their wives be made subject unto strangers."

So spake they, but the son of Cronos vouchsafed not yet fulfilment. And in their midst Priam of the seed of Dardanus uttered his saying: "Hearken to me, Trojans and well-greaved Achaeans. I verily will return back to windy Ilium, seeing that I can in no wise bear to behold with mine eyes my dear son fighting with Menelaus dear to Ares. But Zeus knoweth, and all the immortal gods, for which of the twain the doom of death is appointed."

So spake the godlike man, and laid the lambs in his chariot, and entered in himself, and drew back the reins; and by his side Antenor mounted the splendid chariot. So they departed back again to Ilium; and Hector son of Priam and goodly Odysseus first meted out a space, and then they took the lots, and shook them in a bronze-bound helmet, to know whether of the twain should first cast his spear of bronze. And the people prayed and lifted up their hands to the gods; and thus would say many an one of Achaeans and Trojans: "Father Zeus, that rulest from Ida, most glorious, most great; whichsoe'er it be that brought this trouble upon both peoples, vouchsafe that he may die and enter the house of Hades; that so for us peace may be assured and trusty oaths."

So said they; and great Hector of the glancing plume shook the helmet, looking behind him; and quickly leapt forth the lot of Paris. Then the people sat them down by ranks where each man's high-stepping horses and inwrought armour lay. And upon his shoulders goodly Alexandros donned his beauteous armour, even he that was lord to Helen of the lovely hair. First upon his legs set he his greaves, beautiful, fastened with silver ankle-clasps; next upon his breast he donned the corslet of his brother Lycaon, and fitted it upon himself. And over his shoulders cast he his silver-studded sword of bronze, and then a shield great and sturdy. And on his mighty head he set a wrought helmet of horse-hair crest, whereover the plume nodded terribly, and he took him a strong spear fitted to his grasp. And in like wise warlike Menelaus donned his armour.

So when they had armed themselves on either side in the throng, they strode between Trojans and Achaeans, fierce of aspect, and wonder came on them that beheld, both on the Trojans tamers of horses and on the well-greaved Achaeans. Then took they their stand near together in the measured space, brandishing their spears in wrath each against other. First Alexandros hurled his far-shadowing spear, and smote on Atreides' round shield; but the bronze brake not through, for its point was turned in the stout shield. Next Menelaus son of Atreus lifted up his hand to cast, and made prayer to father Zeus: "King Zeus, grant me revenge on him that was first to do me wrong, even on goodly Alexandros, and subdue thou him at my hands; so that many an one of men that shall be hereafter may shudder to wrong his host that hath shown him kindness."

So said he, and poised his far-shadowing spear, and hurled, and smote on the round shield of the son of Priam. Through the bright shield went the ponderous spear and through the inwrought breastplate it pressed on; and straight beside his flank the spear rent the tunic, but he swerved and escaped black death. Then Atreides drew his silver-studded sword, and lifted up his hand and smote the helmet-ridge; but the sword shattered upon it into three, yea four, and fell from his hand. Thereat Atreides looked up to the wide heaven and cried: "Father Zeus, surely none of the gods is crueller than you. Verily I thought to have gotten vengeance on Alexandros for his wickedness, but now my sword breaketh in my hand, and my spear sped from my grasp in vain, and I have not smitten him."

So saying, he leapt upon him and caught him by his horse-hair crest, and swinging him round dragged him towards the well-greaved Achaeans; and he was strangled by the embroidered strap beneath his soft throat, drawn tight below his chin to hold his helm. Now would Menelaus have dragged him away and won glory unspeakable, but that Zeus' daughter Aphrodite was swift to mark, and tore asunder for him the strap of slaughtered ox's hide; so the helmet came away empty in his stalwart hand. Thereat Menelaus cast it with a swing toward the well-greaved Achaeans, and his trusty comrades took it up; and himself sprang back again eager to slay him with spear of bronze. But Aphrodite snatched up Paris, very easily as a goddess may, and hid him in thick darkness, and set him down in his fragrant perfumed chamber; and herself went to summon Helen. Her she found on the high tower, and about her the Trojan women thronged. So with her hand she plucked her perfumed raiment and shook it and spake to her in the likeness of an aged dame, a wool-comber that was wont to work for her fair wool when she dwelt in Lacedaemon, whom too she greatly loved. Even in her likeness fair Aphrodite spake: "Come hither; Alexandros summoneth thee to go homeward. There is he in his chamber and inlaid bed, radiant in beauty and vesture; nor wouldst thou deem him to be come from fighting his foe, but rather to be faring to the dance, or from the dance to be just resting and set down."

So said she, and stirred Helen's soul within her breast; and when now she marked the fair neck and lovely breast and sparkling eyes of the goddess, she marvelled straight-way and spake a word and called upon her name: "Strange queen, why art thou desirous now to beguile me? Verily thou wilt lead me further on to some one of the peopled cities of Phrygia or lovely Maeonia, if there too thou hast perchance some other darling among mortal men, because even now

Menelaus hath conquered goodly Alexandros, and will lead me, accursed me, to his home. Therefore thou comest hither with guileful intent. Go and sit thou by his side, and depart from the way of the gods; neither let thy feet ever bear thee back to Olympus, but still be vexed for his sake and guard him till he make thee his wife or perchance his slave. But thither will I not go—that were a sinful thing—to array the bed of him; all the women of Troy will blame me hereafter; and I have griefs untold within my soul."

Rape of Helen. (Under guidance of Eneus, Paris carries away Helen, who is guided by Eros and heartened by Aphrodite and Peitho.

PAINTING FROM A SKYPHUS OF MACRON.
(SPINELLI COLL., ACERRA)

Then in wrath bright Aphrodite spake to her: "Provoke me not, rash woman, lest in mine anger I desert thee, and hate thee even as now I love thee beyond measure, and lest I devise grievous enmities between both, even betwixt Trojans and Achaeans, and so thou perish in evil wise."

So said she, and Helen sprung of Zeus was afraid, and went wrapped in her bright radiant vesture, silently, and the Trojan women marked her not; and the goddess led the way.

Now when they were come to the beautiful house of Alexandros the handmaidens turned straightway to their tasks, and the fair lady went to the high-roofed chamber; and laughter-loving Aphrodite took for her a chair and brought it, even she the goddess, and set it before the face of Paris. There Helen took her seat, the child of aegis-bearing Zeus, and with eyes turned askance spake and chided her lord: "Thou comest back from battle; would thou hadst perished there, vanquished of that great warrior that was my former husband. Verily it was once thy boast that thou wast a better man than Menelaus dear to Ares, in the might of thine arm and thy spear. But go, now, challenge Menelaus dear to Ares to fight thee again face to face. Nay, but I, even I, bid thee refrain, nor fight a fight with golden-haired Menelaus man to man, neither attack him recklessly, lest perchance thou fall to his spear anon."

And Paris made answer to her and said: "Chide not my soul, lady, with cruel taunts. For now indeed hath Menelaus vanquished me with Athene's aid, but another day may I do so unto him; for we too have gods with us. But come now, let us have joy of love upon our couch; for never yet hath love so enwrapped my heart—not even then when first I snatched thee from lovely Lacedaemon and sailed with thee on my seafaring ships, and in the isle of Cranae had converse with thee upon thy couch in love—as I love thee now and sweet desire taketh hold upon me." So saying he led the way to the couch, and the lady followed with him.

Thus laid they them upon their fretted couch; but Atreides the while strode through the host like to a wild beast, if anywhere he might set eyes on godlike Alexandros. But none of the Trojans or their famed allies could discover Alexandros to Menelaus dear to Ares. Yet surely did they in no wise hide him for kindliness, could any have seen him; for he was hated of all even as black death. So Agamemnon king of men spake among them there: "Hearken to me, Trojans and Dardanians and allies. Now is victory declared for Menelaus dear to Ares; give ye back Helen of Argos and the possessions with her, and pay ye the recompense such as is seemly, that it may live ever among men that shall be hereafter." So said Atreides, and all the Achaeans gave assent.

IV

The Trojans and Acheans grew hot in fight.

The Truce Is Broken

⟪ Instigated by Athene, Pandarus shoots an arrow at Menelaus wounding him and breaking the truce. Machaon, the surgeon, tends his wound. Agamemnon walks through the camp, speaking to the heroes and encouraging the Greeks as they prepare for battle. The forces march toward each other and join. The feats of many of the heroes are described.

V

Diomedes Triumphs

B<small>UT</small> now to Tydeus' son Diomedes Pallas Athene gave might and courage, for him to be pre-eminent amid all the Argives and win glorious renown. She kindled flame unwearied from his helmet and shield, like to the star of summer that above all others glittereth bright after he hath bathed in the ocean stream. In such wise kindled she flame from his head and shoulders and sent him into the midst, where men thronged the thickest.

Now there was amid the Trojans one Dares, rich and noble, priest of Hephaestus; and he had two sons, Phegeus and Idaeus, well skilled in all the art of battle. These separated themselves and assailed Diomedes face to face, they setting on him from their car and he on foot upon the ground. And when they were now come near in onset on each other, first Phegeus hurled his far-shadowing spear; and over Diomedes' left shoulder the spear point passed, and smote not his body. Then next Diomedes made a spear-cast, and the javelin sped not from his hand in vain, but smote Phegeus' breast between the nipples, and thrust him from the chariot. So Idaeus sprang away, leaving his beautiful car, and dared not to bestride his slain brother; else had neither he himself escaped black fate; but Hephaestus guarded him and saved him in a veil of darkness, that he might not have his aged priest all broken with sorrow. And the son of great-hearted Tydeus drave away the horses and gave them to his men to take to the hollow ships. But when the great-hearted Trojans beheld the sons of Dares, how one was fled, and one was slain beside his chariot, the spirit of all was stirred. But bright-eyed Athene took impetuous Ares by the hand and spake to him and said: "Ares, Ares, blood-stained bane of mortals, thou stormer of walls, can we not now leave the Trojans and Achaeans to fight, on whichso-ever it be that father Zeus bestoweth glory? But let us twain give place, and escape the wrath of Zeus."

So saying she led impetuous Ares from the battle. Then she made him sit down beside loud Scamander, and the Danaans pushed the Trojans back. Each one of the captains slew his man; first Agamemnon king of men thrust from his chariot the lord of the Alizonians, great Odius; for as he first turned to flight Agamemnon thrust his dart into his back be-tween his shoulders, and drave it through his breast. And he fell with a crash, and his armour clanged upon him.

And Idomeneus slew Phaistus son of Borus the Maeonian, that came from deep-soiled Tarne. Him in the act to mount upon his car spear-famed Idomeneus pierced with his long dart through his right shoulder; and he fell from the car and hateful darkness gat hold of him.

Him then Idomeneus' squires despoiled; and Scamandrius son of Strophius, cunning in the chase, fell to the keen-pointed spear of Menelaus son of Atreus; even he the mighty hunter, whom Artemis herself had taught to shoot all man-ner of wild things that the mountain forest breedeth. But now did Archer Artemis avail him naught nor all his marks-manship wherein of old time he excelled; but spear-famed Menelaus son of Atreus smote him with his dart as he fled before him, in his back between his shoulders, and pierced through his breast. So he fell prone and his armour clanged upon him.

And Meriones slew Phereclus son of Tecton, Harmon's son, whose hands were cunning to make all manner of curi-ous work; for Pallas Athene loved him more than all men. He likewise built Alexandros the trim ships, source of ills, that were made the bane of all the Trojans and of himself, be-cause he knew not the oracles of heaven. Him Meriones pursued, and overtaking him smote him in the right buttock, and right through passed the point straight to the bladder beneath the bone; and he fell to his knees with a cry, and death overshadowed him.

Then Meges slew Pedaeus Antenor's son, that was a bastard; yet goodly Theano nurtured him carefully like to her own children, to do her husband pleasure. To him Meges came near, and with keen dart smote him upon the sinew of the head; and right through amid the teeth the point of bronze cleft the tongue's root. So he fell in the dust, and bit the cold bronze with his teeth.

And by Eurypylus Euaemon's son, noble Hypsenor, son of high-hearted Dolopion, that was appointed priest to the river-god Scamander and like to a god was held in honour of the folk—by Eurypylus Euaemon's glorious son, he as he fled before him was pursued and smitten on the shoulder with a sword-thrust, and his heavy arm was shorn away. All bleeding the arm fell upon the earth; and over his eyes came gloomy death and forceful fate.

So laboured these in the violent melee; but of Diomedes man could not tell with whom he were joined, whether he consorted with Trojans or with Achaeans. For he stormed across the plain like a winter torrent at the full, that in swift course scattereth the causeys; neither can the long lines of causeys hold it in, nor the fences of fruitful orchards stay its sudden coming when the rain of heaven driveth it; and so before it perish in multitudes the fair works of the sons of men. Thus before Diomedes the serried battalions of the Trojans were overthrown, and they abode him not for all they were so many.

But when Lycaon's glorious son marked him storming across the plain, overthrowing battalions before him, anon he bent his crooked bow against Diomedes, and smote him as he sped onwards, hitting hard by his right shoulder the plate of his corslet; the bitter arrow flew through and held straight upon its way, and the corslet was dabbled with blood. Over him then loudly shouted Lycaon's glorious son: "Bestir you, great-hearted Trojans, urgers of horses; the best man of the Achaeans is wounded, and I deem that he shall not for long endure the violent dart, if verily the king, the son of Zeus, sped me on my way from Lycia."

So spake he boasting; yet was the other not vanquished of the swift dart, only he gave place and stood before his horses and his chariot and spake to Sthenelus son of Capaneus: "Haste thee, dear son of Capaneus; descend from thy chariot, to draw me from my shoulder the bitter arrow."

So said he, and Sthenelus leapt from his chariot to earth and stood beside him and drew the swift shaft right through, out of his shoulder; and the blood darted up through the pliant tunic. Then Diomedes of the loud war-cry prayed thereat: "Hear me, daughter of aegis-bearing Zeus, unwearied maiden! If ever in kindly mood thou stoodest by my father in the heat of battle, even so now be thou likewise kind to me, Athene. Grant me to slay this man, and bring within my spear-cast him that took advantage to shoot me, and boasteth over me, deeming that not for long shall I see the bright light of the sun."

So spake he in prayer, and Pallas Athene heard him, and made his limbs nimble, his feet and his hands withal, and came near and spake winged words: "Be of good courage now, Diomedes, to fight the Trojans; for in thy breast I have set thy father's courage undaunted, even as it was in knightly Tydeus, wielder of the buckler. Moreover I have taken from thine eyes the mist that erst was on them, that thou mayest well discern both god and man. Therefore if any god come hither to make trial of thee, fight not thou face to face with any of the immortal gods; save only if Aphrodite daughter of Zeus enter into the battle, her smite thou with the keen bronze."

So saying bright-eyed Athene went her way and Tydeus' son returned and entered the forefront of the battle; even though erst his soul was eager to do battle with the Trojans, yet now did threefold courage come upon him, as upon a lion whom some shepherd in the field guarding his fleecy sheep hath wounded, being sprung into the fold, yet hath not vanquished him; he hath roused his might, and then cannot beat him back, but lurketh amid the steading, and his forsaken flock is affrighted; so the sheep are cast in heaps, one upon the other, and the lion in his fury leapeth out of the high fold; even so in fury mingled mighty Diomedes with the Trojans.

There slew he Astynous and Hypeiron shepherd of the host; the one he pierced above the nipple with his bronze-shod dart, the other with his great sword upon the collar-bone beside the shoulder he smote, and severed the shoulder from neck and back. Them left he there, and pursued after Abas and Polvidos, sons of old Eurydamas, dreamer of dreams; yet discerned he no dreams for them when they went, but stalwart Diomedes despoiled them. Then went he after Xanthus and Thoön, sons of Phaenops, striplings both; but their father was outworn of grievous age, and begat no other son for his possessions after him. Then Diomedes slew them and bereft the twain of their dear life, and for their father left only lamentation and sore distress, seeing he welcomed them not alive returned from battle; and kinsmen divided his substance.

Then caught he two sons of Priam of the seed of Dardanus, riding in one chariot, Echemmon and Chromius. As a lion leapeth among the kine and breaketh the neck of cow or heifer grazing in a woodland pasture, so Tydeus' son thrust in ill wise from their chariot both of them unwilling, and thereafter despoiled them of their arms; and the horses gave he to his comrades to drive them to the ships.

Him Aeneas beheld making havoc of the ranks of warriors, and went his way along the battle and amid the hurtling of spears, seeking godlike Pandarus, if haply he might find him. Lycaon's son he found, the noble and stalwart, and stood before his face, and spake a word unto him. "Pandarus, where now are thy bow and thy winged arrows, and the fame wherein no man of this land rivalleth thee, nor any in Lycia boasteth to be thy better? Go to now, lift thy hands in prayer to Zeus and shoot thy dart at this fellow, whoe'er he be that lordeth it here and hath already wrought the Trojans much mischief, seeing he hath unstrung the knees of many a brave man; if indeed it be not some god wroth with the Trojans, in anger by reason of sacrifices; the wrath of god is a sore thing to fall on men."

And Lycaon's glorious son made answer to him: "Aeneas, counsellor of the mail-clad Trojans, in everything liken I him to the wise son of Tydeus; I discern him by his shield and crested helmet, and by the aspect of his horses, yet know I not surely if it be not a god. But if it be the man I deem, even the wise son of Tydeus, then not without help of a god is he thus furious, but some immortal standeth beside him with a cloud wrapped about his shoulders and turned aside from him my swift dart even as it lighted. For already have I shot my dart at him and smote his right shoulder right through the breastplate of his corslet, yea and I thought to hurl him headlong to Hades, yet I vanquished him not; surely it is some wrathful god. And I have no steeds at hand nor any chariot whereon to mount—yet in Lycaon's halls are eleven fair chariots, new wrought, with gear all fresh, and cloths spread over them; and beside each standeth a yoke of horses, champing white barley and spelt. Moreover Lycaon, the aged spearman, at my departing laid instant charge upon me in our well-builded house; he bade me mount horse and chariot to lead the Trojans in the violent melee; but I obeyed him not—far better had that been!—but spared the horses lest in the great crowd of men they should lack fodder that had been wont to feed their fill. Therefore I left them and am come on foot to Ilium, trusting to my bow; and now must my bow not help me. Already have I aimed at two princes, Tydeus' and Atreus' sons, and both I smote and surely drew forth blood, yet only roused them the more. Therefore in an evil hour I took from the peg my curved bow on that day when I led my Trojans to lovely Ilium, to do noble Hector pleasure. But if I return and mine eyes behold my native land and wife and great palace lofty-roofed, then may an alien forthwith cut my head from me if I break not this bow with mine hands and cast it upon the blazing fire; worthless is its service to me as air."

Then Aeneas captain of the Trojans answered him: "Nay,

talk not thus; naught shall be mended before that we with horses and chariot have gone to face this man, and made trial of him in arms. Come then, mount upon my car that thou mayest see of what sort are the steeds of Tros, well skilled for following or for fleeing hither or thither very fleetly across the plain; they will e'en bring us to the city safe and sound, even though Zeus hereafter give victory to Diomedes son of Tydeus. Come therefore, take thou the lash and shining reins, and I will stand upon the car to fight; or else withstand thou him, and to the horses will I look."

To him made answer Lycaon's glorious son: "Aeneas, take thou thyself the reins and thine own horses; better will they draw the curved car for their wonted charioteer, if perchance it hap that we must flee from Tydeus' son; lest they go wild for fear and will not take us from the fight, for lack of thy voice, and so the son of great-hearted Tydeus attack us and slay us both and drive away the whole-hooved horses. So drive thou thyself thy chariot and thy horses, and I will await his onset with my keen spear." So saying mounted they upon the well-dight chariot, and eagerly drave the fleet horses against Diomedes. And Sthenelus the glorious son of Capaneus saw them, and anon spake to Diomedes winged words: "Diomedes son of Tydeus, dear to mine heart, I behold two stalwart warriors eager to fight against thee, endued with might beyond measure. The one is well skilled in the bow, even Pandarus, and he moreover boasteth him to be Lycaon's son; and Aeneas boasteth himself to be born son of great-hearted Anchises, and his mother is Aphrodite. Come now, let us give place upon the chariot, neither rage thou thus, I pray thee, in the forefront of battle, lest perchance thou lose thy life."

Then stalwart Diomedes looked sternly at him and said: "Speak to me no word of flight, for I ween that thou shalt not at all persuade me; not in my blood is it to fight a skulking fight or cower down; my force is steadfast still. I have no mind to mount the chariot, nay, even as I am will I go to face them; Pallas Athene biddeth me not be afraid. And as for these, their fleet horses shall not take both back from us again, even if one or other escape. And this moreover tell I thee, and lay thou it to heart: if Athene rich in counsel grant me this glory, to slay them both, then refrain thou here these my fleet horses, and bind the reins tight to the chariot rim; and be mindful to leap upon Aeneas' horses, and drive them forth from the Trojans amid the well-greaved Achaeans. For they are of that breed whereof farseeing Zeus gave to Tros recompense for Ganymede [1] his child, because they were the best of all horses beneath the daylight and the sun. That blood Anchises king of men stole of Laomedon, privily putting mares to them. Thereof a stock was born him in his palace, even six; four kept he himself and reared them at the stall, and the other twain gave he to Aeneas, deviser of rout. Them could we seize, we should win us great renown."

In such wise talked they one to the other, and anon those other twain came near, driving their fleet horses. First to him spake Lycaon's glorious son: "O thou strong-souled and cunning, son of proud Tydeus, verily my swift dart vanquished thee not, the bitter arrow; so now will I make trial with my spear if I can hit thee."

He spake and poised and hurled his far-shadowing spear, and smote upon Diomedes' shield; right through it sped the point of bronze and reached the breastplate. So over him shouted loudly Lycaon's glorious son: "Thou are smitten on the belly right through, and I ween thou shalt not long hold up thine head; so thou givest me great renown."

But mighty Diomedes unaffrighted answered him: "Thou hast missed, and not hit; but ye twain I deem shall not cease till one or other shall have fallen and glutted with blood Ares the stubborn god of war."

So spake he and hurled; and Athene guided the dart upon his nose beside the eye, and it pierced through his white teeth. So the hard bronze cut through his tongue at the root and the point issued forth by the base of the chin. Pandarus

---

[1] A son of Tros, from whom the Trojans were named. The gods took Ganymede to be cupbearer to Zeus because of his beauty.

fell from his chariot, and his splendid armour gleaming clanged upon him, and the fleet-footed horses swerved aside; so there his soul and strength were unstrung.

Then Aeneas leapt down with shield and long spear, fearing lest perchance the Achaeans might take from him the corpse; and strode over him like a lion confident in his strength, and held before him his spear and the circle of his shield, eager to slay whoe'er should come to face him, crying his terrible cry. Then Diomedes grasped in his hand a stone —a mighty deed—such as two men, as men now are, would not avail to lift; yet he with ease wielded it all alone. Therewith he smote Aeneas on the hip where the thigh turneth in the hip-joint, and this men call the "cup-bone." So he crushed his cup-bone, and brake both sinews withal, and the jagged stone tore apart the skin. Then the hero stayed fallen upon his knees and with stout hand leant upon the earth; and the darkness of night veiled his eyes. And now might Aeneas king of men have perished, but that Aphrodite daughter of Zeus was swift to mark, even his mother that conceived him by Anchises as he tended the kine. About her dear son wound she her white arms, and spread before his face a fold of her radiant vesture, to be a covering from the darts, lest any of the fleet-horsed Danaans might hurl the spear into his breast and take away his life.

So was she bearing her dear son away from battle; but the son of Capaneus forgat not the behest that Diomedes of the loud war-cry had laid upon him; he kept his own whole-hooved horses away from the tumult, binding the reins tight to the chariot-rim, and leapt on the sleek-coated horses of Aeneas, and drave them from the Trojans to the well-greaved Achaeans, and gave them to Deipylus, his dear comrade whom he esteemed above all that were his age-fellows, because he was like-minded with himself; and bade him drive them to the hollow ships. Then did the hero mount his own chariot and take the shining reins and forthwith drive his strong-hooved horses in quest of Diomedes, eagerly. Now Diomedes had made onslaught with pitiless weapon on Aphrodite knowing how she was a coward goddess and none of those that have mastery in battle of the warriors—no Athene she nor Enyo [2] waster of cities. Now when he had pursued her through the dense throng and come on her, then great-hearted Tydeus' son thrust with his keen spear, and leapt on her and wounded the skin of her weak hand; straight through the ambrosial raiment that the Graces themselves had woven her pierced the dart into the flesh, above the springing of the palm. Then flowed the goddess's immortal blood, such ichor as floweth in the blessed gods; for they eat no bread neither drink they gleaming wine, wherefore they are bloodless and are named immortals. And she with a great cry let fall her son: him Phoebus Apollo took into his arms and saved him in a dusky cloud, lest any of the fleet-horsed Danaans might hurl the spear into his breast and take away his life. But over her Diomedes of the loud war-cry shouted afar: "Refrain thee, thou daughter of Zeus, from war and fighting. Is it not enough that thou beguilest feeble women? But if in battle thou wilt mingle, verily I deem that thou shalt shudder at the name of battle, if thou hear it even afar off."

So spake he, and she departed in amaze and was sore troubled: and wind-footed Iris [3] took her and led her from the throng tormented with her pain, and her fair skin was stained. There found she impetuous Ares sitting, on the battle's left; and his spear rested upon a cloud, and his fleet steeds. Then she fell on her knees and with instant prayer besought of her dear brother his golden-frontleted steeds: "Dear brother, save me and give me thy steeds, that I may win to Olympus, where is the habitation of the immortals. Sorely am I afflicted with a wound wherewith a mortal smote me, even Diomedes, who now would fight even with father Zeus."

So spake she, and Ares gave her his golden-frontleted steeds; and she mounted on the chariot sore at heart. By her side mounted Iris, and in her hands grasped the reins and

---

[2] A Greek goddess of battle.
[3] Goddess of the rainbow and a messenger of the gods.

lashed the horses to start them; and they flew onward nothing loth. Thus soon they came to the habitation of the gods, even steep Olympus. There wind-footed fleet Iris loosed the horses from the chariot and stabled them, and set ambrosial forage before them; but fair Aphrodite fell upon Dione's knees that was her mother. She took her daughter in her arms and stroked her with her hand, and spake and called upon her name: "Who now of the sons of heaven, dear child, hath entreated thee thus wantonly, as though thou wert a wrong-doer in the face of all?"

Then laughter-loving Aphrodite made answer to her: "Tydeus' son wounded me, high-hearted Diomedes, because I was saving from the battle my dear son Aeneas, who to me is dearest far of all men. For no more is the fierce battle-cry for Trojans and Achaeans, but the Danaans now are fighting even the immortals."

Then the fair goddess Dione answered her: "Be of good heart, my child, and endure for all thy pain; for many of us that inhabit the mansions of Olympus have suffered through men, in bringing grievous woes one upon another. So suffered Ares, when Otus and stalwart Ephialtes, sons of Aloeus, bound him in a strong prison-house; yea in a vessel of bronze lay he bound thirteen months. Then might Ares insatiate of battle have perished, but that the step-mother of Aloeus' sons, fair Eriboea, gave tidings to Hermes, and he stole away Ares, already pining; for the grievous prison-house was wearing him out. So suffered Hera when Amphitryon's stalwart son smote her on the right breast with a three-barbed arrow, so that pain unassuageable gat hold of her likewise. So suffered awful Hades a swift arrow like the rest, when this same man, the son of aegis-bearing Zeus, smote him in Pylos amid the dead and gave him over to anguish. And he went to the mansion of Zeus and to high Olympus, grieved at heart, pierced through with anguish; for the arrow was driven into his stout shoulder, and vexed his soul. But Paeeon spread soothing drugs upon the wound and healed him; seeing that verily he was of no mortal substance. Headstrong man and violent of deed, that recked not of his evil doings, and with his archery vexed the gods that dwell in Olympus! So upon thee was this man sent by the bright-eyed goddess Athene; fond man—for the heart of Tydeus' son knoweth not this, that he of a surety is not long-lived that fighteth with immortals, nor ever do his children prattle upon his knees at his returning from war and terrible fray. Therefore now let Tydeides, though he be very mighty, beware lest one better than thou encounter him; and so Aegialea, wise daughter of Adrestus, wake from sleep with lamentations all her household, bewailing her wedded lord, the best man of the Achaeans, even she that is the brave wife of horse-taming Diomedes."

So saying with both hands she wiped the ichor from the arm; her arm was comforted, and the grievous pangs assuaged. But Athene and Hera beheld, and with bitter words provoked Zeus the son of Cronos. Of them was the bright-eyed goddess Athene first to speak: "Father Zeus, wilt thou indeed be wroth with me whate'er I say? Verily I ween that Aphrodite was urging some woman of Achaea to join her unto the Trojans whom she so marvellously loveth; and stroking such an one of the fair-robed women of Achaea, she tore upon the golden brooch her delicate hand."

So spake she, and the father of gods and men smiled, and called unto him golden Aphrodite and said: "Not unto thee, my child, are given the works of war; but follow thou after the loving tasks of wedlock, and to all these things shall fleet Ares and Athene look."

Now while they thus spake in converse one with the other, Diomedes of the loud war-cry leapt upon Aeneas, knowing full well that Apollo himself had spread his arms over him; yet reverenced he not even the great god, but still was eager to slay Aeneas and strip from him his glorious armour. So thrice he leapt on him, fain to slay him, and thrice Apollo beat back his glittering shield. And when the fourth time he sprang at him like a god, then Apollo the Far-darter spake to him with terrible shout: "Think, son of Tydeus, and shrink, nor desire to match thy spirit with gods; seeing there is no comparison of the race of immortal gods and of men that walk upon the earth."

So said he, and Diomedes shrank a short space backwards, to avoid the wrath of Apollo the Far-darter. Then Apollo set Aeneas away from the throng in holy Pergamus where his temple stood. There Leto and Archer Artemis healed him in the mighty sanctuary, and gave him glory; but Apollo of the silver bow made a wraith like unto Aeneas' self, and in such armour as his; and over the wraith Trojans and goodly Achaeans each hewed the others' bucklers on their breasts, their round shields and fluttering targes.

Then to impetuous Ares said Phoebus Apollo: "Ares, Ares, blood-stained bane of mortals, thou stormer of walls, wilt thou not follow after this man and withdraw him from the battle, this son of Tydeus, who now would fight even with father Zeus? First in close fight he wounded Aphrodite in her hand hard by the wrist, and then sprang he upon myself like unto a god."

So saying he sate himself upon the height of Pergamus, and baleful Ares entered among the Trojan ranks and aroused them in the likeness of fleet Acamas, captain of the Thracians. On the heaven-nurtured sons of Priam he called saying: "O ye sons of Priam, the heaven-nurtured king, how long will ye yet suffer your host to be slain of the Achaeans? Shall it be even until they fight about our well-builded gates? Low lieth the warrior whom we esteemed like unto goodly Hector, even Aeneas, son of Anchises great of heart. Go to now, let us save from the tumult our valiant comrade."

So saying he aroused the spirit and soul of every man. Thereat Sarpedon sorely chided noble Hector: "Hector, where now is the spirit gone that erst thou hadst? Thou saidst forsooth that without armies or allies thou wouldest hold the city, alone with thy sisters' husbands and thy brothers; but now can I not see any of these neither perceive them, but they are cowering like hounds about a lion; and we are fighting that are but allies among you. Yea I being an ally

am come from very far; far off is Lycia upon eddying
Xanthus, where I left my dear wife and infant son, and left
my great wealth that each one coveteth that is in need. Yet
for all that I urge on my Lycians, and myself am eager to
fight my man, though here is naught of mine such as the
Achaeans might plunder or harry. But thou standest, nay
thou dost not even urge all thine hosts to abide and guard
their wives. Only beware lest, as though tangled in meshes
of all-ensnaring flax, ye be made unto your foeman a prey
and a spoil; and they will soon lay waste your well-peopled
city. Thee it behoveth to give thought to all these things
both by night and day, and to beseech the captains of thy
far-famed allies to hold on unflinchingly; and so shalt thou
put away their sore rebuking from thee."

So spake Sarpedon, and his word stung Hector to the
heart. Forthwith he leapt from his chariot in his armour to
the earth, and brandishing two keen spears went everywhere through the host, urging them to fight, and roused the
dread battle-cry. So they were rallied and stood to face the
Achaeans: and the Argives withstood them in close array and
fled not. Even as a wind carrieth the chaff about the sacred
threshing-floors when men are winnowing, what time golden-
haired Demeter in rush of wind maketh division of grain and
chaff, and so the chaff-heaps grow white—so now grew the
Achaeans white with falling dust which in their midst the
horses' hooves beat up into the brazen heaven, as fight was
joined again, and the charioteers wheeled round. Thus bare
they forward the fury of their hands; and impetuous Ares
drew round them a veil of night to aid the Trojans in the
battle, ranging everywhere; so fulfilled he the behest of Phoebus Apollo of the golden sword, who bade him rouse the
Trojans' spirit when he beheld Pallas Athene departed; for
she was helper to the Danaans. And Apollo himself sent
forth Aeneas from his rich sanctuary and put courage in the
heart of him, shepherd of the hosts. So Aeneas took his place
amid his comrades, and they were glad to see him come
among them alive and sound and full of valiant spirit. Yet
they questioned him not at all, for all the toil forbade them

that the god of the silver bow was stirring and Ares bane of men and Strife raging insatiably.

And on the other side the two Aiantes [4] and Odysseus and Diomedes stirred the Danaans to fight; yet these of themselves feared neither the Trojans' violence nor assaults, but stood like mists that Zeus Cronos' son setteth in windless air on the mountain tops, at peace, while the might of the north wind sleepeth and of all the violent winds that blow with keen breath and scatter apart the shadowing clouds. Even so the Danaans withstood the Trojans steadfastly and fled not. And Atreides ranged through the throng exhorting instantly: "My friends, quit you like men and take heart of courage, and shun dishonour in one another's eyes amid the stress of battle. Of men that shun dishonour more are saved than slain, but for them that flee is neither glory found nor any safety."

So saying he darted swiftly with his javelin and smote a foremost warrior, even great-hearted Aeneas' comrade Deïcoon son of Pergasus, whom the Trojans held in like honour with Priam's sons, because he was swift to do battle amid the foremost. Him lord Agamemnon smote with his dart upon the shield, and it stayed not the spear, but the point passed through, so that he drave it through the belt into his nethermost belly: and he fell with a crash and his armour clanged upon him.

Then did Aeneas slay two champions of the Danaans, even the sons of Diocles, Crethon and Orsilochus, whose father dwelt in Phere, a man full of substance, whose lineage was of the river Alpheus, that floweth in broad stream through the land of the Pylians; Alpheus begat Orsilochus to be king of many men, and Orsilochus begat great-hearted Diocles, and of Diocles were born twin sons, even Crethon and Orsilochus, well skilled in all the ways of war. Now when these were of full age, they bare the Argives company

---

[4] *Aiantes* is the plural of *Aias:* (1) son of the Locrian King Oïleus, called the Lesser Aias, in contrast to (2) the Telamonian Aias (son of Telamon of Salamis) or Great Aias, so-called because of his height.

on their black ships to Ilium home of horses, to win recompense for Atreus' sons, Agamemnon and Menelaus; but now the issue of death shrouded them about. Like them, two lions on the mountain tops are nurtured by their dam in the deep forest thickets; and these harry the kine and goodly sheep and make havoc of the farmsteads of men, till in their turn they too are slain at men's hands with the keen bronze; in such wise were these twain vanquished at Aeneas' hands and fell like tall pine-trees.

But Menelaus dear to Ares had pity of them in their fall, and strode through the forefront, harnessed in flashing bronze, brandishing his spear; and Ares stirred his courage, with intent that he might fall beneath Aeneas' hand. But Antilochus, great-hearted Nestor's son, beheld him, and strode through the forefront; because he feared exceedingly for the shepherd of the host, lest aught befall him and disappoint them utterly of their labour. So those two, Menelaus and Aeneas, were now holding forth their hands and sharp spears each against the other, eager to do battle; when Antilochus came and stood hard by the shepherd of the host. But Aeneas faced them not, keen warrior though he was, when he beheld two men abiding side by side; so these haled away the corpses to the Achaeans' host, and laid the hapless twain in their comrades' arms, and themselves turned back and fought on amid the foremost.

Then slew they Pylaemenes, peer of Ares, captain of the great-hearted Paphlagonians bearers of the shield. Him as he stood still Atreus' son, spear-famed Menelaus, pierced with his javelin, smiting upon the collar-bone; and Antilochus hurled at Mydon, his squire and charioteer, Atymnius' brave son, even as he was wheeling the whole-hooved horses, and with a stone smote his elbow in the midst; so the reins white with ivory fell from his hands to earth, even into the dust. Then Antilochus sprang on him and drove the sword into his temple, and he fell gasping from the well-wrought chariot headlong in the dust on crown and shoulders. A while he stood there, being lighted on deep sand, until his horses spurned him and cast him to earth, even in the dust; and them Antilochus lashed, and drove them to the Achaeans' host.

But Hector marked them across the ranks, and sprang on them with a shout, and the battalions of the Trojans followed him in their might: and Ares led them on and dread Enyo, she bringing ruthless turmoil of war, the while Ares wielded in his hands his monstrous spear, and ranged now before Hector's face, and now behind.

Then Diomedes of the loud war-cry shuddered to behold him; and even as a shiftless man crossing a great plain cometh on a swift-streaming river flowing on to the sea, and seeing it boil with foam springeth backwards, even so now Diomedes shrank back and spake to the host: "Friends, how marvel we that noble Hector is a spearman and bold man of war! Yet ever is there beside him some god that wardeth off destruction; even as now Ares is there by him in likeness of a mortal man. But with faces towards the Trojans still give ground backwards, neither be desirous to fight amain with gods."

So said he, and the Trojans came very close upon them. Then Hector slew two that knew well the battle joy, riding in one chariot, even Menesthes and Anchialus. And the great Telamonian Aias had pity of them in their fall, and came hard by and darted with his bright javelin, and smote Amphius son of Selagus, that dwelt in Paesus, a man rich in substance, rich in meadow land; but fate led him to bring succour to Priam and his sons. Him Telamonian Aias smote upon the belt, and in his nether belly the far-shadowing spear stuck and he fell with a crash. Then glorious Aias ran at him to strip him of his armour, and the Trojans rained on him keen javelins glittering, and his shield caught many thereof. But he set his heel upon the corpse and plucked forth the spear of bronze; only he could not strip from his shoulders all the fair armour therewith, being overwhelmed of spears. Moreover he feared the haughty Trojans' stout defence, they being many and brave that with their spears pressed on him, so that for all he was so great and valiant and proud they thrust him from them; and he was shaken and shrank back.

Thus toiled these in violent battle; and Tlepolemus son of Heracles, valiant and tall, was driven of forceful fate against godlike Sarpedon. Then when the twain were come nigh in onset on each other, even the son and grandson of Zeus the cloud-gatherer, then first to the other spake Tlepolemus: "Sarpedon, counsellor of the Lycians, why must thou be skulking here, being a man unskilled in battle? Falsely do men say that thou art offspring of aegis-bearing Zeus, seeing thou art found lacking greatly beside those men that in days of old were born of Zeus. Ah, what an one do men say was mighty Heracles, even my father the steadfast lion-heart, who erst came hither for Laomedon's mares with but six ships and a scantier host than ours, yet sacked the city of Ilium and made her highways desolate. But thine is a base spirit, and thy folk are minishing. I ween that thou art in no wise come from Lycia to be a bulwark unto the Trojans, for all thy great strength, but that thou shalt be vanquished at my hand and pass the gates of Hades."

Then Sarpedon captain of the Lycians answered him: "Tlepolemus, Heracles verily overthrew holy Ilium because of the folly of the proud man Laomedon, that rewarded his good deed with harsh upbraiding, and paid him not the steeds wherefor he came from afar. And for thee I say that slaughter and black death shall come about here at my hands; vanquished by my spear thou shalt yield to me my glory, and thy life to Hades of the goodly steeds."

So spake Sarpedon, and Tlepolemus lifted his ashen spear, and both their long javelins sped from their hands together. Sarpedon smote the midst of his neck, and the grievous point passed right through, and the darkness of night fell on his eyes and shrouded him: and Tlepolemus with long spear smote the other's left thigh, and the point sped through furiously, grazing the bone; but his father yet warded off destruction.

So his goodly comrades bare away godlike Sarpedon from

the battle, but the long spear dragging was heavy upon him, and no man marked it or took thought in their haste to draw the ashen spear out from his thigh that he might stand upright; such labour had they in tending him. And over against them the well-greaved Achaeans bare Tlepolemus from the battle. And noble Odysseus of the patient soul marked it, and his heart was stirred within him. Then doubted he in mind and soul whether first to pursue the son of Zeus the loud thunderer, or take the lives of the common sort of the Lycians. But it was not destined to great-hearted Odysseus to slay with his keen blade the mighty son of Zeus; so Athene turned his fury upon the multitude of the Lycians. Then slew he Coeranus and Alastor and Chromius and Alcander and Halius and Noemon and Prytanis; and yet more Lycians had noble Odysseus slain but that great Hector of the glancing helm was swift to mark him, and strode through the forefront of battle, harnessed in flashing bronze, and brought terror to the Danaans; but Sarpedon the son of Zeus was glad at his coming, and spake to him a word of pain: "O son of Priam, let me not now be left a prey unto the Danaans, but bring me succour; howbeit thereafter let my life depart from me in your city, seeing it might not be that I should return home to my dear native land, to make glad my dear wife and infant son."

So said he, but Hector of the glancing helm spake no word to him, but hastened on, desirous with all speed to thrust back the Argives and take the lives of many. So his goodly comrades made godlike Sarpedon to sit beneath a fair oak-tree of aegis-bearing Zeus, and valiant Pelagon that was his dear comrade drew forth from his thigh the ashen spear; and his spirit failed him and mist overspread his eyes. Then breathed he again, and the breath of the north wind blew round about him and brought him to life from the grievous swoon of his soul.

Now the Argives before the face of Ares and mail-clad Hector neither turned them round about toward their black ships, nor charged forward in battle, but still fell backward, when they heard of Ares amid the Trojans. And now who first was slaughtered, and who last, by Hector son of Priam and brazen Ares? Even godlike Teuthras, and thereafter Orestes the charioteer, and Trechus, spearman of Aetolia, and Oenomaus and Helenus, son of Oenops and Oresbius with gleaming taslets, who dwelt in Hyle and had great care of his substance, lying beside the Cephisian mere; and near him dwelt all the Boeotians, inhabiters of a full rich domain.

Now when the white-armed goddess Hera marked them making havoc of the Argives in the press of battle, anon she spake winged words to Athene: "Out on it, thou daugh-

Birth of Athene from the Brain of Zeus, in front of
Poseidon, Hephaestos, Ilithye and Artemis.

PAINTING FROM A PELIKE FOUND AT VULCI.
(BRITISH MUSEUM)

ter of aegis-bearing Zeus, unwearied maiden! Was it for naught we pledged our word to Menelaus, that he should not depart till he had laid waste well-walled Ilium,—if thus we let baleful Ares rage? Go to now, let us twain also take thought of impetuous valour."

So said she, and the bright-eyed goddess Athene disregarded not. So Hera the goddess queen, daughter of great

Cronos, went her way to harness the gold-frontleted steeds;
and Hebe quickly put to the car the curved wheels of
bronze, eight-spoked, upon their axle-tree of iron. Golden is
their felloe,[5] imperishable, and tires of bronze are fitted
thereover, a marvel to look upon; and the naves are of silver, to turn about on either side. And the car is plaited tight
with gold and silver thongs, and two rails run round about
it. And the silver pole stood out therefrom; upon the end
bound she the fair golden yoke, and set thereon the fair
breaststraps of gold, and Hera led beneath the yoke the
horses fleet of foot, and hungered for strife and the battle-
cry. And Athene, daughter of aegis-bearing Zeus, cast down
at her father's threshold her woven vesture many-coloured,
that herself had wrought and her hands had fashioned, and
put on her the tunic of Zeus the cloud-gatherer, and arrayed
her in her armour for dolorous battle. About her shoulders
cast she the tasselled aegis terrible, whereon is Panic as a
crown all round about, and Strife is therein and Valour
and horrible Onslaught withal, and therein is the dreadful
monster's Gorgon head, dreadful and grim, portent of
aegis-bearing Zeus. Upon her head set she the two-crested
golden helm with fourfold plate, bedecked with men-at-
arms of a hundred cities. Upon the flaming chariot set she
her foot, and grasped her heavy spear, great and stout, wherewith she vanquished the ranks of men, even of heroes with
whom she of the awful sire is wroth. Then Hera swiftly
smote the horses with the lash; self-moving groaned upon
their hinges the gates of heaven whereof the Hours are
warders, to whom is committed great heaven and Olympus,
whether to throw open the thick cloud or set it to. There
through the gates guided they their horses patient of the
lash. And they found the son of Cronos sitting apart from
all the gods on the topmost peak of many-ridged Olympus.
Then the white-armed goddess Hera stayed her horses and
questioned the most high Zeus, the son of Cronos, and
said: "Father Zeus, hast thou no indignation with Ares for

---

[5] The circular rim of a wheel, supported by the spokes.

these violent deeds? How great and goodly a company of Achaeans hath he destroyed recklessly and in unruly wise, unto my sorrow. But here in peace Aphrodite and Apollo of the silver bow take their pleasure, having set on this mad one that knoweth not any law. Father Zeus, wilt thou at all be wroth with me if I smite Ares and chase him from the battle in sorry plight?"

And Zeus the cloud-gatherer answered and said to her: "Go to now, set upon him, Athene driver of the spoil, who most is wont to bring sore pain upon him."

So spake he, and the white-armed goddess Hera disregarded not, and lashed her horses; they nothing loth flew on between earth and starry heaven. As far as a man seeth with his eyes into the haze of distance as he sitteth on a place of outlook and gazeth over the wine-dark sea, so far leap the loudly neighing horses of the gods. Now when they came to Troy and the two flowing rivers, even to where Simoïs and Scamander join their streams, there the white-armed goddess Hera stayed her horses and loosed them from the car and poured thick mist round about them, and Simois made ambrosia spring up for them to graze. So the goddesses went their way with step like unto turtledoves, being fain to bring succour to the men of Argos. And when they were now come where the most and most valiant stood, thronging about mighty Diomedes tamer of horses, in the semblance of ravening lions or wild boars whose strength is nowise feeble, then stood the white-armed goddess Hera and shouted in the likeness of great-hearted Stentor with voice of bronze, whose cry was loud as the cry of fifty other men: "Fie upon you, Argives, base things of shame, so brave in semblance! While yet noble Achilles entered continually into battle, then issued not the Trojans even from the Dardanian gate; for they had dread of his terrible spear. But now fight they far from the city at the hollow ships."

So saying she aroused the spirit and soul of every man. And to Diomedes' side sprang the bright-eyed goddess Athene. That lord she found beside his horses and chariot, cooling the wound that Pandarus with his dart had pierced, for his sweat vexed it by reason of the broad baldrick of his round shield; therewith was he vexed and his arm grew weary, so he was lifting up the baldrick and wiping away the dusky blood. Then the goddess laid her hand on his horses' yoke, and said: "Of a truth Tydeus begat a son little after his own likeness. Tydeus was short of stature, but a man of war; yea even when I would not have him fight nor make display—what time he came apart from the Achaeans on an embassage to Thebes, to the midst of the multitude of the Cadmeians, I bade him feast in their halls at peace; but he, possessing his valiant soul as of old time, challenged the young men of the Cadmeians and in everything vanquished easily; so sure a helper was I unto him. But for thee, beside thee stand I and guard thee and with all my heart bid thee fight the Trojans; yet either hath weariness of much striving entered into thy limbs, or disheartening terror hath taken hold of thee. If that be so, no offspring art thou of Tydeus, the wise son of Oeneus."

And stalwart Diomedes made answer to her and said: "I know thee, goddess daughter of aegis-bearing Zeus: therefore with my whole heart will I tell thee my thought and hide it not. Neither hath disheartening terror taken hold upon me, nor any faintness, but I am still mindful of thy behest that thou didst lay upon me. Thou forbadest me to fight face to face with all the blessed gods, save only if Zeus' daughter Aphrodite should enter into battle, then to wound her with the keen bronze. Therefore do I now give ground myself and have bidden all the Argives likewise to gather here together; for I discern Ares lording it in the fray."

Then the bright-eyed goddess Athene answered him: "Diomedes son of Tydeus, thou joy of mine heart, fear thou, for that, neither Ares nor any other of the immortals; so great a helper am I to thee. Go to now, at Ares first guide thou thy whole-hooved horses, and smite him hand to hand, nor have any awe of impetuous Ares, raving here, a curse incarnate, the renegade that of late in converse with me and Hera pledged him to fight against the Trojans and give succour to the Argives, but now consorteth with the Trojans and hath forgotten these."

So speaking, with her hand she drew back Sthenelus and

thrust him from the chariot to earth, and instantly leapt he down, so the goddess mounted the car by noble Diomedes' side right eagerly. The oaken axle creaked loud with its burden, bearing the dread goddess and the man of might. Then Pallas Athene grasped the whip and reins; forthwith against Ares first guided she the whole-hooved horses. Now he was stripping huge Periphas, most valiant far of the Aitolians, Ochesius' glorious son. Him was blood-stained Ares stripping; and Athene donned the helm of Hades, that terrible Ares might not behold her. Now when Ares scourge of mortals beheld noble Diomedes, he left huge Periphas lying there, where at the first he had slain him and taken away his life, and made straight at Diomedes tamer of horses. Now when they were come nigh in onset on one another, first Ares thrust over the yoke and horses' reins with spear of bronze, eager to take away his life. But the bright-eyed goddess Athene with her hand seized the spear and thrust it up over the car, to spend itself in vain. Next Diomedes of the loud war-cry attacked with spear of bronze; and Pallas Athene drave it home against Ares' nethermost belly, where his taslets were girt about him. There smote he him and wounded him, rending through his fair skin, and plucked forth the spear again. Then brazen Ares bellowed loud as nine thousand warriors or ten thousand cry in battle as they join in strife and fray. Thereat trembling gat hold of Achaeans and Trojans for fear, so mightily bellowed Ares insatiate of battle.

Even as gloomy mist appeareth from the clouds when after heat a stormy wind ariseth, even so to Tydeus' son Diomedes brazen Ares appeared amid clouds, faring to wide heaven. Swiftly came he to the gods' dwelling, steep Olympus, and sat beside Zeus son of Cronos with grief at heart, and shewed the immortal blood flowing from the wound, and piteously spake to him winged words: "Father Zeus, hast thou no indignation to behold these violent deeds? For ever cruelly suffer we gods by one another's devices, in shewing men grace. With thee are we all at variance, because thou didst beget that reckless maiden and baleful, whose thought is ever of iniquitous deeds. For all the other gods that are in Olympus hearken to thee, and we are subject every one; only her thou chastenest not, neither in deed nor word, but settest her on, because this pestilent one is thine own offspring. Now hath she urged on Tydeus' son, even overweening Diomedes, to rage furiously against the immortal gods. Aphrodite first he wounded in close fight, in the wrist of her hand, and then assailed he me, even me, with the might of a god. Howbeit my swift feet bare me away; else had I long endured anguish there amid the grisly heaps of dead, or else had lived strengthless from the smitings of the spear."

Then Zeus the cloud-gatherer looked sternly at him and said: "Nay, thou renegade, sit not by me and whine. Most hateful to me art thou of all gods that dwell in Olympus; thou ever lovest strife and wars and battles. Truly thy mother's spirit is intolerable, unyielding, even Hera's; her can I scarce rule with words. Therefore I deem that by her prompting thou art in this plight. Yet will I no longer endure to see thee in anguish; mine offspring art thou, and to me thy mother bare thee. But wert thou born of any other god unto this violence, long ere this hadst thou been lower than the sons of Heaven."

So spake he and bade Paeeon heal him. And Paeeon laid assuaging drugs upon the wound and healed him; seeing he was verily of no mortal substance. Even as fig juice maketh haste to thicken white milk, that is liquid but curdleth speedily as a man stirreth, even so swiftly healed he impetuous Ares. And Hebe bathed him, and clothed him in gracious raiment, and he sate him down by Zeus son of Cronos, glorying in his might.

Then fared the twain back to the mansion of great Zeus, even Hera of Argos and Alalcomenean [6] Athene, having stayed Ares scourge of mortals from his man-slaying.

---

[6] Alalcomeneas was a primordial man, said to have been the tutor of Athene.

VI

Hector Returns to the City

❡ *Many more feats of valor are described. Glaucus the Lycian and Diomedes, challenging each other, discover that they are family friends; leaping from their chariots, they clasp each other by the hands, pledge faith, and exchange armor. The Trojans being hard pressed, Hector returns to Troy to ask his mother and the Trojan women to pray to Athene for them.*

Now when Hector came to the Scaean gates and to the oak-tree, there came running round about him the Trojans' wives and daughters, enquiring of sons and brethren and friends and husbands. But he bade them thereat all in turn pray to the gods; but sorrow hung over many.

But when he came to Priam's beautiful palace, adorned with polished colonnades—and in it were fifty chambers of polished stone, builded hard by one another, wherein Priam's sons slept beside their wedded wives; and for his daughters over against them on the other side within the courtyard were twelve roofed chambers of polished stone builded hard by one another, wherein slept Priam's sons-in-law beside their chaste wives—then came there to meet him his bountiful mother, leading with her Laodice, fairest of her daughters to look on; and she clasped her hand in his, and spake, and called upon his name: "My son, why hast thou left violent battle to come hither? Surely the sons of the Achaeans —name of evil!—press thee hard in fight about thy city, and so thy spirit hath brought thee hither, to come and stretch forth thy hands to Zeus from the citadel. But tarry till I bring thee honey-sweet wine, that thou mayest pour libation to Zeus and all the immortals first, and then shalt thou thyself also be refreshed if thou wilt drink. When a man is aweariled wine greatly maketh his strength to wax, even as thou art aweariled in fighting for thy fellows."

Then great Hector of the glancing helm answered her: "Bring me no honey-hearted wine, my lady mother, lest

Hector, in presence of Priam, takes leave of Hecuba.
PAINTING FROM AN AMPHORA FOUND AT NOLA.
(VATICAN MUSEUM)

thou cripple me of my courage and I be forgetful of my might. Moreover I have awe to make libation of gleaming wine to Zeus with hands unwashen; nor can it be in any wise that one should pray to the son of Cronos, god of the storm-cloud, all defiled with blood and filth. But go thou to the temple of Athene driver of the spoil, with offerings, and gather the aged wives together; and the robe that seemeth to thee the most gracious and greatest in thy palace, and dearest unto thyself, that lay thou upon the knees of beauteous-haired Athene, and vow to her to sacrifice in her temple twelve sleek kine, that have not felt the goad, if she will have mercy on the city and the Trojans' wives and little children. So may she perchance hold back Tydeus' son from holy Ilium, the furious spearman, the mighty deviser of rout. So go thou to the temple of Athene driver of the spoil; and I will go after Paris, to summon him, if perchance he will hearken to my voice. Would that the earth forthwith might swallow him up! The Olympian fostered him to be a sore bane to the Trojans and to great-hearted Priam, and to Priam's sons. If I but saw him going down to the gates of death, then might I deem that my heart had forgotten its sorrow."

So said he, and she went unto the hall, and called to her handmaidens, and they gathered the aged wives throughout the city. Then she herself went down to her fragrant chamber where were her embroidered robes, the work of Sidonian women, whom godlike Alexandros himself brought from Sidon, when he sailed over the wide sea, that journey wherein he brought home high-born Helen. Of these Hecabe took one to bear for an offering to Athene, the one that was fairest for adornment and greatest, and shone like a star, and lay nethermost of all. Then went she her way and the multitude of aged wives hasted after her.

Now when they came to the temple of Athene in the citadel, fair-cheeked Theano opened them the doors, even Cisseus' daughter, wife of horse-taming Antenor; for her the Trojans had made priestess of Athene. Then lifted they all their hands to Athene with lamentation: and fair-cheeked Theano took the robe and laid it on the knees of beauteous-haired Athene, and lifted up her voice and prayed to the daughter of great Zeus: "Lady Athene, saviour of the city, fair among goddesses, break now Diomedes' spear, and grant moreover that himself may fall prone before the Scaean gates; that we may sacrifice thee now forthwith in thy temple twelve sleek kine, that have not felt the goad, if thou wilt have mercy on the city and the Trojans' wives and little children." So spake she praying, but Pallas Athene denied the prayer.

So were these praying to the daughter of great Zeus; and Hector was come to Alexandros' fair palace, that himself had builded with them that were most excellent carpenters then in deep-soiled Troy-land; these made him his chamber and hall and courtyard hard by to Priam and Hector, in the upper city. There entered in Hector dear to Zeus, and his hand bare his spear, eleven cubits long: before his face glittered the bronze spear-point, and a ring of gold ran round about it. And he found Paris in his chamber busied with his beauteous arms, his shield and breastplate, and handling his curved bow; and Helen of Argos sate among her serving-women and appointed brave handiwork for her handmaidens. Then when Hector saw him he rebuked him with scornful words: "Good sir, thou dost not well to cherish this rancour in thy heart. The folk are perishing about the city and high wall in battle, and for thy sake the battle-cry is kindled and war around this city; yea thyself wouldest thou fall out with another, didst thou see him shrinking from hateful war. Up then, lest the city soon be scorched with burning fire."

And godlike Alexandros answered him: "Hector, since in measure thou chidest me and not beyond measure, therefore will I tell thee; lay thou it to thine heart and hearken to me. Not by reason so much of the Trojans, for wrath and indignation, sate I me in my chamber, but fain would I yield me to my sorrow. Even now my wife hath persuaded me with soft words, and urged me into battle; and I moreover, even I, deem that it will be better so; for victory shifteth from man to man. Go to then, tarry awhile, let me put on my armour of war; or else fare thou forth, and I will follow; and I think to overtake thee."

So said he, but Hector of the flashing helm answered him not a word. But Helen spake to him with gentle words: "My brother, even mine that am a dog, mischievous and abominable, would that on the day when my mother bare me at the first, an evil storm-wind had caught me away to a mountain or a billow of the loud-sounding sea, where the billow might have swept me away before all these things came to pass. Howbeit, seeing the gods devised all these ills in this wise, would that then I had been mated with a better man that felt dishonour and the multitude of men's reproachings. But as for him, neither hath he now sound heart, nor ever will have; thereof deem I moreover that he will reap the fruit. But now come, enter in and sit thee here upon this bench, my brother, since thy heart chiefly trouble hath encompassed, for the sake of me, that am a dog, and for Alexandros' sin; on whom Zeus bringeth evil doom, that even in days to come we may be a song in the ears of men that shall be hereafter."

Then great Hector of the flashing helm answered her: "Bid me not sit, Helen, of thy love; thou wilt not persuade me. Already my heart is set to succour the men of Troy, that have great desire for me that am not with them. But rouse thou this fellow, yea let himself make speed, to overtake me yet within the city. For I shall go into mine house to behold my housefolk and my dear wife, and infant boy; for I know not if I shall return home to them again, or if the gods will now overthrow me at the hands of the Achaeans."

So spake Hector of the flashing helm and departed; and anon he came to his well-stablished house. But he found not white-armed Andromache in the halls; she with her boy and fair-robed handmaiden had taken her stand upon the tower, weeping and wailing. And when Hector found not his noble wife within, he came and stood upon the threshold, and spake amid the serving-women: "Come tell me now true, my serving-women. Whither went white-armed Andromache forth from the hall? Hath she gone out to my sisters or unto my brothers' fair-robed wives, or to Athene's temple, where all the fair-tressed Trojan women propitiate the awful goddess?"

Then a busy housedame spake in answer to him: "Hector, seeing thou straitly chargest us tell thee true, neither hath she gone out to any of thy sisters or thy brothers' fair-robed wives, neither to Athene's temple, where all the fair-tressed Trojan women are propitiating the awful goddess; but she went to the great tower of Ilium, because she heard the Trojans were hard pressed, and great victory was for the Achaeans. So hath she come in haste to the wall, like unto one frenzied; and the nurse with her beareth the child."

So spake the housedame, and Hector hastened from his house back by the same way down the well-builded streets. When he had passed through the great city and was come to the Scaean gates, whereby he was minded to issue upon the plain, then came his dear-won wife, running to meet him, even Andromache daughter of great-hearted Eëtion, Eëtion that dwelt beneath wooded Placus, in Thebe under Placus, and was king of the men of Cilicia; for his daughter was wife to bronze-harnessed Hector. So she met him now, and with her went the handmaid bearing in her bosom the tender boy, the little child, Hector's loved son, like unto a beautiful star. Him Hector called Scamandrius, but all the folk Astyanax; [1] for only Hector guarded Ilium. So now he smiled and gazed at his boy silently, and Andromache stood by his side weeping, and clasped her hand in his, and spake and called upon his name. "Dear my lord, this thy hardihood will undo thee, neither hast thou any pity for thine infant boy, nor for me forlorn that soon shall be thy widow; for soon will the Achaeans all set upon thee and slay thee. But it were better for me to go down to the grave if I lose thee; for never more will any comfort be mine, when once thou, even thou, hast met thy fate, but only sorrow. Moreover I have no father nor lady mother: my father was slain of goodly Achilles, for he wasted the populous city of the Cilicians, even high-gated Thebe, and slew Eëtion; yet he despoiled him not, for his soul had shame of that, but he burnt him in his inlaid armour and raised a barrow over him; and all about were elm-trees planted by the mountain nymphs, daughters of aegis-bearing Zeus. And the

---

[1] *Astyanax* means "Lord of the City."

seven brothers that were mine within our halls, all these on the selfsame day went within the house of Hades; for fleet-footed goodly Achilles slew them all amid their kine of trailing gait and white-fleeced sheep. And my mother, that was queen beneath wooded Placus, her brought he hither with the other spoils, but afterward took a ransom untold to set her free; but in her father's halls was she smitten by the Archer Artemis. Nay, Hector, thou art to me father and lady mother, yea and brother, even as thou art my goodly husband. Come now, have pity and abide here upon the tower, lest thou make thy child an orphan and thy wife a widow. And stay thy folk beside the fig-tree, where best the city may be scaled and the wall is assailable. Thrice came thither the most valiant that are with the two Aiantes and famed Idomeneus and the sons of Atreus and Tydeus' valiant son, and essayed to enter; whether one skilled in soothsaying revealed it to them, or whether their own spirit urgeth and biddeth them on."

Then great Hector of the flashing helm answered her: "Surely I take thought for all these things, my wife; but I have very sore shame of the Trojans and Trojan dames with trailing robes, if like a coward I shrink away from battle. Moreover mine own soul forbiddeth me, seeing I have learnt ever to be valiant and fight in the forefront of the Trojans, winning my father's great glory and mine own. Yea of a surety I know this in heart and soul; the day shall come for holy Ilium to be laid low, and Priam and the folk of Priam of the good ashen spear. Yet doth the anguish of the Trojans hereafter not so much trouble me neither Hecabe's own, neither king Priam's, neither my brethren's, the many and brave that shall fall in the dust before their foemen, as doth thine anguish in the day when some mail-clad Achaean shall lead thee weeping and rob thee of the light of freedom. So shalt thou abide in Argos and ply the loom at another woman's bidding, and bear water from fount Messeis or Hypereia, being grievously treated, and sore constraint shall be laid upon thee. And then shall one say that beholdeth thee weep: 'This is the wife of Hector, that was foremost in battle of the horse-taming Trojans when men fought about Ilium.' Thus shall one say hereafter, and fresh grief will be thine for lack of such an husband as thou hadst to ward off the day of thraldom. But me in death may the heaped-up earth be covering, ere I hear thy crying and thy carrying into captivity."

So spake glorious Hector, and stretched out his arm to his boy. But the child shrunk crying to the bosom of his fair-girdled nurse, dismayed at his dear father's aspect, and in dread at the bronze and horse-hair crest that he beheld nodding fiercely from the helmet's top. Then his dear father laughed aloud, and his lady mother; forthwith glorious Hector took the helmet from his head, and laid it, all gleaming, upon the earth; then kissed he his dear son and dandled him in his arms, and spake in prayer to Zeus and all the gods, "O Zeus and all ye gods, vouchsafe ye that this my son may likewise prove even as I, pre-eminent amid the Trojans, and as valiant in might, and be a great king of Ilium. Then may men say of him, 'Far greater is he than his father' as he returneth home from battle; and may he bring with him blood-stained spoils from the foeman he hath slain, and may his mother's heart be glad."

So spake he, and laid his son in his dear wife's arms; and she took him to her fragrant bosom, smiling tearfully. And her husband had pity to see her, and caressed her with his hand, and spake and called upon her name: "Dear one, I pray thee be not of oversorrowful heart; no man against my fate shall hurl me to Hades; only destiny, I ween, no man hath escaped, be he coward or be he valiant, when once he hath been born. But go thou to thine house and see to thine own tasks, the loom and distaff, and bid thine handmaidens ply their work; but for war shall men provide and I in chief of all men that dwell in Ilium."

So spake glorious Hector, and took up his horse-hair crested helmet; and his dear wife departed to her home oft looking back, and letting fall big tears. Anon she came to the well-stablished house of man-slaying Hector, and found therein her many handmaidens, and stirred lamentation in them all. So bewailed they Hector, while yet he lived, within his house: for they deemed that he would no more come back to them from battle, nor escape the fury of the hands of the Achaeans.

Neither lingered Paris long in his lofty house, but clothed on him his brave armour, bedight with bronze, and hasted through the city, trusting to his nimble feet. Even as when a stalled horse, full-fed at the manger, breaketh his tether and speedeth at the gallop across the plain, being wont to bathe him in the fair-flowing stream, exultingly; and holdeth his head on high, and his mane floateth about his shoulders, and he trusteth in his glory, and nimbly his limbs bear him to the haunts and pasturage of mares; even so Priam's son Paris, glittering in his armour like the shining sun, strode down from high Pergamus laughingly, and his swift feet bare him. Forthwith he overtook his brother noble Hector, even as he was on the point to turn him away from the spot where he had dallied with his wife. To him first spake godlike Alexandros: "Sir, in good sooth I have delayed thee in thine haste by my tarrying, and came not rightly as thou badest me."

And Hector of the flashing helm answered him and said: "Good brother, no man that is rightminded could make light of thy doings in fight, seeing thou art strong: but thou art wilfully remiss and hast no care; and for this my heart is grieved within me, that I hear shameful words concerning thee in the Trojans' mouths, who for thy sake endure much toil. But let us be going; all this will we make good hereafter, if Zeus ever vouchsafe us to set before the heavenly gods that are for everlasting the cup of deliverance in our halls, when we have chased out of Troy-land the well-greaved Achaeans."

VII

Voting of the Achaians.

PAINTING FROM A KYLIX.
(BASSEGGIO COLL., ROME)

Aias and Hector Fight

❴ Hector proposes to the Achaeans that he engage a champion of theirs in combat. Aias is chosen by lot, and they fight until night stops them.

Among the Trojans, Antenor proposes that Helen and her wealth be sent back to the Achaeans. Paris is willing to send her wealth, and more, but not Helen. At dawn the herald goes to the Achaeans with this word. Being confident of the destruction of Troy, they refuse the offer, but agree to a truce so that the Trojans may burn their dead. After the dead of both sides have been burned, the Achaeans build a wall before the ships, digging a deep ditch in front of it, and planting a row of stakes in the ditch.

VIII

Zeus thundered terribly and darted his white lightning.

The Trojans Reach the Achaean Wall

❬ On Olympus, Zeus, with threats, forbids the immortals to give help to either side. Then he goes to Mt. Ida to watch the war from the mountain tops. All day the battle wavers to and fro with, however, the best of it going to Hector. When night comes, the Trojans camp: "Even as when in heaven the stars about the bright moon shine clear to see, when the air is windless, and all the peaks appear and the tall headlands and glades, and from heaven breaketh open the infinite air, and all stars are seen, and the shepherd's heart is glad; even in like multitude between the ships and the streams of Xanthus appeared the watchfires that the Trojans kindled in front of Ilium."

IX

Agamemnon Tries to Heal the Quarrel

Thus kept the Trojans watch; but the Achaeans were holden of heaven-sent panic, handmaid of palsying fear, and all their best were stricken to the heart with grief intolerable. Like as two winds stir up the main, the home of fishes, even the north wind and the west wind that blow from Thrace, coming suddenly; and the dark billow straightway lifteth up its crest and casteth much tangle out along the sea; even so was the Achaeans' spirit troubled in their breast.

But Atreides was stricken to the heart with sore grief, and went about bidding the clear-voiced heralds summon every man by name to the assembly, but not to shout aloud; and himself he toiled amid the foremost. So they sat sorrowful in assembly, and Agamemnon stood up weeping like unto a fountain of dark water that from a beetling cliff poureth down its black stream; even so with deep groaning he spake amid the Argives and said: "My friends, leaders and captains of the Argives, Zeus son of Cronos hath bound me with might in grievous blindness of soul; hard of heart is he, for that erewhile he promised and gave his pledge that not till I had laid waste well-walled Ilium should I depart, but now hath planned a cruel wile, and biddeth me return in dishonour to Argos with the loss of many of my folk. Such meseemeth is the good pleasure of most mighty Zeus that hath laid low the heads of many cities, yea and shall lay low; for his is highest power. So come, even as I shall bid let us all obey; let us flee with our ships to our dear native land, for now shall we never take wide-wayed Troy."

So said he, and they all held their peace and kept silence. Long time were the sons of the Achaeans voiceless for grief, but at the last Diomedes of the loud war-cry spake amid them and said: "Atreides, with thee first in thy folly will I contend, where it is just, O king, even in the assembly; be not thou wroth therefor. My valour didst thou blame in chief amid the Danaans, and saidst that I was no man of war but a coward; and all this know the Argives both young and old. But the son of crooked-counselling Cronos hath endowed thee but by halves; he granted thee to have the honour of the sceptre above all men, but valour he gave thee not, wherein is highest power. Sir, deemest thou that the sons of the Achaeans are thus indeed cowards and weaklings as thou sayest? But and if thine own heart be set on departing, go thy way; the way is before thee, and thy ships stand beside the sea, even the great multitude that followed thee from Mycene. But all the other flowing-haired Achaeans will tarry here until we lay waste Troy. Nay, let them too flee on their ships to their dear native land; yet will we twain, even I and Sthenelus, fight till we attain the goal of Ilium; for in God's name are we come."

So said he, and all the sons of the Achaeans shouted aloud, applauding the saying of horse-taming Diomedes. Then knightly Nestor arose and said amid them: "Son of Tydeus, in battle art thou passing mighty, and in council art thou best among thine equals in years; none of all the Achaeans will make light of thy word nor gainsay it; but thou hast not made a full end of thy words. Moreover thou art a young man indeed, and mightest even be my son, my youngest-born; yet thou counsellest prudently the princes of the Achaeans, because thou speakest according unto right. But lo, I that avow me to be older than thou will speak forth and expound everything; neither shall any man despise my saying, not even the lord Agamemnon. A tribeless, lawless, homeless man is he that loveth bitter civil strife. Howbeit now let us yield to black night and make ready our meal;

and let the sentinels bestow them severally along the deep-delved fosse without the wall. This charge give I to the young men; and thou, Atreides, lead then the way, for thou art the most royal. Spread thou a feast for the councillors; that is thy place and seemly for thee. Thy huts are full of wine that the ships of the Achaeans bring thee by day from Thrace across the wide sea; all entertainment is for thee, being king over many. In the gathering of many shalt thou listen to him that deviseth the most excellent counsel; sore need have all the Achaeans of such as is good and prudent, because hard by the ships our foemen are burning their watch-fires in multitude; what man can rejoice thereat? This night shall either destroy or save the host."

So said he, and they gladly hearkened to him and obeyed. Forth sallied the sentinels in their harness, around Thrasymedes Nestor's son, shepherd of the host, and Ascalaphus and Ialmenus sons of Ares, and Meriones and Aphareus and Deipyrus and Creon's son noble Lycomedes. Seven were the captains of the sentinels, and with each went fivescore young men bearing their long spears in their hands; and they took post midway betwixt fosse and wall, and kindled a fire and made ready each man his meal.

Then Atreides gathered the councillors of the Achaeans, and led them to his hut, and spread before them an abundant feast. So they put forth their hands to the good cheer that lay before them. And when they had put away from them the desire of meat and drink, then the old man first began to weave his counsel, even Nestor, whose rede of old time was approved the best. He of good intent spake to them and said: "Most noble son of Atreus, Agamemnon king of men, in thy name will I end and with thy name begin, because thou art king over many hosts, and to thy hand Zeus hath entrusted sceptre and law, that thou mayest take counsel for thy folk. Thee therefore more than any it behoveth both to speak and hearken, and to accomplish what another than thou may say, when his heart biddeth him speak for profit: wheresoever thou leadest all shall turn on thee, so I will speak as meseemeth best. No other man shall have a more excellent thought than this that I bear in mind from old time even until now, since the day when thou, O heaven-sprung king, didst go and take the damsel Briseis from angry Achilles' hut by no consent of ours. Nay, I right heartily dissuaded thee; but thou yieldedst to thy proud spirit, and dishonouredest a man of valour whom even the immortals honoured; for thou didst take and keepest from him his meed of valour. Still let us even now take thought how we may appease him and persuade him with gifts of friendship and kindly words."

And Agamemnon king of men answered and said to him: "Old sir, in no false wise hast thou accused my folly. Fool was I, I myself deny it not. Worth many hosts is he whom Zeus loveth in his heart, even as now he honoureth this man and destroyeth the host of the Achaeans. But seeing I was a fool in that I yielded to my sorry passion, I will make amends and give a recompense beyond telling. In the midst of you all I will name the excellent gifts; seven tripods untouched of fire, and ten talents of gold and twenty gleaming caldrons, and twelve stalwart horses, winners in the race, that have taken prizes by their speed. No lackwealth were that man, neither undowered of precious gold, whose substance were as great as the prizes my whole-hooved steeds have borne me off. And seven women will I give, skilled in excellent handiwork, Lesbians whom I chose me from the spoils the day that he himself took stablished Lesbos, surpassing womankind in beauty. These will I give him, and with them shall be she whom erst I took from him, even the daughter of Briseus; moreover I will swear a great oath that never I went up into her bed nor slept with her as is the wont of mankind, even of men and women. All these things shall be set straightway before him; and if hereafter the gods grant us to lay waste the great city of Priam, then let him enter in when we Achaeans be dividing the spoil, and load his ship full of gold and bronze, and himself choose twenty Trojan women, the fairest that there be after Helen of Argos. And if we win to the richest of lands, even Achaean Argos, he shall be my son and I will hold him in like honour with Orestes, my stripling boy that is nurtured in all abundance. Three daughters are mine in my well-builded hall, Chrysothemis and Laodice and Iphianassa; let him take of them which he will, without gifts of wooing, to Peleus' house; and I will add a great dower such as no man ever yet gave with his daughter. And seven well-peopled cities will I give him, Cardamyle and Enope and grassy Hire and holy Pherae and Antheia deep in meads, and fair Aepeia and Pedasus land of vines. And all are nigh to the salt sea, on the uttermost border of sandy Pylos; therein dwell men abounding in flocks and kine, men that shall worship him like a god with gifts, and beneath his sway fulfil his prosperous ordinances. All this will I accomplish so he but cease from wrath. Let him yield; Hades I ween is not to be softened neither overcome, and therefore is he hatefullest of all gods to mortals. Yea, let him be ruled by me, inasmuch as I am more royal and avow me to be the elder in years."

Then knightly Nestor of Gerenia[1] answered and said: "Most noble son of Atreus, Agamemnon king of men, now are these gifts not lightly to be esteemed that thou offerest king Achilles. Come therefore, let us speed forth picked men to go with all haste to the hut of Peleus' son Achilles. Lo now, whomsoever I appoint let them consent. First let Phoenix dear to Zeus lead the way, and after him great Aias and noble Odysseus; and for heralds let Odius and Eurybates be their companions. And now bring water for our hands, and bid keep holy silence, that we may pray unto Zeus the son of Cronos, if perchance he will have mercy upon us."

So said he, and spake words that were well-pleasing unto all. Forthwith the heralds poured water on their hands, and the young men filled the bowls to the brim with drink and gave each man his portion after they had poured the libation in the cups. And when they had made libation

---

[1] So called because he lived for a time among the Gerenians in Messenia.

and drunk as their heart desired, they issued forth from the hut of Agamemnon son of Atreus. And knightly Nestor of Gerenia gave them full charge, with many a glance to each, and chiefest to Odysseus, how they should essay to prevail on Peleus' noble son.

So the twain went along the shore of the loud-sounding sea, making many a prayer to the earth-embracer, the Shaker of the Earth, that they might with ease prevail on Achilles'

Phoenix, Aias, Odysseus entreat Achilles to fight the Trojans.

PAINTING FROM A CALYXKRATER FOUND AT CAERE.
(LOUVRE MUSEUM)

great heart. So they came to the huts and ships of the Myrmidons, and found their king taking his pleasure of a loud lyre, fair, of curious work, with a silver cross-bar upon it; one that he had taken from the spoils when he laid Eëtion's city waste. Therein he was delighting his soul, and singing the glories of heroes. And over against him sate Patroclus alone in silence, watching till Achilles should cease from singing. So the twain came forward, and noble Odysseus led the way, and they stood before his face; and Achilles sprang up amazed with the lyre in his hand, and left the seat where he was sitting, and in like manner Patroclus when he beheld the men arose. Then Achilles fleet of foot

greeted them and said: "Welcome; verily ye are friends that
are come—sore indeed is the need—even ye that are dearest
of the Achaeans to me even in my wrath."

So spake noble Achilles and led them forward, and made
them sit on settles and carpets of purple; and anon he spake
to Patroclus being near: "Bring forth a greater bowl, thou
my lord Patroclus; mingle stronger drink, and prepare each
man a cup, for dearest of men are these that are under my
roof."

So said he, and Patroclus hearkened to his dear comrade.
He cast down a great bench in the fire-light, and laid thereon
a sheep's back and a fat goat's, and a great hog's chine rich
with fat. And Automedon held them for him, while Achilles
carved. Then he sliced well the meat and pierced it through
with spits, and Patroclus, that godlike hero, made the fire
burn high. Then when the fire was burned down and the
flame waned, he scattered the embers and laid the spits
thereover, resting them on the spit-racks, when he had sprinkled them with holy salt. Then when he had roasted the
meat and apportioned it in the platters, Patroclus took bread
and dealt it forth on the table in fair baskets, and Achilles
dealt the meat. And he sate him over against godlike
Odysseus by the other wall, and bade his comrade Patroclus
do sacrifice to the gods; so he cast the first-fruits into the
fire. Then put they forth their hands to the good cheer
lying before them. And when they had put from them the
desire of meat and drink, Aias nodded to Phoenix. But noble
Odysseus marked it, and filled a cup with wine and pledged
Achilles:

"Hail, O Achilles! The fair feast lack we not either in
the hut of Agamemnon son of Atreus neither now in thine;
for feasting is there abundance to our heart's desire, but our
thought is not for matters of the delicious feast; nay, we behold very sore destruction, thou fosterling of Zeus, and are
afraid. Now is it in doubt whether we save the benched ships
or behold them perish, if thou put not on thy might. Nigh
unto ships and wall have the high-hearted Trojans and
famed allies pitched their camp, and kindled many fires

throughout their host, and ween that they shall no more be withheld but will fall on our black ships. And Zeus son of Cronos sheweth them signs upon the right by lightning, and Hector greatly exulteth in his might and rageth furiously, trusting in Zeus, and recketh not of god nor man, for mighty madness hath possessed him. He prayeth bright Dawn to shine forth with all speed, for he hath passed his word to smite off from the ships the ensigns' tops, and to fire the hulls with devouring flame, and hard thereby to make havoc of the Achaeans confounded by the smoke. Therefore am I sore afraid in my heart lest the gods fulfil his boastings, and it be fated for us to perish here in Troy-land, far from Argos pasture-land of horses. Up then! if thou art minded even at the last to save the failing sons of the Achaeans from the war-din of the Trojans. Thyself shalt have grief hereafter, and when the ill is done is there no way to find a cure therefor; in good time rather take thou thought to ward the evil day from the Danaans. Friend, surely to thee thy father Peleus gave commandment the day he sent thee to Agamemnon forth from Phthia: 'My son, strength shall Athene and Hera give thee if they will; but do thou refrain thy proud soul in thy breast, for gentlemindedness is the better part; and withdraw from mischievous strife, that so the Argives may honour thee the more, both young and old.' Thus the old man charged thee, but thou forgettest. Yet cease now at the last, and eschew thy grievous wrath; Agamemnon offereth thee worthy gifts, so thou wilt cease from anger. Lo now, hearken thou to me, and I will tell thee all the gifts that in his hut Agamemnon promised thee: seven tripods untouched of fire, and ten talents of gold and twenty gleaming caldrons and twelve stalwart horses, win-ners in the race, that have taken prizes by their speed. No lackwealth were that man, neither undowered of precious gold, whose substance were as great as the prizes Agamem-non's steeds have borne him off. And seven women will he give, skilled in excellent handiwork, Lesbians whom he chose him from the spoils the day that thou thyself tookest Lesbos, surpassing womankind in beauty. These will he give thee, and with them shall be she whom erst he took from thee, even the daughter of Briseus; moreover he will swear a great oath that never he went up into her bed nor slept with her as is the wont of mankind, O king, even of men and women. All these things shall be set straightway before thee; and if hereafter the gods grant us to lay waste the great city of Priam, then enter thou in when we Achaeans be dividing the spoil, and load thy ship full of gold and bronze, and thyself choose twenty Trojan women, the fairest that there be after Helen of Argos. And if we win to the richest of lands, even Achaean Argos, thou shalt be his son and he will hold thee in like honour with Orestes, his stripling boy that is nurtured in all abundance. Three daughters are his in his well-builded hall, Chrysothemis and Laodice and Iphianassa; take thou of them which thou wilt, without gifts of wooing, to Peleus' house; and he will add a great dower such as no man ever yet gave with his daughter. And seven well-peopled cities will he give thee, Cardamyle and Enope and grassy Hire and holy Pherae and Antheia deep in meads, and fair Aepeia and Pedasus land of vines. And all are nigh to the sea, on the uttermost border of sandy Pylos; therein dwell men abounding in flocks and kine, men that shall worship thee like a god with gifts, and beneath thy sway fulfil thy prosperous ordinances. All this will he accomplish so thou but cease from wrath. But and if Agamemnon be too hateful to thy heart, both he and his gifts, yet have thou pity on all the Achaeans that faint throughout the host; these shall honour thee as a god, for verily thou wilt earn exceeding great glory at their hands. Yea now mightest thou slay Hector, for he would come very near thee in his deadly madness, because he deemeth that there is no man like unto him among the Danaans that the ships brought hither."

And Achilles fleet of foot answered and said unto him: "Heaven-sprung son of Laertes, Odysseus of many wiles, in openness must I now declare unto you my saying, even as I am minded and as the fulfilment thereof shall be, that ye may not sit before me and coax in turn. For hateful to me even as the gates of hell is he that hideth one thing in his heart and uttereth another: but I will speak what meseemeth best. Not me, I ween, shall Agamemnon son of Atreus persuade, nor the other Danaans, seeing we were to have no thank for battling with the foemen ever without respite. He that abideth at home hath equal share with him that fighteth his best, and in like honour are held both the coward and the brave; death cometh alike to the untoiling and to him that hath toiled long. Neither have I any profit for that I endured tribulation of soul, ever staking my life in fight. Even as a hen bringeth her unfledged chickens each morsel as she winneth it, and with herself it goeth hard, even so I was wont to watch out many a sleepless night and pass through many bloody days of battle, warring with folk for their women's sake. Twelve cities of men have I laid waste from ship-board, and from land eleven, throughout deep-soiled Troy-land; out of all these took I many goodly treasures and would bring and give them all to Agamemnon son of Atreus, and he staying behind amid the fleet ships would take them and portion out some few but keep the most. Now some he gave to be meeds of honour to the princes and the kings, and theirs are left untouched; only from me of all the Achaeans took he my darling lady and keepeth her—let him sleep beside her and take his joy!

"But why must the Argives make war on the Trojans? why hath Atreides gathered his host and led them hither? is it not for lovely-haired Helen's sake? Do then the sons of Atreus alone of mortal men love their wives? surely whatsoever man is good and sound of mind loveth his own and cherisheth her, even, as I too loved mine with all my heart, though but the captive of my spear. But now that he hath taken my meed of honour from mine arms and hath deceived me, let him not tempt me that know him full well; he shall not prevail.

"Nay, Odysseus, let him take counsel with thee and all the princes to ward from the ships the consuming fire. Verily without mine aid he hath wrought many things, and built a wall and dug a fosse about it wide and deep, and set a palisade therein; yet even so can he not stay murderous Hector's might. But so long as I was fighting amid the Achaeans, Hector had no mind to array his battle far from the city wall, but scarce came unto the Scaean gates and to the oak-tree; there once he awaited me alone and scarce escaped my onset. But now, seeing I have no mind to fight with noble Hector, I will to-morrow do sacrifice to Zeus and all the gods, and store well my ships when I have launched them on the salt sea—then shalt thou see, if thou wilt and hast any care therefor, my ships sailing at break of day over Hellespont, the fishes' home, and my men right eager at the oar; and if the great Shaker of the Earth grant me good journey, on the third day should I reach deep-soiled Phthia. There are my great possessions that I left when I came hither to my hurt; and yet more gold and ruddy bronze shall I bring home hence, and fair-girdled women and grey iron, all at least that were mine by lot; only my meed of honour hath he that gave it me taken back in his despitefulness, even lord Agamemnon son of Atreus.

"To him declare ye everything even as I charge you, openly, that all the Achaeans likewise may have indignation, if haply he hopeth to beguile yet some other Danaan, for that he is ever clothed in shamelessness. Verily not in my face would he dare to look, for all his impudence. Neither will I devise counsel with him nor any enterprise, for utterly he hath deceived me and done wickedly; but never again shall he beguile me with fair speech—let this suffice him. Let him begone in peace; Zeus the lord of counsel hath taken away his wits.

"Hateful to me are his gifts, and I hold him at a straw's worth. Not even if he gave me ten times, yea twenty, all that now is his, and all that may come to him otherwhence, even all the revenue of Orchomenus or Egyptian Thebes where the treasure-houses are stored fullest—Thebes of the hundred gates, whence sally forth two hundred warriors through each with horses and chariots—nay, nor gifts in number as sand or dust; not even so shall Agamemnon persuade my soul till he have paid me back all the bitter despite.

"And the daughter of Agamemnon son of Atreus will I not wed, not were she rival of golden Aphrodite for fairness and for handiwork matched bright-eyed Athene—not even then will I wed her; let him choose him of the Achaeans another that is his peer and is more royal than I. For if the gods indeed preserve me and I come unto my home, then will Peleus himself seek me a wife. Many Achaean maidens are there throughout Hellas and Phthia, daughters of princes that ward their cities; whomsoever of these I wish will I make my dear lady. Very often was my high soul moved to take me there a wedded wife, a help meet for me, and have joy of the possessions that the old man Peleus possesseth. For not of like worth with life hold I even all the wealth that men say was possessed of the well-peopled city of Ilium in days of peace gone by, before the sons of the Achaeans came; neither all the treasure that the stone threshold of the archer Phoebus Apollo encompasseth in rocky Pytho. For kine and goodly flocks are to be had for the harrying, and tripods and chestnut horses for the purchasing; but to bring back man's life neither harrying nor earning availeth when once it hath passed the barrier of his lips. For thus my goddess mother telleth me, Thetis the silver-footed, that twain fates are bearing me to the issue of death. If I abide here and besiege the Trojans' city, then my returning home is taken from me, but my fame shall be imperishable; but if I go home to my dear native land, my high fame is taken from me, but my life shall endure long while, neither shall the issue of death soon reach me.

"Moreover I would counsel you all to set sail homeward, seeing ye shall never reach your goal of steep Ilium; of a surety far-seeing Zeus holdeth his hand over her and her folk are of good courage. So go your way and tell my answer to the princes of the Achaeans, even as is the office of elders, that they may devise in their hearts some other better counsel, such as shall save them their ships and the host of the Achaeans amid the hollow ships: since this counsel availeth them naught that they have now devised, by reason of my fierce wrath. But let Phoenix now abide with us and lay him to rest, that he may follow with me on my ships to our dear native land to-morrow, if he will; for I will not take him perforce."

So spake he, and they all held their peace and were still, and marvelled at his saying; for he denied them very vehemently. But at the last spake to them the old knight Phoenix, bursting into tears, because he was sore afraid for the ships of the Achaeans: "If indeed thou ponderest departure in thy heart, glorious Achilles, and hast no mind at all to save the fleet ships from consuming fire, because that wrath hath entered into thy heart; how can I be left of thee, dear son, alone thereafter? To thee did the old knight Peleus send me the day he sent thee to Agamemnon forth from Phthia, a stripling yet unskilled in equal war and in debate wherein men wax pre-eminent. Therefore sent he me to teach thee all these things, to be both a speaker of words and a doer of deeds. So would I not be left alone of thee, dear son, not even if god himself should take on him to strip my years from me, and make me fresh and young as in the day when first I left Hellas the home of fair women, fleeing from strife against my father Amyntor son of Ormenus: for he was sore angered with me by reason of his lovely-haired concubine, whom he ever cherished and wronged his wife my mother. So she besought me continually by my knees to go in first unto the concubine, that the old man might be hateful to her. I hearkened to her and did the deed; but my sire was ware thereof forthwith and cursed me mightily, and called the dire Erinyes to look that never should any dear son sprung of my body sit upon my knees; and the gods fulfilled his curse, even Zeus of the underworld and dread Persephone. Then took I counsel to slay him with the keen sword; but some immortal stayed mine anger, bringing to my mind the people's voice and all the reproaches of men, lest I should be called a father-slayer amid the Achaeans. Then would my soul no more be restrained all within my breast to tarry in the halls of mine angered father. Now my fellows and my kinsmen came about me with many prayers, and restrained me there within the halls, and slaughtered many goodly sheep and shambling kine with crooked horns; and many swine rich with fat were stretched to singe over the flames of Hephaestus, and wine from that old man's jars was drunken without stint. Nine nights long slept they all night around my body; they kept watch in turn, neither were the fires quenched, one beneath the colonnade of the fenced courtyard and another in the porch before the chamber doors. But when the tenth dark night was come upon me, then burst I my cunningly fitted chamber doors, and issued forth and overleapt the courtyard fence lightly, unmarked of watchmen and handmaidens. Then fled I far through Hellas of wide lawns, and came to deep-soiled Phthia, mother of flocks, even unto king Peleus; and he received me kindly and cherished me as a father cherisheth his only son, his stripling heir of great possessions; and he made me rich and gave much people to me, and I dwelt in the uttermost part of Phthia and was king over the Dolopians.

"Yea, I reared thee to this greatness, thou godlike Achilles, with my heart's love; for with none other wouldest thou go unto the feast, neither take meat in the hall, till that I had set thee upon my knees and stayed thee with the savoury morsel cut first for thee, and put the wine-cup to thy lips. Oft hast thou stained the doublet on my breast with sputtering of wine in thy sorry helplessness. Thus I suffered much with thee and much I toiled, being mindful that the gods in nowise created any issue of my body; but I made thee my son, thou godlike Achilles, that thou mayest yet save me from grievous destruction.

"Therefore, Achilles, rule thy high spirit; neither beseemeth it thee to have a ruthless heart. Nay, even the very gods can bend, and theirs withal is loftier majesty and honour and might. Their hearts by incense and reverent vows and drink-offering and burnt-offering men turn with prayer, so oft as any transgresseth and doeth sin. Moreover Prayers of penitence are daughters of great Zeus, halting and wrinkled and of eyes askance, that have their task withal to go in the steps of Sin. For Sin is strong and fleet of foot, wherefore she far outrunneth all prayers, and goeth before them over all the earth making men fall, and Prayers follow behind to heal the harm. Now whosoever reverenceth Zeus' daughters when they draw near, him they greatly bless and hear his petitions; but when one denieth them and stiffly refuseth, then depart they and make prayer unto Zeus the son of Cronos that sin may come upon such an one, that he may fall and pay the price. Nay, Achilles, look thou too that there attend upon the daughters of Zeus the reverence that bendeth the heart of all men that be right-minded. For if Atreides brought thee not gifts and foretold thee not more hereafter, but were ever furiously wroth, then I were not he that should bid thee cast aside thine anger and save the Argives, even in their sore need of thee. But now he both offereth thee forthwith many gifts, and promiseth thee more hereafter, and hath sent heroes to beseech thee, the best men chosen throughout the host of the Achaeans and that to thyself are dearest of the Argives; dishonour not thou their petition nor their journey hither; though erst it were no wrong that thou wast wroth."

Phoenix tells the story of Meleager, who nursed his wrath when injured, but who was finally persuaded to help save his city.

"Nay, come for the gifts; the Achaeans shall honour thee even as a god. But if without gifts thou enter into battle the bane of men, thou wilt not be held in like honour, even though thou avert the fray."

And Achilles fleet of foot made answer and said to him: "Phoenix my father, thou old man fosterling of Zeus, such honour need I in no wise; for I deem that I have been honoured by the judgment of Zeus, which shall abide upon me amid my beaked ships as long as breath tarrieth in my body and my limbs are strong. Moreover I will say this thing to thee and lay thou it to thine heart; trouble not my soul by weeping and lamentation, to do the pleasure of warrior Atreides; neither beseemeth it thee to cherish him, lest thou be hated of me that cherish thee. It were good that thou with me shouldest vex him that vexeth me. Be thou king even as I, and share my sway by halves, but these shall bear my message. So tarry thou here and lay thee to rest in a soft bed, and with break of day will we consider whether to depart unto our own, or to abide."

He spake, and nodded his brow in silence unto Patroclus to spread for Phoenix a thick couch, that the others might bethink them to depart from the hut with speed. Then spake to them Aias, Telamon's godlike son, and said: "Heaven-sprung son of Laertes, Odysseus of many wiles, let us go hence; for methinks the purpose of our charge will not by this journey be accomplished; and we must tell the news, though it be no wise good, with all speed unto the Danaans, that now sit awaiting. But Achilles hath wrought his proud soul to fury within him—stubborn man, that recketh naught of his comrades' love, wherein we worshipped him beyond all men amid the ships—unmerciful! Yet doth a man accept recompense of his brother's murderer or for his dead son; and so the man-slayer for a great price abideth in his own land, and the kinsman's heart is appeased, and his proud soul, when he hath taken the recompense. But for thee, the gods have put within thy breast a spirit implacable and evil, by reason of one single damsel. And now we offer thee seven damsels, far best of all, and many other gifts besides; entertain thou then a kindly spirit, and have respect unto thine home; because we are guests of thy roof, sent of the multitude of Danaans, and we would fain be nearest to thee and dearest beyond all other Achaeans, as many as there be."

And Achilles fleet of foot made answer and said to him: "Aias sprung of Zeus, thou son of Telamon, prince of the folk, thou seemest to speak all this almost after mine own mind; but my heart swelleth with wrath as oft as I bethink me of those things, how Atreides entreated me arrogantly among the Argives, as though I were some worthless sojourner. But go ye and declare my message; I will not take thought of bloody war until that wise Priam's son, noble Hector, come to the Myrmidons' huts and ships, slaying the

Argives, and smirch the ships with fire. But about mine hut and black ship I ween that Hector, though he be very eager for battle, shall be refrained."

So said he, and they took each man a two-handled cup, and made libation and went back along the line of ships; and Odysseus led the way. And Patroclus bade his fellows and handmaidens spread with all speed a thick couch for Phoenix; and they obeyed and spread a couch as he ordained, fleeces and rugs and fine flock of linen. Then the old man laid him down and tarried for bright Dawn. And Achilles slept in the corner of the morticed hut, and by his side lay a woman that he brought from Lesbos, even Phorbas' daughter fair-cheeked Diomede. And on the other side Patroclus lay, and by his side likewise fair-girdled Iphis, whom noble Achilles gave him at the taking of steep Scyros, the city of Enyeus.

Now when those were come unto Atreides' huts, the sons of the Achaeans stood up on this side and on that, and pledged them in cups of gold, and questioned them; and Agamemnon king of men asked them first: "Come now, tell me, Odysseus full of praise, thou great glory of the Achaeans; will he save the ships from consuming fire, or said he nay, and hath wrath yet hold of his proud spirit?"

And steadfast goodly Odysseus answered him: "Most noble son of Atreus, Agamemnon king of men, he yonder hath no mind to quench his wrath, but is yet more filled of fury, and spurneth thee and thy gifts. He biddeth thee take counsel for thyself amid the Argives, how to save the ships and folk of the Achaeans. And for himself he threateneth that at break of day he will launch upon the sea his trim well-benched ships. Moreover he said that he would counsel all to sail for home, because ye now shall never reach your goal of steep Ilium; surely far-seeing Zeus holdeth his hand over her and her folk are of good courage. Even so said he, and here are also these to tell the tale that were my companions, Aias and the two heralds, both men discreet. But the old man Phoenix laid him there to rest, even as Achilles bade him, that he may follow with him on his ships to his dear native land to-morrow, if he will; for he will not take him perforce."

So said he, and they all held their peace and were still, marvelling at his saying, for he harangued very vehemently. Long were the sons of the Achaeans voiceless for grief, but at the last Diomedes of the loud war-cry spake amid them: "Most noble son of Atreus, Agamemnon king of men, would thou hadst never besought Peleus' glorious son with offer of gifts innumerable; proud is he at any time, but now hast thou yet far more encouraged him in his haughtiness. Howbeit we will let him bide, whether he go or tarry; hereafter he shall fight, whenever his heart within him biddeth and god arouseth him. Come now, even as I shall say let us all obey. Go ye now to rest, full to your hearts' desire of meat and wine, wherein courage is and strength; but when fair rosy-fingered Dawn appeareth, array thou with all speed before the ships thy folk and horsemen, and urge them on; and fight thyself amid the foremost."

So said he, and all the princes gave assent, applauding the saying of Diomedes tamer of horses. And then they made libation and went every man to his hut, and there laid them to rest and took the boon of sleep.

X

Odysseus with Diomedes takes one of the horses of Rhesos.

PAINTING FROM A CALYX KRATER.
(AUSTRIAN MUSEUM, VIENNA)

The Night Raid on the Trojan Camp

(The Achaeans send Diomedes and Odysseus as spies to the
Trojan camp. They capture the Trojan Dolon, who is on his way
to spy on the Achaeans. He gives them much information, particularly about Rhesus of Thrace and his beautiful swift horses.
For his pains, Dolon receives death. Because these Thracians
lie apart from the rest of the hosts, Diomedes and Odysseus
quite easily slay Rhesus with twelve of his men and drive his
horses into the Achaean camp.

XI

Argives Arming Themselves.
PAINTING FROM A CUP BY EUPHRONIUS FOUND AT VULCI.
(PERUGIA MUSEUM)

The Achaeans Suffer

⟨ The next morning the battle begins again. Agamemnon leads in driving the Trojans back to their walls. A messenger from Zeus tells Hector to keep out of the fight until Agamemnon is wounded; at this time Hector will drive the Achaeans back to their ships. The word of Zeus is fulfilled. Agamemnon is wounded, and so are Odysseus and Diomedes—so also is Machaon the physician, who is taken out of the battle by Nestor. Achilles sees Nestor driving someone into the camp and sends Patroclus to make sure who it is. For Patroclus, this is the beginning of evil. Nestor suggests that if Achilles will not fight, he allow Patroclus to fight in his armor, leading his men.

XII

The Trojans March Against the Danaans.

Hector Storms the Achaean Wall

⟨ Led by Hector fighting like a whirlwind, the Trojans storm
the dike and the walls before the Achaean ships. But an eagle
appears at the left hand of the Trojans, bearing a blood-red
snake, which attacks it so that it drops the snake. Polydamus
interprets this as an evil omen. Hector reminds him of the
promise of Zeus and continues: "But thou bidst us be obedient
to birds long of wing, whereto I give no heed, nor take any
care thereof, whether they fare to the right, to the dawn and to
the sun, or to the left, to mist and darkness. Nay, for us, let us
trust to the counsel of mighty Zeus, who is king over all mortals and immortals. One omen is best, to fight for our own
country."

XIII

On the both sides, the arrows fly and men fall.

The Fight Among the Ships

(Zeus now leaves the Trojans to their toil and turns his glance elsewhere. Taking advantage of Zeus' preoccupation, Poseidon comes to help the Achaeans.

XIV

Hera Tricks Zeus

⟨ *Though wounded, Agamemnon, Diomedes and Odysseus go to the forefront of the battle to cheer the Achaeans, as does the aged Nestor. With them goes Poseidon in the guise of an ancient man, uttering a war-cry loud as nine thousand men.*

Now Hera of the golden throne stood on the peak of Olympus, and saw with her eyes, and anon knew Poseidon going to and fro through the glorious fight, and she rejoiced in her heart. And she beheld Zeus sitting on the topmost crest of many-fountained Ida, and to her heart he was hateful. Then she took thought, the ox-eyed lady Hera, how she might beguile the mind of aegis-bearing Zeus. And this seemed to her in her heart to be the best counsel, namely to fare to Ida, when she had well adorned herself, if perchance he would desire to sleep beside her and embrace her body in love, and a sweet sleep and a kindly she could pour on his eyelids and his crafty wits. And she set forth to her bower, that her dear son Hephaestus had fashioned, and therein had made fast strong doors on the pillars, with a secret bolt, that no other god might open. There did she enter in and closed the shining doors. With ambrosia first did she cleanse every stain from her winsome body, and anointed her with olive oil, ambrosial, soft, and of a sweet savour; if it were but shaken, in the bronze-floored mansion of Zeus, the savour thereof went right forth to earth and heaven.

Therewith she anointed her fair body, and combed her hair, and with her hands plaited her shining tresses, fair and ambrosial, flowing from her immortal head. Then she clad her in her fragrant robe that Athene wrought delicately for her and lavishly embroidered, and fastened it over her breast with clasps of gold. And she girdled it with a girdle arrayed with a hundred tassels, and she set earrings in her pierced ears, earrings of three drops, and glistering, therefrom shone grace abundantly. And with a veil over all the peerless goddess veiled herself, a fair new veil, bright as the sun, and beneath her shining feet she bound goodly sandals. But when she had adorned her body with all her array, she went forth from her bower, and called Aphrodite apart from the other gods, and spake to her saying: "Wilt thou obey me, dear child, in that which I shall tell thee? or wilt thou refuse, with a grudge in thy heart, because I succour the Danaans, and thou the Trojans?"

Then Aphrodite the daughter of Zeus answered her: "Hera, goddess queen, daughter of mighty Cronos, say the thing that is in thy mind, my heart bids me fulfil it, if fulfil it I may, and if it may be accomplished."

Then with crafty purpose the lady Hera answered her: "Give me now Love and Desire wherewith thou dost overcome all the Immortals, and mortal men. For I am going to visit the limits of the bountiful Earth, and Oceanus, father of the gods, and mother Tethys, who reared me well and nourished me in their halls, having taken me from Rhea, when far-seeing Zeus imprisoned Cronos beneath the earth and the unharvested sea. Them am I going to visit, and their endless strife will I loose, for already this long time they hold apart from each other, apart from love and the marriage bed, since wrath had settled in their hearts. If with words I might persuade their hearts, and bring them back to love and the marriage bed, ever should I be called dear to them and worshipful."

Then laughter-loving Aphrodite answered her again: "It may not be, nor seemly were it to deny that thou askest, for thou sleepest in the arms of Zeus, the chief of gods."

Therewith from her breast she loosed the broidered girdle, fair-wrought, wherein are all her enchantments; therein are love, and desire, and loving converse, that steals the wits even of the wise. This girdle she laid in her hands, and spake, and said: "Lo now, take this girdle and lay it up in thy bosom, this fair-wrought girdle, wherein all things are fashioned; methinks thou wilt not return with that unaccomplished, which in thy heart thou desirest."

So spake she, and the ox-eyed lady Hera smiled, and smiling laid up the zone within her breast.

Then the daughter of Zeus, Aphrodite, went to her house, and Hera, rushing down, left the peak of Olympus, and touched on Pieria and pleasant Emathia, and sped over the snowy hills of the Thracian horsemen, even over the topmost crests, nor grazed the ground with her feet, and from Athos she fared across the foaming sea, and came to Lemnos, the city of godlike Thoas. There she met Sleep, the brother of Death, and clasped her hand in his, and spake and called him by name: "Sleep, lord of all gods and of all men, if ever thou didst hear my word, obey me again even now, and I will be grateful to thee always. Lull me, I pray thee, the shining eyes of Zeus beneath his brows, so soon as I have laid me down by him in love. And gifts I will give to thee, even a fair throne, imperishable for ever, a golden throne, that Hephaestus the Lame, mine own child, shall fashion skilfully, and will set beneath it a footstool for the feet, for thee to set thy shining feet upon, when thou art at a festival."

Then sweet Sleep answered her and said: "Hera, goddess and queen, daughter of mighty Cronos, another of the eternal gods might I lightly lull to slumber, yea, were it the streams of Oceanus himself, that is the father of them all. But to Zeus the son of Cronos might I not draw near, nor lull him to slumber, unless himself commanded it. For ere now did a behest of thine teach me a lesson, on the day when Heracles that famed high-hearted son of Zeus sailed from Ilium, when he had sacked the city of the Trojans. Then verily I lulled the soul of aegis-bearing Zeus, with my sweet influence poured about him, and thou didst contrive evil against him in thy heart, and didst rouse over the sea the blasts of violent winds, and Heracles thou then didst bear to well-peopled Cos, far from all his friends. But Zeus, when he wakened, was wrathful, and dashed the gods about his mansion, and me above all he sought, and he would have cast me from the upper air to perish in the deep, if Night had not saved me, Night, that subdues both gods and men. To her I came as a suppliant in my flight, and he ceased from pursuing, wrathful as he was, for he was in awe of doing aught displeasing to swift Night. And now again thou biddest me accomplish this other task that may not be accomplished."

Then the ox-eyed lady Hera answered him again: "Sleep, wherefore dost thou consider these things in thy heart? dost thou deem that Zeus of the far-borne voice will succour the Trojans even as he was wroth for the sake of Heracles, his own child? Nay come, and I will give thee one of the younger of the Graces, to wed and to be called thy wife, even Pasitheë, that ever thou longest for all thy days."

So she spake, and Sleep was glad, and answered and said: "Come now, swear to me by the inviolable water of Styx, and with one of thy hands grasp the bounteous earth, and with the other the shining sea, that all may be witnesses to us, even all the gods below that are with Cronos, that verily thou wilt give me one of the younger of the Graces, even Pasitheë, that myself do long for all my days."

So spake he, nor did she disobey, the white-armed goddess Hera; she swore as he bade her, and called all the gods by name, even those below Tartarus that are called Titans. But when she had sworn and ended that oath, the twain clothed in mist left the citadel of Lemnos, and of Imbros, and swiftly they accomplished the way. To many-fountained Ida they came, the mother of wild beasts, to Lecton, where first they left the sea, and they twain fared above the dry land, and the topmost forest waveth beneath their feet. There Sleep halted, ere the eyes of Zeus beheld him, and alighted on a tall pine-tree, the loftiest pine that then in all

Ida rose through the nether to the upper air. Therein sat he, hidden by the branches of the pine, in the likeness of the shrill bird that on the mountains the gods call bronze-throat, but men nightjar. But Hera swiftly drew nigh to topmost Gargarus, the highest crest of Ida, and Zeus the cloud-gatherer beheld her. And as he saw her, so love came over his deep heart, even as when first they mingled with each other in delight, and went together to the couch, their dear parents knowing it not. And he stood before her, and spoke, and said: "Hera, with what desire comest thou thus hither from Olympus, and thy horses and chariot are not here, whereon thou mightst ascend?"

Then with crafty purpose lady Hera answered him: "I am going to visit the limits of the bountiful earth, and Oceanus, father of the gods, and mother Tethys, who reared me well and cherished me in their halls. Them am I going to visit, and their endless strife will I loose, for already this long time they hold apart from each other, from love and the marriage bed, since wrath hath settled in their hearts. But my horses are standing at the foot of many-fountained Ida, my horses that shall bear me over wet and dry. And now it is because of thee that I am thus come hither, down from Olympus, lest perchance thou mightest be wroth with me hereafter, if silently I were gone to the mansion of deep-flowing Oceanus."

Then Zeus, the gatherer of the clouds, answered her and said: "Hera, thither mayst thou go on a later day. But come let us twain take pleasure in the bed of love. For never once as thus did the love of goddess or woman so mightily over-flow and conquer the heart within my breast. Not when I loved the wife of Ixion, who bore Peirithous, the peer of gods in counsel, nor when I loved Danaë of the fair ankles, daughter of Acrisius, who bore Perseus, most renowned of all men, nor when I loved the famed daughter of Phoenix, who bore me Minos, and godlike Rhadamanthus, nay, nor even when I loved Semele, nor Alcmene in Thebes, and she bore Heracles, a child hardy of heart, but Semele bore Dionysus, a delight to mortals, nay, nor when I loved the fair-tressed queen, Demeter, nor renowned Leto, nay, nor thy very self, as now I love thee, and sweet desire possesses me."

And him the lady Hera answered with crafty purpose: "Most dread son of Cronos, what a word thou hast spoken! If now thou dost long to be couched in love on the crests of Ida, and all stands plain to view, how would it be if some one of the eternal gods should see us slumbering, and go and tell it to all the gods? It is not I that could arise from the couch and go again to thy house, nay, it would be a thing for righteous anger. But if thou wilt, and it is dear to thy heart, thou hast a chamber that thine own son Hephaestus builded, and fastened strong doors to the pillars, thither let us go and lie down, if the couch be thy desire."

Then Zeus the cloud-gatherer answered her and said: "Hera, fear not lest any god, or any man should spy the thing, so great a golden cloud will I cast all over thee. Nay, methinks not even the sun might see through it, the sun, whose light is keenest of all to behold."

So spake he, and the son of Cronos clasped his consort in his arms. And beneath them the divine earth sent forth fresh new grass, and dewy lotus, and crocus, and hyacinth, thick and soft, that raised them aloft from the ground. Therein they lay, and were clad on with a fair golden cloud, whence fell drops of glittering dew.

⁋ *Sleep hurries to tell Poseidon that Zeus is asleep. Poseidon again rallies the Achaeans, and they drive the Trojans out. Hector is wounded by Aias, but his comrades carry him out of the battle.*

XV

The Trojans Press Forward Again

Now when they had sped in flight across the palisade and trench, and many were overcome at the hands of the Danaans, the rest were stayed, and abode beside the chariots in confusion, and pale with terror, and Zeus awoke, on the peaks of Ida, beside Hera of the golden throne. Then he leaped up, and stood, and beheld the Trojans and Achaeans, those in flight, and these driving them on from the rear, even the Argives, and among them the prince Poseidon. And Hector he saw lying on the plain, and around him sat his comrades, and he was gasping with difficult breath, and his mind wandering, and was vomiting blood, for it was not the weakest of the Achaeans that had smitten him. Beholding him, the father of men and gods had pity on him, and terribly he spoke to Hera, with fierce look: "O thou ill to deal with, Hera, verily it is thy crafty wile that has made noble Hector cease from the fight, and has terrified the host. Nay, but yet I know not whether thou mayst not be the first to reap the fruits of thy cruel treason, and I beat thee with stripes. Dost thou not remember, when thou wert hung from on high, and from thy feet I suspended two anvils, and round thy hands fastened a golden bond that might not be broken? And thou didst hang in the clear air and the clouds, and the gods were wroth in high Olympus, but they could not come round and unloose thee. Nay, whomsoever I might take, I would clutch, and throw from the threshold, to come fainting to the earth, yet verily not even so did the

ceaseless sorrow leave my soul free: sorrow for godlike
Heracles. Him didst thou drive, when thou hadst suborned
the tempest, with the help of the North Wind, over the unharvested deep, out of thine evil counsel, and then didst
carry him away to well-peopled Cos. Him did I rescue
thence, and lead again to Argos, the pasture-land of horses,
after his much labour. Of these things will I mind thee
again, that thou mayst cease from thy wiles, that thou mayst
know if it profit thee at all, the dalliance and the love,
wherein thou didst lie with me, when thou hadst come from
among the gods, and didst beguile me."

So spake he, and the ox-eyed lady Hera shuddered, and
spake unto him winged words, saying: "Let earth now be
witness hereto, and wide heaven above, and that falling water of Styx, the greatest oath and the most terrible to the
blessed gods, and thine own sacred head, and our own bridal
bed, whereby never would I forswear myself, that not by my
will does earth-shaking Poseidon trouble the Trojans and
Hector, and succour them of the other part. Nay, it is his
own soul that urgeth and commandeth him, and he had pity
on the Achaeans, when he beheld them hard pressed beside
the ships. I would even counsel him also to go even where
thou, lord of the storm-cloud, mayst lead him."

So spake she, and the father of gods and men smiled, and
answering her he spake winged words: "If thou, of a truth,
O ox-eyed lady Hera, wouldst hereafter abide of one mind
with me among the immortal gods, thereon would Poseidon,
howsoever much his wish be contrariwise, quickly turn his
mind otherwhere, after thy heart and mine. But if indeed
thou speakest the truth and soothly, go thou now among the
tribes of the gods, and call Iris to come hither, and Apollo,
the renowned archer, that Iris may go among the host of
mail-clad Achaeans and tell Poseidon the prince to cease
from the war, and get him unto his own house. But let
Phoebus Apollo spur Hector on to the war, and breathe
strength into him again, and make him forget his anguish,
that now wears down his heart, and drive the Achaeans back

again, when he hath stirred in them craven fear. Let them flee and fall among the many-benched ships of Achilles son of Peleus, and he shall rouse his own comrade, Patroclus; and him shall renowned Hector slay with the spear, in front of Ilium, after that he has slain many other youths, and among them my son, noble Sarpedon. In wrath therefor shall goodly Achilles slay Hector. From that hour verily will I cause a new pursuit from the ships, that shall endure continually, even until the Achaeans take steep Ilium, through the counsels of Athene. But before that hour neither do I cease in my wrath, nor will I suffer any other of the Immortals to help the Danaans there, before I accomplish that desire of the son of Peleus, as I promised him at the first, and confirmed the same with a nod of my head, on that day when the goddess Thetis clasped my knees, imploring me to honour Achilles, the sacker of cities."

So spake he, nor did the white-armed goddess Hera disobey him, and she sped down from the hills of Ida to high Olympus. And even as when the mind of a man darts speedily, of one that hath travelled over far lands, and considers in his wise heart, "Would that I were here or there," and he thinketh him of many things, so swiftly fled she in her eagerness, the lady Hera, and came to steep Olympus, and went among the gathering of the immortal gods in the house of Zeus, and when they beheld her they all rose up together, and held out their cups to her in welcome. The others she left alone, but took the cup of Themis of the fair cheeks, for she was the first that came running to meet her, and speaking winged words accosted her: "Hera, wherefore hast thou come? thou seemest like one confounded; verily the son of Cronos hath made thee adread, thine own husband."

Then the white-armed goddess Hera answered her, saying: "Ask me not concerning this, O goddess Themis; thyself knowest it, how overweening is his heart, and unyielding. But do thou begin the equal banquet of the gods in the halls, and thus shalt thou hear among all the Immortals, even what evil deeds Zeus declareth. Nay, methinks, not equally will it delight the minds of all, neither of gods nor mortals, if even now any still sit with pleasure at the feast."

So spake the lady Hera, and sat her down, while the gods were heavy at heart in the hall of Zeus. And she laughed with her lips, but her forehead above her dark brows was not gladdened, and indignantly she spake among them all: "Witless that we are to be wroth in our folly against Zeus! Even still we are eager to draw nigh to him, and keep him from his will, by word or deed, but he sits apart and careth not, nor takes any thought thereof, for he deems that among the immortal gods he is manifestly pre-eminent in force and might. Wherefore do ye content yourselves with whatsoever sorrow he sends on each of you. Already, methinks, has sorrow been wrought for Ares, for his son has fallen in the fight, even the dearest of men, Ascalaphus, that dread Ares deemeth to be verily his own."

So spake she, but Ares smote his strong thighs with the flat of his hands, and sorrowing he spake: "Hold me not now to blame, ye that keep the mansions of Olympus, if I avenge the slaying of my son, and go to the ships of the Achaeans, even if it be my doom to be smitten with the bolt of Zeus, and lie among the dead, in the dust and blood."

So spake he, and bade yoke his horses, Fear and Dread, and himself put on his shining harness. Thereby would yet a greater and more implacable wrath and anger have been caused between Zeus and the Immortals, had not Athene, in terror for the sake of all the gods, leaped out through the doorway, and left the throne wherein she sat, and taken from Ares' head the helmet, and the shield from his shoulders, and drawn the spear of bronze from his stalwart hand, and set it apart, and then with words she rebuked the impetuous Ares: "Mad that thou art, and distraught of wit— this is thy bane! Verily thou hast ears and hearest not, and perished have thine understanding and thine awe. Hearest thou not what she saith, the white-armed goddess Hera, that even now is come from Olympian Zeus? Dost thou wish both thyself to fill up the measure of mischief and so return to Olympus ruefully, of necessity, and for all the other gods to sow the seed of a great wrong? For straightway will he leave the high-hearted Trojans and the Achaeans, and to us will he come to make tumult in Olympus: and he will clutch us each in turn, the blameless with the guilty. Wherefore now again I bid thee to abate thine anger for thy son, for already many a man stronger than he, and more hardy of his hands, has fallen, or yet will fall; and a hard thing it is to save the lineage and offspring of all men."

So spake she, and made impetuous Ares sit down on his throne. But Hera called Apollo without the hall, and Iris, that is the messenger of the immortal gods, and she spake winged words, and addressed them, saying: "Zeus bids you go to Ida as swiftly as may be, and when ye have gone, and looked on the face of Zeus, do ye whatsoever he shall order and command."

So spake she, and returned again, the lady Hera, and sat down on her throne, and they flew forward speedily, and came to many-fountained Ida, mother of wild beasts, and found far-seeing Zeus seated on topmost Gargarus, and round him a fragrant cloud was circled like a crown. And these twain came before the face of Zeus the cloud-gatherer, and stood there, and he was no wise displeased at heart when he beheld them, for that speedily they had obeyed the words of his dear wife. And to Iris first he spake winged words: "Go, get thee, swift Iris, to the prince Poseidon, and tell him all these things, nor be a false messenger. Command him to cease from war and battle, and to go among the tribes of the gods, or into the bright sea. But if he will not obey my words, but will hold me in no regard, then let him consider in his heart and mind, lest he dare not for all his strength to abide me when I come against him, since I deem me to be far mightier than he, and elder born. But this his heart feareth not,—to call himself the peer of me whom even the other gods do hold in dread."

So spake he, nor did the wind-footed fleet Iris disobey

him, but went down the hills of Ida to sacred Ilium. And as when snow or chill hail fleets from the clouds beneath the stress of the North Wind born in the clear air, so fleetly she fled in her eagerness, swift Iris, and drew near the renowned Earth-shaker and spake to him, saying: "A certain message to thee, O dark-haired embracer of the earth, have I come hither to bring from aegis-bearing Zeus. He biddeth thee cease from the battle and war, and go among the tribes of the gods, or into the bright sea. And if thou wilt not obey his word, but wilt hold him in no regard, he threatens that even himself will come hither against thee in battle, and he biddeth thee avoid thee out of his hands, since he deemeth him far mightier than thou, and elder born, but thy heart feareth not to call thyself the peer of him whom even the other gods do hold in dread."

Then, in great displeasure the renowned Shaker of the earth answered her: "Out on it, verily now, for as strong as he is, he hath spoken over-haughtily, if indeed he will subdue by force, against my will, me that am his equal in honour. For three brethren are we, and sons of Cronos, whom Rhea bare, Zeus, and myself, and Hades is the third, the ruler of the folk in the under-world. And in three lots are all things divided, and each drew a domain of his own, and to me fell the hoary sea, to be my habitation for ever, when we shook the lots: and Hades drew the murky darkness, and Zeus the wide heaven, in clear air and clouds, but the earth and high Olympus are yet common to all. Wherefore no whit will I walk after the will of Zeus, but quietly let him abide, for all his strength, in his third portion. And with the might of his hands let him not strive to terrify me withal, as if I were a coward. Better for him were it to threaten with terrible words his daughters and his sons, that himself begat, who will perforce listen to whatso he enjoins."

Then the fleet wind-footed Iris answered him: "Is it indeed thy will, O dark-haired embracer of the earth, that even thus I shall carry to Zeus this message, hard and froward, or wilt thou turn thee at all, for the hearts of the good may be turned? Thou knowest how the Erinyes [1] do always follow to aid the elder-born."

Then he answered her again, Poseidon, the Shaker of the earth: "Goddess Iris, most duly hast thou spoken this word. Yea, an excellent thing is this, when the bearer of a message has a prudent wit. Yet this is a terrible grief that cometh on heart and spirit, whenso any desireth to upbraid with angry words his peer to whom fate hath assigned an equal share with himself. But verily now will I yield, for all mine anger; but another thing will I tell thee, and make this threat in my heart, that if against my will, and the will of Athene, the driver of the prey, and of Hera and Hermes, and prince Hephaestus, Zeus shall spare steep Ilium, nor choose utterly to destroy it, and give great might to the Argives, let him know this, that our wrath will be inappeasable."

So spake the Shaker of the earth, and left the host of the Achaeans, and passed to the sea, and sank, and sorely they missed him, the heroes of the Achaeans.

Then Zeus, the gatherer of the clouds, spake to Apollo, saying: "Go now, dear Phoebus, to Hector of the helm of bronze, for, lo, already the embracer of the world, the Earth-shaker, is gone to the bright sea, shunning our utter wrath, ay, and had he not done so, even the others would have heard of our strife, even the gods of the nether world, that are with Cronos. But better far is this, both for me, and for him, that, despite his wrath, he should yield to my hands, for not without sweat would this strife have been accomplished. But do thou take in thy hands the tasselled aegis, and shake it fiercely and affright the Achaean heroes. But, thou Archer-God, let glorious Hector be thy care, and rouse in him great wrath even till the Achaeans come in their flight to the ships, and the Hellespont. And from that moment will I devise word and deed wherewithal the Achaeans may take breath again from their toil."

So spake he, nor was Apollo deaf to the word of the Fa-

---

[1] Divinities who are ministers of justice.

ther, but he went down the hills of Ida like a fleet falcon,
the bane of doves, that is the swiftest of flying things. And
he found the son of wise-hearted Priam, noble Hector, sitting up, no longer lying, for he had but late got back his
life, and knew the comrades around him, and his gasping
and his sweat had ceased, from the moment when the will
of aegis-bearing Zeus began to revive him. Then far-darting
Apollo stood near him, and spake to him: "Hector, son of
Priam, why dost thou sit fainting apart from the others? Is
it perchance that some trouble cometh upon thee?"

Acheans Fight the Trojans.

PAINTING FROM A CALYXKRATER.
(MUNICH PINAKOTHEK)

Then, with faint breath answered him Hector of the
glancing helm: "Nay, but who art thou, best of the gods,
who inquirest of me face to face? Dost thou not know that
by the hindmost row of the ships of the Achaeans, Aias of
the loud war-cry smote me on the breast with a stone, as I
was slaying his comrades, and made me cease from mine impetuous might? And verily I deemed that this very day I
should pass to the dead, and the house of Hades, when I
had gasped my life away."

Then prince Apollo the Far-darter answered him again:
"Take courage now, so great an ally hath the son of Cronos
sent thee out of Ida, to stand by thee and defend thee, even
Phoebus Apollo of the golden sword, me who of old defend
thee, thyself and the steep citadel. But come now bid thy
many charioteers drive their swift steeds against the hollow

ships, and I will go before and make smooth all the way for
the chariots, and will put to flight the Achaean heroes."

❨ *Revived, Hector leads his hosts into battle, and once more
the Achaeans are driven over the moat. Apollo goes with the
Trojans, bearing the aegis of Zeus, and they carry the fight even
to the ships, for Zeus desires to give glory to Hector that
Agamemnon may be repaid for the slight to Achilles. Patroclus sees the danger and goes to beg Achilles to join the battle.
The Trojans try to fire the ships, but are prevented by Aias.*

XVI

The Valor and Death of Patroclus

So they were warring round the well-timbered ship, but Patroclus drew near Achilles, shepherd of the host, and he shed warm tears, even as a fountain of dark water that down a steep cliff pours its cloudy stream. And noble swift-footed Achilles when he beheld him was grieved for his sake, and accosted him, and spake winged words, saying: "Wherefore weepest thou, Patroclus, like a fond little maid, that runs by her mother's side, and bids her mother take her up, snatching at her gown, and hinders her in her going, and tearfully looks at her, till the mother takes her up? like her, Patroclus, dost thou let fall soft tears. Hast thou aught to tell to the Myrmidons, or to me myself, or is it some tidings out of Phthia that thou alone hast heard? They say that Menoetius son of Actor still lives: and Peleus son of Aeacus lives yet among the Myrmidons, for which twain, were they dead, right sore would we sorrow. Or dost thou lament for the sake of the Argives,—how they perish by the hollow ships through their own transgression? Speak out, and hide it not within thy spirit, that we may both know all."

But with a heavy groan didst thou speak unto him, O knight Patroclus: "O Achilles, son of Peleus, far the bravest of the Achaeans, be not wroth, seeing that so great calamity has beset the Achaeans. For verily all of them that aforetime were the best are lying among the ships, smitten and wounded. Smitten is the son of Tydeus, strong Diomedes, and wounded is Odysseus, spearman renowned, and Aga-

memnon; and smitten is Eurypylus on the thigh with an arrow. And about them the leeches skilled in medicines are
busy, healing their wounds, but thou art hard to reconcile,
Achilles. Never then may such wrath take hold of me as
that thou nursest; thou brave to the hurting of others. What
other man later born shall have anything to thank thee for,
if thou dost not ward off base ruin from the Argives?
Pitiless that thou art, the knight Peleus was not then thy
father, nor Thetis thy mother, but the grey sea bare thee,
and the sheer cliffs, so untoward is thy spirit. But if in thy
heart thou art shunning some oracle, and thy lady mother
hath told thee somewhat from Zeus, yet me do thou send
forth quickly, and make the rest of the host of the Myrmidons follow me, if yet any light may arise from me to the
Danaans. And give me thy harness to buckle about my
shoulders, if perchance the Trojans may take me for thee,
and so abstain from battle, and the warlike sons of the
Achaeans may take breath, wearied as they be, for brief is
the breathing in war. And lightly might we that are fresh
drive men wearied with the battle back to the citadel, away
from the ships and the huts."

So he spake and besought him, in his unwittingness, for
truly it was to be his own evil death and fate that he prayed
for. Then to him in great heaviness spake swift-footed
Achilles: "Ah me, Patroclus of the seed of Zeus, what word
hast thou spoken? Neither take I heed of any oracle that I
wot of, nor yet has my lady mother told me somewhat
from Zeus, but this dread sorrow comes upon my heart and
spirit, from the hour that a man wishes to rob me who am
his equal, and to take away my prize, for that he excels me
in power. A dread sorrow to me is this, after all the toils
that my heart hath endured. The maiden that the sons of
the Achaeans chose out for me as my prize, and that I won
with my spear when I sacked a well-walled city, her has
mighty Agamemnon the son of Atreus taken back out of my
hands, as though I were but some sojourner dishonourable.

"But we will let bygones be bygones. No man may be angry
of heart for ever, yet verily I said that I would not cease

from my wrath, until that time when to mine own ships should come the war-cry and the battle. But do thou put on thy shoulders my famous harness, and lead the war-loving Myrmidons to the fight, if indeed the dark cloud of the Trojans hath mightily surrounded the ships, and if the Argives have given back to the shore of the sea, holding but a narrow space of land, and the whole town of Troy hath come boldly against them. Yea, for they behold not the vizor of my helm shining hard at hand; swiftly would they flee, and fill the watercourses with dead, if mighty Agamemnon had been but kindly to me,—but now are they warring round the camp. For not in the hands of Diomedes, the son of Tydeus, rageth the spear, to ward off destruction from the Danaans. Neither as yet have I heard the voice of the son of Atreus, shouting out of his hated mouth, but of Hector the slayer of men doth the voice burst around me, as he calls on the Trojans, and they with their cries fill all the plain, overcoming the Achaeans in the battle. But even so, Patroclus, to ward off destruction from the ships, do thou fall on mightily, lest they even burn the ships with blazing fire, and take away our desired return. But do thou obey, even as I shall put into thy mind exactly how far to go, that in my sight thou mayst win great honour and fame of all the Danaans, and they may give me back again the fairest maiden, and thereto add splendid gifts. When thou hast driven them from the ships, return, and even if the loud-thundering lord of Hera grant thee to win glory, yet long not thou apart from me to fight with the war-loving Trojans; thereby wilt thou diminish mine honour. Neither do thou, exulting in war and strife, and slaying the Trojans, lead on toward Ilium, lest one of the eternal gods from Olympus come against thee; right dearly doth Apollo the Far-darter love them. Nay, return back when thou hast brought safety to the ships, and suffer the rest to fight along the plain. For would, O father Zeus, and Athene, and Apollo, would that not one of all the Trojans might escape death, nor one of the Argives, but that we twain might avoid destruction, that alone we might pull down Troy's sacred crown of towers."

So spake they each to other, but Aias no longer abode the onset, for he was overpowered by darts; the counsel of Zeus was subduing him, and the shafts of the proud Trojans; and his bright helmet, being smitten, kept ringing terribly about his temples: for always it was smitten upon the fair-wrought cheek-pieces. Moreover his left shoulder was wearied, as steadfastly he held up his glittering shield, nor yet could they make him give ground, as they pressed on with their darts around him. And ever, he was worn out with difficult breath, and much sweat kept running from all his limbs, nor had he a moment to draw breath, so on all sides was evil heaped on evil.

Tell me now, ye Muses that have mansions in Olympus, how first fire fell on the ships of the Achaeans. Hector drew near, and the ashen spear of Aias he smote with his great sword, hard by the socket, behind the point, and shore it clean away, and the son of Telamon brandished in his hand no more than a pointless spear, and far from him the head of bronze fell ringing on the ground.

And Aias knew in his noble heart, and shuddered at the deeds of the gods, even how Zeus that thundereth on high did utterly cut off from him avail in war, and desired victory for the Trojans. Then Aias gave back out of the darts. But the Trojans cast on the swift ship unwearying fire, and instantly the inextinguishable flame streamed over her: so the fire begirt the stern, whereon Achilles smote his thighs, and spake to Patroclus: "Arise, Patroclus of the seed of Zeus, commander of the horsemen, for truly I see by the ships the rush of the consuming fire. Up then, lest they take the ships, and there be no more retreat; do on thy harness speedily, and I will summon the host."

So spake he, while Patroclus was harnessing him in shining bronze. His goodly greaves, fitted with silver clasps, he first girt round his legs, and next did on around his breast the well-dight starry corslet of the swift-footed son of Aeacus. And round his shoulders he cast a sword of bronze, with studs of silver, and next took the great and mighty shield, and on his proud head set a well-wrought helm with a horse-hair crest, and terribly nodded the crest from above. Then seized he two strong lances that fitted his grasp, only he took not the spear of noble Peleus, heavy, and huge, and stalwart, that none other of the Achaeans could wield, but Achilles alone availed to wield it: even the ashen spear from a peak of Pelion, that Cheiron gave to his father dear to be the death of warriors. And Patroclus bade Automedon to yoke the horses speedily, even Automedon whom most he honoured after Achilles, the breaker of the ranks of

Patroclus orders Automedon to yoke the horses.
PAINTING FROM AN ARCHAIC HYDRIA WITH BLACK FIGURES.
(BERLIN MUSEUM)

men, and whom he held trustiest in battle to abide his call. And for him Automedon led beneath the yoke the swift horses, Xanthus and Balius, that fly as swift as the winds, the horses that the harpy Podarge bare to the West Wind, as she grazed on the meadow by the stream of Oceanus. And in the sidetraces he put the goodly Pedasus, that Achilles carried away, when he took the city of Eëtion; and being but a mortal steed, he followed with the immortal horses.

Meanwhile Achilles went and harnessed all the Myrmidons in the huts with armour, and they gathered like ravening wolves with strength in their hearts unspeakable, that have slain a great horned stag in the hills and rend him piecemeal; and all their jaws are red with blood, and in a

herd they go, to lap with their thin tongues the surface of
the dark water in a dusky well, belching out the blood of
the slaughter, their heart steadfast within their breasts, and
their bellies swollen, even so hastened the leaders and chiefs
of the Myrmidons around the good squire of swift-footed
Achilles. And among them all stood warlike Achilles, urging
on the horses and the shield-bearers.

Fifty were the swift ships which Achilles, beloved of Zeus,
led to Troy, and in each ship on the benches sat fifty men
his comrades, and five leaders he made, wherein he trusted
to give command, and himself with great lordship was chief
of them all. One rank led Menesthius of the shining corslet,
the son of Spercheus, the River that falleth from Zeus.
Him did the daughter of Peleus bear, beautiful Polydora,
to tireless Spercheus, a woman couched with a god. But by
name was he the son of Borus, Perieres' son, who openly
wedded her, giving countless gifts of wooing. And the next
company did warlike Eudorus lead, the son of an unwedded
girl, and him bare Polymele, fair in the dance, the daughter
of Phylas. Her did Hermes the strong slayer of Argus [1] love,
when he had beheld her with his eyes among the singing
maidens, in the choir of Artemis, the swift-rushing goddess
of the golden arrows. Then straightway he went up into her
upper chamber, and lay with her secretly, even Hermes the
bearer of all things good, and gat by her a glorious son,
Eudorus, swift of foot and a man of war. But when Eileithyia,
goddess of the pains of travail, had brought him to the light,
and he saw the rays of the sun, then the strong Echecles, son
of Actor, led Polymele to his halls, after he had given countless gifts of wooing, but Eudorus did the old Phylas rear
well and nourish tenderly, loving him dearly as he had been
his own son.

And the third company led warlike Peisander, the son
of Maemalus, most excellent among the Myrmidons in fight-

---

[1] Argus was the herdsman with eyes all over his body who was set
by jealous Hera to watch Io, beloved of Zeus, whom he had vainly
turned into a heifer to escape the attention of Hera.

ing with the spear, after the comrade of the son of Peleus.
And the ancient knight Phoenix led the fourth company,
and the fifth Alcimedon the noble son of Laerces led.
But when Achilles had stationed them all, and arrayed them
well with their leaders, he laid on them a strong command:
"Myrmidons, let me find none of you forgetful of the
threats wherewith by the swift ships ye threatened the Trojans, through all the time of my wrath, and ye did each ac-
cuse me, saying, 'Hard-hearted son of Peleus, surely on gall
thy mother reared thee, thou pitiless one that restrainest thy
comrades at the ships, against their will. Nay, homewards let
us return again with our seafaring ships, since such an evil
wrath has sunk into thy heart.' Even thus did ye often clamour against me in your gatherings, but now hath appeared
the mighty work of war, wherewith in time past ye were in
love. Therefore let each man keep a stout heart in the battle
with the Trojans."

So spake he, and aroused the heart and valour of each of
them, and the ranks were yet the closer serried when they
heard the prince. And as when a man builds the wall of a
high house with close-set stones, to avoid the might of the
winds, even so close were arrayed the helmets and bossy
shields, and shield pressed on shield, helm on helm, and
man on man, and the horse-hair crests on the bright helmet-
ridges touched each other when they nodded, so close they
stood by each other.

But in front of them all were two men harnessed,
Patroclus and Automedon, both of one heart, to war in the
van of the Myrmidons. But Achilles went into his hut, and
opened the lid of a fair and well-wrought coffer, that silver-
footed Thetis placed on board his ship to carry with him,
and filled it well with doublets, and cloaks to keep the wind
away, and thick carpets. Therein had he a fair-fashioned
cup, and neither was any other man wont to drink therefrom the bright wine, nor to any other god was he wont to
do libation therewith, save to Zeus the Father only. This
cup he took from the coffer, and first purified it with brimstone, and then washed it in fair streams of water, and him-

self washed his hands, and drew bright wine. Then prayed he, standing in the mid-court, and poured forth the wine, looking up to heaven, and Zeus that hath joy of the thunder was ware of him: "King Zeus, Dodonean,[2] Pelasgian,[3] thou that dwellest afar, ruling over wintry Dodona—and around thee dwell the Helli, thy prophets, with unwashen feet, and couching on the ground,—even as once thou didst hear my voice in prayer, and didst honour me, and mightily afflict the host of the Achaeans, even now too fulfil for me this my desire. For I myself will abide in the gathering of the ships, but my comrade I send with many Myrmidons to war: to him do thou speed the victory, O far-seeing Zeus, and strengthen his heart within him, that Hector too may know whether my squire hath skill to war even alone,—or whether his hands invincible rage only when I enter the moil of war. But when he has driven from the ships the war and din of battle, scathless then let him return to me at the swift ships with all his arms, and his comrades that fight hand to hand."

So spake he in his prayer, and wise-counselling Zeus heard him, and the Father granted part to him, and part he denied. He granted him that Patroclus should drive the war and the fight from the ships, but denied him to return safe out of the fight. Then Achilles, having made libation and prayer to father Zeus, went back into his hut, and placed the cup in the coffer again, and came forth and stood in front of his hut, for still his heart desired to see the dread strife of the Trojans and Achaeans.

But they that were armed about the high-hearted Patroclus marched forward till they rushed in their pride on the Trojans. And straightway they poured forth like wasps that have their dwelling by the wayside, and that boys are ever wont to vex, always tormenting them in their nests beside the way in childish sport, and a common evil they make for many. And they, if ever some wayfaring man passing by stir

---

[2] Dodona was the site of a famous oracle of Zeus.
[3] The Pelasgians were the original inhabitants of Greece.

them unwittingly, fly forth every one of them, with a heart of valour, and each defends his children; with heart and spirit like theirs the Myrmidons poured out now from the ships, and a cry arose unquenchable, and Patroclus called on his comrades, shouting aloud: "Myrmidons, ye comrades of Achilles son of Peleus, be men, my friends, and be mindful of your impetuous valour, that so we may win honour for the son of Peleus, that is far the bravest of the Argives by the ships, and whose close-fighting squires are the best. And let wide-ruling Agamemnon the son of Atreus learn his own blindness of heart, in that he nothing honoured the best of the Achaeans."

So spake he, and aroused each man's heart and courage, and all in a mass they fell on the Trojans, and the ships around echoed wondrously to the cry of the Achaeans. But when the Trojans beheld Patroclus the strong son of Menoetius, himself and his squire, shining in their armour, the heart was stirred in all of them, and the companies wavered, for they deemed that by the ships the swift-footed son of Peleus had cast away his wrath, and chosen reconcilement: then each man glanced round, to see where he might flee sheer destruction.

But Patroclus first with a shining spear cast straight into the press, where most men were thronging, even by the stern of the ship of great-hearted Protesilaus, and he smote Pyraechmes, who led his Paeonian horsemen out of Amydon, from the wide water of Axius; him he smote on the right shoulder, and he fell on his back in the dust with a groan, and his comrades around him, the Paeonians, were afraid, for Patroclus sent fear among them all, when he slew their leader that was ever the best in fight. Then he drove them out from the ships, and quenched the burning fire. And the half-burnt ship was left there, and the Trojans fled, with a marvellous din, and the Danaans poured in among the hollow ships, and ceaseless was the shouting. And as when from the high crest of a great hill Zeus, the gatherer of the lightning, hath stirred a dense cloud, and forth shine all the peaks, and sharp promontories, and glades, and from heaven the

infinite air breaks open, even so the Danaans, having driven
the blazing fire from the ships, for a little while took breath,
but there was no pause in the battle. For not yet were the
Trojans driven in utter rout by the Achaeans, dear to Ares,
from the black ships, but they still stood up against them,
and only perforce gave ground from the ships.

*The Trojans, however, are finally driven back toward Troy;
Patroclus, chief of the pursuing Achaeans, performs incredible
deeds of valor.*

But when Sarpedon beheld his comrades with ungirdled
doublets, subdued beneath the hands of Patroclus son of
Menoetius, he cried aloud, upbraiding the godlike Lycians:
"Shame, ye Lycians, whither do ye flee? Now be ye strong,
for I will encounter this man that I may know who he is
that conquers here, and verily many evils hath he wrought
the Trojans, in that he hath loosened the knees of many
men and noble."

So spake he, and leaped with his arms from the chariot
to the ground. But Patroclus, on the other side, when he
beheld him leaped from his chariot. And they, like vultures
of crooked talons and curved beaks, that war with loud yells
on some high cliff, even so they rushed with cries against
each other. And beholding then the son of Cronos of the
crooked counsels took pity on them, and he spake to Hera,
his sister and wife: "Ah woe is me for that it is fated that
Sarpedon, the best-beloved of men to me, shall be subdued
under Patroclus son of Menoetius. And in two ways my heart
within my breast is divided, as I ponder whether I should
catch him up alive out of the tearful war, and set him down
in the rich land of Lycia, or whether I should now subdue
him beneath the hands of the son of Menoetius."

Then the ox-eyed lady Hera made answer to him: "Most
dread son of Cronos, what word is this thou hast spoken?
A mortal man long doomed to fate dost thou desire to deliver again from death of evil name? Work thy will, but all
we other gods will in no wise praise thee. And another thing
I will tell thee, and do thou lay it up in thy heart; if thou

dost send Sarpedon living to his own house, consider lest
thereon some other god likewise desire to send his own dear
son away out of the strong battle. For round the great citadel of Priam war many sons of the Immortals, and among
the Immortals wilt thou send terrible wrath. But if he be
dear to thee, and thy heart mourns for him, truly then suffer him to be subdued in the strong battle beneath the
hands of Patroclus son of Menoetius, but when his soul and
life leave that warrior, send Death and sweet Sleep to bear
him, even till they come to the land of wide Lycia, there
will his kindred and friends bury him, with a barrow and a
pillar, for this is the due of the dead."

So spake she, nor did the father of gods and men disregard her. But he shed bloody raindrops on the earth, hon-
ouring his dear son, that Patroclus was about to slay in the
deep-soiled land of Troy, far off from his own country. Now
when they were come near each other in onset, there verily
did Patroclus smite the renowned Thrasymelus, the good
squire of the prince Sarpedon, on the lower part of the belly,
and loosened his limbs. But Sarpedon missed him with his
shining javelin, as he in turn rushed on, but wounded the
horse Pedasus on the right shoulder with the spear, and he
shrieked as he breathed his life away, and fell crying in the
dust, and his spirit fled from him. But the other twain reared
this way and that, and the yoke creaked, and the reins were
confused on them, when their trace-horse lay in the dust.
But thereof did Automedon, the spearman renowned, find
a remedy, and drawing his long-edged sword from his stout
thigh, he leaped forth, and cut adrift the horse, with no delay, and the pair righted themselves, and strained in the
reins, and they met again in life-devouring war.

Then again Sarpedon missed with his shining dart, and
the point of the spear flew over the left shoulder of Patroclus and smote him not, but he in turn arose with the
bronze, and his javelin flew not vainly from his hand, but
struck Sarpedon even where the midriff clasps the beating
heart. And he fell as falls an oak, or a silver poplar, or a
slim pine-tree, that on the hills the shipwrights fell with

whetted axes, to be timber for shipbuilding; even so before the horses and chariot he lay at length, moaning aloud, and clutching at the bloody dust. And as when a lion hath fallen on a herd, and slain a bull, tawny and high of heart, among the kine of trailing gait, and he perishes groaning beneath the claws of the lion, even so under Patroclus did the leader of the Lycian shieldmen rage, even in death, and he called to his dear comrade: "Dear Glaucus, warrior among warlike men, now most doth it behove thee to be a spearman, and a hardy fighter: now let baneful war be dear to thee, if indeed thou art a man of might. First fare all about and urge on the heroes that be leaders of the Lycians, to fight for Sarpedon, and thereafter thyself do battle for me with the sword. For to thee even in time to come shall I be shame and disgrace for ever, all thy days, if the Achaeans strip me of mine armour, fallen in the gathering of the ships. Nay, hold out manfully, and spur on all the host."

Even as he spake thus, the end of death veiled over his eyes and his nostrils, but Patroclus, setting foot on his breast, drew the spear out of his flesh, and the midriff followed with the spear, so that he drew forth together the spear point, and the soul of Sarpedon. . . . And ever men thronged about the dead, as in a steading flies buzz around the full milk-pails, in the season of spring, when the milk drenches the bowls, even so thronged they about the dead. Nor ever did Zeus turn from the strong fight his shining eyes, but ever looked down on them, and much in his heart he debated of the slaying of Patroclus, whether there and then above divine Sarpedon glorious Hector should slay him likewise in strong battle with the sword, and strip his harness from his shoulders, or whether to more men yet he should deal sheer labour of war. And thus to him as he pondered it seemed the better way, that the gallant squire of Achilles, Peleus' son, should straightway drive the Trojans and Hector of the helm of bronze towards the city, and should rob many of their life. And in Hector first he put a weakling heart, and leaping into his car Hector turned in flight, and cried on the rest of the Trojans to flee, for he knew the turning of the sacred scales of Zeus. Thereon neither did the strong Lycians abide, but fled all in fear, when they beheld their king stricken to the heart, lying in the company of the dead, for many had fallen above him, when Cronion made fierce the fight. Then the others stripped from the shoulders of Sarpedon his shining arms of bronze, and these the strong son of Menoetius gave to his comrades to bear to the hollow ships. Then Zeus that gathered the clouds spake to Apollo: "Prithee, dear Phoebus, go take Sarpedon out of range of darts, and cleanse the black blood from him, and thereafter bear him far away, and bathe him in the streams of the river, and anoint him with ambrosia, and clothe him in garments that wax not old, and send him to be wafted by fleet convoy, by the twin brethren Sleep and Death, that quickly will set him in the rich land of wide Lycia. There will his kinsmen and clansmen give him burial, with barrow and pillar, for such is the due of the dead."

So spake he, nor was Apollo disobedient to his father. He went down the hills of Ida to the dread battle-din, and straightway bore goodly Sarpedon out of the darts, and carried him far away, and bathed him in the streams of the river, and anointed him with ambrosia, and clad him in garments that wax not old, and sent him to be wafted by fleet convoy, the twin brethren Sleep and Death, that swiftly set him down in the rich land of wide Lycia. But Patroclus cried to his horses and Automedon, and after the Trojans and Lycians went he, and so was blindly forgetful, in his witlessness, for if he had kept the saying of the son of Peleus, verily he should have escaped the evil fate of black death. But ever is the wit of Zeus stronger than the wit of men, for he driveth the valiant man in flight, and easily taketh away the victory, and then again himself rouseth men to fight, so now he roused the spirit of Patroclus in his breast. There whom first, whom last didst thou slay, Patroclus, when the gods called thee deathward? Adrestus first, and Autonous, and Echeclus, and Perimus, son of Megas, and Epistor, and Melanippus, and thereafter Elasus, and Mulius, and Pylartes; these he slew, but the others were each man of them fain of flight. Then would the sons of the Achaeans have taken high-gated Troy, by the hands of Patroclus, for around and before him he raged with the spear, but that Phoebus Apollo stood on the well-builded wall, with baneful thoughts towards Patroclus, and succouring the Trojans. Thrice did Patroclus climb on the corner of the lofty wall, and thrice did Apollo force him back and smote the shining shield with his immortal hands. But when for the fourth time he came on like a god, then cried far-darting Apollo terribly, and spake winged words: "Give back, Patroclus of the seed of Zeus! Not beneath thy spear is it fated that the city of the valiant Trojans shall fall, nay nor beneath Achilles, a man far better than thou."

So spake he, and Patroclus retreated far back, avoiding the wrath of far-darting Apollo. But Hector within the Scaean gates was restraining his whole-hooved horses, pondering whether he should drive again into the din and fight, or should call unto the host to gather to the wall. While thus he was thinking, Phoebus Apollo stood by him in the guise of a young man and a strong, Asius, who was the mother's brother of horse-taming Hector, being own brother of Hecabe, and son of Dymas, who dwelt in Phrygia, on the streams of Sangarius. In his guise spake Apollo, son of Zeus, to Hector: "Hector, wherefore dost thou cease from fight? It doth not behove thee. Would that I were as much stronger than thou as I am weaker, thereon quickly shouldst thou stand aloof from war to thy hurt. But come turn against Patroclus thy strong-hooved horses, if perchance thou mayst slay him, and Apollo give thee glory."

So spake the god, and went back again into the moil of men. But renowned Hector bade wise-hearted Cebriones to lash his horses into the war. Then Apollo went and passed into the press, and sent a dread panic among the Argives, but to the Trojans and Hector gave he renown. And Hector let the other Argives be, and slew none of them, but against Patroclus he turned his strong-hooved horses, and Patroclus on the other side leaped from his chariot to the ground, with a spear in his left hand, and in his other hand grasped a shining jagged stone, that his hand covered. Firmly he planted himself and hurled it, nor long did he shrink from his foe, nor was his cast in vain, but he struck Cebriones the charioteer of Hector, the bastard son of renowned Priam, on the brow with the sharp stone, as he held the reins of the horses. Both his brows the stone drove together, and his bone held not, but his eyes fell to the ground in the dust, there, in front of his feet. Then he, like a diver, fell from the well-wrought car, and his spirit left his bones. Then taunting him didst thou address him, knightly Patroclus: "Out on it, how nimble a man, how lively he diveth! Yea, if perchance he were on the teeming deep, this man would satisfy many by seeking for oysters, leaping from the ship, even if it were stormy weather, so lightly now he diveth from the chariot into the plain. Verily among the Trojans too there be diving men."

So speaking he set on the hero Cebriones with the rush of a lion, that while wasting the cattle-pens is smitten in the breast, and his own valour is his bane, even so against Cebriones, Patroclus, didst thou leap furiously. But Hector, on the other side, leaped from his chariot to the ground. And these twain strove for Cebriones like lions, that on the mountain peaks fight, both hungering, both high of heart, for a slain hind. Even so for Cebriones' sake these two masters of the war-cry, Patroclus and renowned Hector, were eager each to hew the other's flesh with the ruthless bronze.

Hector then seized him by the head, and slackened not hold, while Patroclus on the other side grasped him by the foot, and thereon the others, Trojans and Danaans, joined strong battle. And as the East Wind and the South contend with one another in shaking a deep wood in the dells of a mountain, shaking beech, and ash, and smooth-barked cornel tree, that clash against each other their long boughs with marvellous din, and a noise of branches broken, so the Trojans and Achaeans were leaping on each other and slaying, nor had either side any thought of ruinous flight. And many sharp darts were fixed around Cebriones, and winged arrows leaping from the bow-string, and many mighty stones smote the shields of them that fought around him. But he in the whirl of dust lay mighty and mightily fallen, forgetful of his chivalry.

Now while the sun was going about mid-heaven, so long the darts smote either side, and the host fell, but when the sun turned to the time of the loosing of oxen, lo, then beyond their doom the Achaeans proved the better. The hero Cebriones drew they forth from the darts, out of the tumult of the Trojans, and stripped the harness from his shoulders, and with ill design against the Trojans, Patroclus rushed upon them. Three times then rushed he on, peer of swift Ares, shouting terribly, and thrice he slew nine men. But when the fourth time he sped on like a god, thereon to thee, Patroclus, did the end of life appear, for Phoebus met thee in the strong battle, in dreadful wise. And Patroclus was not ware of him coming through the press, for hidden in thick mist did he meet him, and stood behind him, and smote his back and broad shoulders with a down-stroke of his hand, and his eyes were dazed. And from his head Phoebus Apollo smote the helmet that rolled rattling away with a din beneath the hooves of the horses, the helm with upright socket, and the crests were defiled with blood and dust. Not of old was it suffered that the helm with horse-hair crest should be defiled with dust, nay, but it protected the head and beautiful face of a man divine, even of Achilles. But then Zeus gave it to Hector, to bear on his head, yet was destruction near him. And all the long-shadowed spear was shattered in the hands of Patroclus, the spear great and heavy and strong, and sharp, while from his shoulders the tasselled shield with the baldric fell to the ground.

And the prince Apollo, son of Zeus, loosed his corslet, and blindness seized his heart and his shining limbs were unstrung, and he stood in amaze, and at close quarters from behind a Dardanian [4] smote him on the back, between the shoulders, with a sharp spear, even Euphorbus, son of Panthous, who excelled them of his age in casting the spear, and

---

[4] A Trojan; Dardanus was the ancestor of the Kings of Troy.

in horsemanship, and in speed of foot. Even thus, verily, had he cast down twenty men from their chariots, though then first had he come with his car to learn the lesson of war. He it was that first smote a dart into thee, knightly Patroclus, nor overcame thee, but ran back again and mingled with the throng, first drawing forth from the flesh his ashen spear, nor did he abide the onset of Patroclus, unarmed as he was, in the strife. But Patroclus, being overcome by the stroke of the god, and by the spear, gave ground, and retreated to the host of his comrades, avoiding Fate. But Hector, when he beheld great-hearted Patroclus give ground, being smitten with the keen bronze, came nigh unto him through the ranks, and wounded him with a spear, in the lowermost part of the belly, and drove the bronze clean through. And he fell with a crash, and sorely grieved the host of Achaeans. And as when a lion hath overcome in battle an untiring boar, they twain fighting with high heart on the crests of a hill, about a little well, and both are desirous to drink, and the lion hath by force overcome the boar that draweth difficult breath; so after that he had slain many did Hector son of Priam take the life away from the strong son of Menoetius, smiting him at close quarters with the spear; and boasting over him he spake winged words: "Patroclus, surely thou saidst that thou wouldst sack my town, and from Trojan women take away the day of freedom, and bring them in ships to thine own dear country: fool! nay, in front of these were the swift horses of Hector straining their speed for the fight; and myself in wielding the spear excel among the war-loving Trojans, even I who ward from them the day of destiny: but thee shall vultures here devour. Ah, wretch, surely Achilles for all his valour, availed thee not, who straitly charged thee as thou camest, he abiding there, saying, 'Come not to me, Patroclus lord of steeds, to the hollow ships, till thou hast torn the gory doublet of man-slaying Hector about his breast;' so, surely, he spake to thee, and persuaded the wits of thee in thy witlessness."

Then faintly didst thou answer him, knightly Patroclus: "Boast greatly, as now, Hector, for to thee have Zeus, son of

Cronos, and Apollo given the victory, who lightly have subdued me; for themselves stripped my harness from my shoulders. But if twenty such as thou had encountered me, here had they all perished, subdued beneath my spear. But me had ruinous Fate and the son of Leto slain, and of men Euphorbus, but thou art the third in my slaying. But another thing will I tell thee, and do thou lay it up in thy heart; verily thou thyself art not long to live, but already doth Death stand hard by thee, and strong Fate, that thou art to be subdued by the hands of noble Achilles, of the seed of Aeacus."

Even as so he spake the end of death overshadowed him. And his soul, fleeting from his limbs, went down to the house of Hades, wailing its own doom, leaving manhood and youth.

Then renowned Hector spake to him even in his death: "Patroclus, wherefore to me dost thou prophesy sheer destruction? who knows but that Achilles, the child of fair-tressed Thetis, will first be smitten by my spear, and lose his life?"

So spake he, and drew the spear of bronze from the wound, setting his foot on the dead, and cast him off on his back from the spear. And straightway with the spear he went after Automedon, the godlike squire of the swift-footed Achilles, for he was eager to smite him; but his swift-footed immortal horses bare him out of the battle, horses that the gods gave to Peleus a splendid gift.

XVII

Ajax Leaving the Body of Patroclus.
PAINTING FROM AN ARCHAIC AMPHORA.
(BASSEGGIO COLL., ROME)

The Fight over Patroclus' Body

❦ Menelaus stands over the body of Patroclus, guarding it from the enemy until the appearance of Hector forces him to flee. With Aias and his shield like a tower to help him, he returns to the fight, but too late to save the armor of Achilles, which Hector has seized and put on. At least Menelaus has saved the body of Patroclus. Around it the fight waxes wild.

Menelaus bids Antilochus, the son of Nestor, carry to Achilles the news of Patroclus' death. Menelaus and Meriones struggle to bear the body of Patroclus from the battle while the Aiantes try to hold back the Trojans.

XVIII

The Forging of Achilles' New Armour

Thus fought the rest in the likeness of blazing fire, while to Achilles came Antilochus, a messenger fleet of foot. Him found he in front of his ships of upright horns, boding in his soul the things which even now were accomplished. And sore troubled he spake to his great heart: "Ay me, wherefore again are the flowing-haired Achaeans flocking to the ships and flying in rout over the plain? May the gods not have wrought against me the grievous fears at my heart, even as my mother revealed and told me that while I am yet alive the best man of the Myrmidons must by deed of the men of Troy forsake the light of the sun. Surely now must Menoetius' valiant son be dead—foolhardy! surely I bade him when he should have beaten off the fire of the foe to come back to the ships nor with Hector fight amain."

While thus he held debate in his heart and soul, there drew nigh unto him noble Nestor's son, shedding hot tears, and spake his grievous tidings: "Ay me, wise Peleus' son, very bitter tidings must thou hear, such as I would had never been. Fallen is Patroclus, and they are fighting around his body, naked, for his armour is held by Hector of the glancing helm."

Thus spake he, and a black cloud of grief enwrapped Achilles, and with both hands he took dark dust and poured it over his head and defiled his comely face, and on his fragrant doublet black ashes fell. And himself in the dust lay mighty and mightily fallen, and with his own hands tore and marred his hair. And the handmaidens, whom Achilles and Patroclus took captive, cried aloud in the grief of their hearts, and ran forth around valiant Achilles, and all beat on their breasts with their hands, and the knees of each of them were unstrung. And Antilochus on the other side wailed and shed tears, holding Achilles' hands while he groaned in his noble heart, for he feared lest he should cleave his throat with the sword. Then terribly moaned Achilles; and his lady mother heard him as she sat in the depths of the sea beside her ancient sire. And thereon she uttered a cry, and the goddesses flocked around her, all the daughters of Nereus that were in the deep of the sea. There were Glauce, and Thaleia, and Cymodoce, Nesaea and Speio and Thoe and ox-eyed Halie and Cymothoe and Actaee and Limnoreia and Melite and Iaera and Amphithoe and Agaue and Doto and Proto and Pherusa and Dynamene and Dexamene and Amphinome and Callianeira, Doris and Panope and noble Galatea, and Nemertes, and Apseudes and Callianassa, and there were Clymene and Ianeira and Ianassa and Maera, and Oreithuia, and fair-tressed Amatheia, and other Nereids that were in the deep of the sea. With these the bright cave was filled, and they all beat together on their breasts, and Thetis led the lament: "Listen, sister Nereids, that ye all hear and know well what sorrows are in my heart. Ay me unhappy, ay me that bare to my sorrow the first of men! For after I had born a son noble and strong, the chief of heroes, and he shot up like a young branch, then when I had reared him as a plant in a very fruitful field I sent him in beaked ships to Ilium to fight against the men of Troy; but never again shall I welcome him back to his home, to the house of Peleus. And while he yet liveth in my sight and beholdeth the light of the sun, he sorroweth, neither can I help him any whit though I go unto him. But I will go, that I may look upon my dear child, and learn what sorrow hath come to him though he abide aloof from the war."

Thus spake she and left the cave; and the nymphs went

with her weeping, and around them the surge of the sea was sundered. And when they came to deep-soiled Troy-land they went up upon the shore in order, where the ships of the Myrmidons were drawn up thickly around fleet Achilles. And as he groaned heavily his lady mother stood beside him, and with a shrill cry clasped the head of her child, and spake unto him winged words of lamentation: "My child, why weepest thou? what sorrow hath come to thy heart? Tell it forth, hide it not. One thing at least hath been accomplished of Zeus according to the prayer thou madest, holding up to him thy hands, that the sons of the Achaeans should all be pent in at the ships, through lack of thee, and should suffer hateful things."

Then groaning heavily spake unto her Achilles fleet of foot: "My mother, that prayer truly hath the Olympian accomplished for me. But what delight have I therein, since my dear comrade is dead, Patroclus, whom I honoured above all my comrades as it were my very self? Him have I lost, and Hector that slew him hath stripped from him the armour great and fair, a wonder to behold, that the gods gave to Peleus a splendid gift, on the day when they laid thee in the bed of a mortal man. Would thou hadst abode among the deathless daughters of the sea, and Peleus had wedded a mortal bride! But now, that thou mayest have sorrow a thousandfold in thy heart for a dead son, never shalt thou welcome him back home, since my soul biddeth me also live no longer nor abide among men, if Hector be not first smitten by my spear and yield his life, and pay for his slaughter of Patroclus, Menoetius' son."

Then answered unto him Thetis shedding tears: "Short-lived, I ween, must thou be then, my child, by what thou sayest, for straightway after Hector is death appointed unto thee."

Then mightily moved spake unto her Achilles fleet of foot: "Straightway may I die, since I might not succour my comrade at his slaying. He hath fallen afar from his country and lacked my help in his sore need. Now therefore, since I go not back to my dear native land, neither have at all been succour to Patroclus nor to all my other comrades that have been slain by noble Hector, but I sit beside my ships a profitless burden of the earth, I that in war am such an one as is none else of the mail-clad Achaeans, though in council are others better—may strife perish utterly among gods and men, and wrath that stirreth even a wise man to be vexed, wrath that far sweeter than trickling honey waxeth like smoke in the breasts of men, even as I was wroth even now against Agamemnon king of men. But bygones will we let be, for all our pain, curbing the heart in our breasts under necessity. Now go I forth, that I may light on the destroyer of him I loved, on Hector; then will I accept my death whensoever Zeus willeth to accomplish it and the other immortal gods. For not even the mighty Heracles escaped death, albeit most dear to Cronian Zeus the king, but Fate overcame him and Hera's cruel wrath. So also shall I, if my fate hath been fashioned likewise, lie low when I am dead. But now let me win high renown, let me set some Trojan woman, some deep-bosomed daughter of Dardanos, staunching with both hands the tears upon her tender cheeks and wailing bitterly; yea, let them know that I am come back, though I tarried long from the war. Hold not me then from the battle in thy love, for thou shalt not prevail with me."

Then Thetis the silver-footed goddess answered him saying: "Yea verily, my child, no blame is in this, that thou ward sheer destruction from thy comrades in their distress. But thy fair glittering armour of bronze is held among the Trojans. Hector of the glancing helm beareth it on his shoulders in triumph, yet not for long, I ween, shall he glory therein, for death is hard anigh him. But thou go not yet down into the melee of war until thou see me with thine eyes come hither. In the morning will I return, at the coming up of the sun, bearing fair armour from the king Hephaestus."

Thus spake she and turned to go from her son, and as she turned she spake among her sisters of the sea: "Ye now go down within the wide bosom of the deep, to visit the Ancient One of the Sea and our father's house, and tell him all. I am going to high Olympus to Hephaestus of noble skill, if haply he will give unto my son noble armour shining gloriously."

Thus spake she, and they forthwith went down beneath the surge of the sea. And the silver-footed goddess Thetis went on to Olympus that she might bring noble armour to her son.

So her unto Olympus her feet bore. But the Achaeans with terrible cries were fleeing before man-slaying Hector till they came to the ships and to the Hellespont. Nor might the well-greaved Achaeans drag the corpse of Patroclus, Achilles' squire, out of the darts, for now again overtook him the host and the horses of Troy, and Hector son of Priam, in might as it were a flame of fire. Thrice did glorious Hector seize him from behind by the feet, resolved to drag him away, and mightily called upon the men of Troy. Thrice did the two Aiantes, clothed on with impetuous might, beat him off from the dead man, but he nevertheless, trusting in his might, anon would charge into the press, anon would stand and cry aloud, but he gave ground never a whit. As when shepherds in the field avail nowise to chase a fiery lion in fierce hunger away from a carcase, so availed not the two warrior Aiantes to scare Hector son of Priam from the dead. And now would he have won the body and gained renown unspeakable, had not fleet wind-footed Iris come speeding from Olympus with a message to the son of Peleus to array him, unknown of Zeus and the other gods, for Hera sent her. And she stood anigh and spake to him winged words: "Rouse thee, son of Peleus, of all men most redoubtable! Succour Patroclus, for whose body is terrible battle afoot before the ships. There slay they one another, these guarding the dead corpse, while the men of Troy are fierce to hale him unto windy Ilium, and chiefliest noble Hector is fain to drag him, and his heart biddeth him fix the head on the stakes of the wall when he hath sundered it from the tender neck. But

arise, lie thus no longer! let awe enter thy heart to forbid
that Patroclus become the sport of dogs of Troy. Thine were
the shame if he go down mangled amid the dead."

Then answered her fleet-footed noble Achilles: "Goddess
Iris, what god sent thee a messenger unto me?"

And to him again spake wind-footed fleet Iris: "It was
Hera that sent me, the wise wife of Zeus, nor knoweth the
high-throned son of Cronos nor any other of the Immortals
that on snowy Olympus have their dwelling-place."

And Achilles fleet of foot made answer to her and said:
"And how may I go into the fray? The Trojans hold my
arms; and my dear mother bade me forbear to array me until
I behold her with my eyes returned, for she promised to bring
fair armour from Hephaestus. Other man know I none whose
noble armour I might put on, save it were the shield of
Aias Telamon's son. But himself, I ween, is in the fore-front
of the press, dealing death with his spear around Patroclus
dead."

Then again spake unto him wind-footed fleet Iris: "Well
are we also aware that thy noble armour is held from thee.
But go forth unto the trench as thou art and show thyself to
the men of Troy, so that haply they will shrink back and refrain them from battle, and the warlike sons of the Achaeans
take breath amid their toil, for small breathing-time is in the
thick of fight."

Thus spake fleet-footed Iris and went her way. But Achilles dear to Zeus arose, and around his strong shoulders
Athene cast her tasselled aegis, and around his head the
bright goddess set a crown of a golden cloud, and kindled
therefrom a blazing flame. And as when a smoke issueth
from a city and riseth up into the upper air, from an island
afar off that foes beleaguer, while the others from their city
fight all day in hateful war,—but with the going down of the
sun blaze out the beacon-fires in line, and high aloft rusheth
up the glare for dwellers round about to behold, if haply
they may come with ships to help in need—thus from the
head of Achilles soared that blaze toward the heavens. And
he went and stood beyond the wall beside the trench, yet

mingled not among the Achaeans, for he minded the wise bidding of his mother. There stood he and shouted aloud, and afar off Pallas Athene uttered her voice, and spread terror unspeakable among the men of Troy. Clear as the voice of a clarion when it soundeth by reason of slaughterous foemen that beleaguer a city, so clear rang forth the voice of Achilles. And when they heard the brazen voice of Achilles, the souls of all of them were dismayed, and the horses of goodly manes were fain to turn the chariots backward, for they boded anguish in their hearts. And the charioteers were amazed when they saw the unwearying fire blaze fierce on the head of the great-hearted son of Peleus, for the bright-eyed goddess Athene made it blaze. Thrice from over the trench shouted mightily noble Achilles, and thrice were the men of Troy confounded and their proud allies. Yea there and then perished twelve men of their best by their own chariot wheels and spears. But the Achaeans with joy drew Patroclus forth of the darts and laid him on a litter, and his dear comrades stood around lamenting him; and among them followed fleet-footed Achilles, shedding hot tears, for his true comrade he saw lying on the bier, mangled by the keen bronze. Him sent he forth with chariot and horses unto the battle, but home again welcomed never more.

Then Hera the ox-eyed queen sent down the unwearying Sun to be gone unwillingly unto the streams of Ocean. So the Sun set, and the noble Achaeans made pause from the stress of battle and the hazardous war.

Now the men of Troy on their side when they were come back out of the violent fray loosed their swift horses from the chariots and gathered themselves in assembly or ever they would sup. Upon their feet they stood in the assembly, neither had any man heart to sit, for fear was fallen upon all because Achilles was come forth, after long ceasing from fell battle. Then began to speak among them wise Polydamas, son of Panthous, for he alone saw before and after. Comrade of Hector was he, and in the same night were both born, but the one in speech was far the best, the other with the spear. So with good intent toward them he made harangue and spake: "Take good heed on both sides, O my friends; for my part I would have ye go up now to the city, nor wait for bright morning on the plain beside the ships, for we are far off from the wall. So long as this man was wroth with noble Agamemnon, so long were the Achaeans easier to fight against, ay and I too rejoiced when I couched nigh their swift ships, trusting that we should seize the curved ships for a prey. But now am I sore afraid of the fleet son of Peleus; so exceeding fierce is his heart, he will not choose to abide in the plain where Trojans and Achaeans both in the midst share the spirit of war, but the prize he doeth battle for will be our city and our wives. Now go we up to our fastness; hearken unto me, for thus will it be. Now hath divine night stayed the fleet son of Peleus, but if to-morrow full-armed for the onset he shall light upon us abiding here, well shall each know that it is he, for gladly will whosoever fleeth win to sacred Ilium, and many of the men of Troy shall dogs and vultures devour—far be that from my ear. But if, though loth, we hearken unto my words, this night in counsel we shall possess our strength, and the city shall be guarded of her towers and high gates and tall well-polished doors that fit thereon close-shut. But at dawn of day in armour harnessed will we take our stand along the towers. Ill will he fare if he come forth from the ships to fight with us for our wall. Back to his ships shall he betake him when in vain chase he hath given his strong-necked horses their fill of hasting every-whither beneath the town. But within it never will he have heart to force his way, nor ever lay it waste; ere then shall he be devoured of swift dogs."

Then with stern gaze spake unto him Hector of the glancing helm: "Polydamas, no longer to my liking dost thou speak now, in that thou biddest us go back and be pent within the town. Have ye not had your fill already of being pent behind the towers? Of old time all mortal men would tell of this city of Priam for the much gold and bronze thereof, but now are its goodly treasures perished out of its dwellings, and much goods are sold away to Phrygia and pleasant Maeonia, since mighty Zeus dealt evilly with us.

But now when the son of crooked-counselling Cronos hath given me to win glory at the ships and to pen the Achaeans beside the sea, no longer, fond man, put forth such counsels among the folk. No man of Troy will hearken unto thee, I will not suffer it. But come let us all be persuaded as I shall say. Sup now in your ranks throughout the host, and keep good ward, and each watch in his place. And whoso of the Trojans is grieved beyond measure for his goods, let him gather them together and give them to the people to consume in common, for it is better they have joy thereof than the Achaeans. Then at dawn of day in armour harnessed at the hollow ships we will arouse keen war. What though in very truth noble Achilles be arisen beside the ships, ill shall he fare, if he will have it so. I at least will not flee from him out of the dread-sounding war, but full facing him will I stand, to try whether he win great victory, or haply I. The war-god is alike to all and a slayer of him that would slay."

Thus Hector spake, and the men of Troy applauded with fond hearts, for Pallas Athene bereft them of their wit. And they gave assent to the ill advising of Hector, but none hearkened to Polydamas who devised good counsel. Then they supped throughout the host; but the Achaeans all night made moan in lamentation for Patroclus. And first of them in the loud lamentation was the son of Peleus, laying upon the breast of his comrade his man-slaying hands and moaning very sore, even as a deep-bearded lion whose whelps some stag-hunter hath snatched away out of a deep wood; and the lion coming afterward grieveth, and through many glens he rangeth on the track of the footsteps of the man, if anywhere he might find him, for most bitter anger seizeth him;—thus Achilles moaning heavily spake among the Myrmidons: "Ay me, vain verily was the word I uttered on that day when I cheered the hero Menoetius in his halls and said that I would bring back to Opus his son in glory from the sack of Ilium with the share of spoil that should fall unto him. Not all the purposes of men doth Zeus accomplish for them. It is appointed that both of us redden the same earth with our blood here in Troy-land, for neither shall the old knight Peleus welcome me back home within his halls, nor my mother Thetis, but even here shall earth keep hold on me. Yet now, O Patroclus, since I follow thee under earth, I will not hold thy funeral till I have brought hither the armour and the head of Hector, thy high-hearted slayer, and before thy pyre I will cut the throats of twelve noble sons of the men of Troy, for mine anger thou art slain. Till then beside the beaked ships shalt thou lie as thou art, and around thee deep-bosomed women, Trojan and Dardanian, shall mourn thee weeping night and day, even they whom we toiled to win by our strength and our long spears when we sacked rich cities of mortal men."

Thus spake noble Achilles, and bade his comrades set a great tripod on the fire, that with all speed they might wash from Patroclus the bloody gore. So they set a tripod of ablution on the burning fire, and poured therein water and took wood and kindled it beneath; and the fire wrapped the belly of the tripod, and the water grew hot. And when the water boiled in the bright bronze, then washed they him and anointed with olive oil, and filled his wounds with fresh ointment, and laid him on a bier and covered him with soft cloth from head to foot, and thereover a white robe. Then all night around Achilles fleet of foot the Myrmidons made lament and moan for Patroclus.

Meanwhile Zeus spake unto Hera his sister and wife: "Thou hast accomplished this, O Hera, ox-eyed queen, thou hast aroused Achilles fleet of foot. Verily of thine own children must the flowing-haired Achaeans be."

Then answered unto him Hera the ox-eyed queen: "Most dread son of Cronos, what is this word thou hast said? Truly even a man, I ween, is to accomplish what he may for another man, albeit he is mortal and hath not wisdom as we. How then was I who avow me the first of goddesses both by birth and for that I am called thy wife, and thou art king among all Immortals—how was I not in mine anger to devise evil against the men of Troy?"

So debated they on this wise with one another. But Thetis of the silver feet came unto the house of Hephaestus, imperishable, starlike, far seen among the dwellings of Immortals, a house of bronze, wrought by the crook-footed god himself. Him found she sweating in toil and busy about his bellows, for he was forging tripods twenty in all to stand around the wall of his stablished hall, and beneath the base of each he had set golden wheels, that of their own motion they might enter the assembly of the gods and again return unto his house, a marvel to look upon. Thus much were they finished that not yet were the handles of cunning work set thereon; these was he making ready, and welding chains. While hereat he was labouring with wise intent, then drew nigh unto him Thetis, goddess of the silver feet. And Charis went forward and beheld her, fair Charis of the shining chaplet whom the renowned lame god had wedded. And she clasped her hand in hers and spake and called her by her name: "Wherefore, long-robed Thetis, comest thou to our house, honoured that thou art and dear? No frequent comer art thou hitherto. But come onward with me that I may set guest-cheer before thee."

Thus spake the bright goddess and led her on. Then set she her on a silver-studded throne, goodly, of cunning work, and a footstool was beneath her feet; and she called to Hephaestus, the famed artificer, and said unto him: "Hephaestus, come forth hither, Thetis hath need of thee."

And the renowned lame god made answer to her: "Verily a dread and honoured goddess in my sight is she that is within, seeing that she delivered me when pain came upon me from my great fall through the ill-will of my shameless mother who would have fain hid me away, for that I was lame. Then had I suffered anguish of heart had not Eurynome and Thetis taken me into their bosom—Eurynome daughter of Ocean that floweth back ever upon himself. Nine years with them I wrought much cunning work of bronze, brooches and spiral arm-bands and cups and necklaces, in the hollow cave, while around me the stream of Ocean with murmuring foam flowed infinite. Neither knew thereof any other of gods or of mortal men, save only Thetis and Eurynome who delivered me. And now cometh Thetis to our house; wherefore behoveth it me verily in all wise to repay fair-tressed Thetis for the saving of my life. But do thou now set beside her fair entertainment, while I put away my bellows and all my gear."

He said, and from the anvil rose limping, a huge bulk, but under him his slender legs moved nimbly. The bellows he set away from the fire, and gathered all his gear wherewith he worked into a silver chest; and with a sponge he wiped his face and hands and sturdy neck and shaggy breast, and put on his doublet, and took a stout staff and went forth limping; but there were handmaidens of gold that moved to help their lord, the semblances of living maids. In them is understanding at their hearts, in them are voice and strength, and they have skill of the immortal gods. These supported their lord, and he gat him haltingly near to where Thetis was, and set him on a bright seat, and clasped her hand in his and spake and called her by her name: "Wherefore, long-robed Thetis, comest thou to our house, honoured that thou art and dear? No frequent comer art thou hitherto. Speak what thou hast at heart; my soul is fain to accomplish it, if accomplish it I can, and if it be appointed for accomplishment."

Then answered unto him Thetis shedding tears: "Hephaestus, hath there verily been any of all goddesses in Olympus that hath endured so many grievous sorrows at heart as are the woes that Cronian Zeus hath laid upon me above all others? He chose me from among the sisters of the sea to enthrall me to a man, even Peleus Aeacus' son, and with a man I endured wedlock sore against my will. Now lieth he in his halls forspent with grievous age, but other griefs are mine. A son he gave me to bear and nourish, the chief of heroes, and he shot up like a young branch. Like a plant in a very fruitful field I reared him and sent him forth on beaked ships to Ilium to fight against the men of Troy, but never again shall I welcome him back to his home within the house of Peleus. And while he yet liveth in my sight and beholdeth the light of the sun, he sorroweth, neither can I help him any whit though I go unto him. The maiden whom the sons of the Achaeans chose out to be his prize, her hath the lord Agamemnon taken back out of his hands. In grief for her wasted he his heart; while the men of Troy were driving the Achaeans on their ships, nor suffered them to come forth. And the elders of the Argives entreated him, and told over many noble gifts. Then albeit himself he refused to ward destruction from them, he put his armour on Patroclus and sent him to the war, and much people with him. All day they fought around the Scaean gates and that same day had sacked the town, but that when now Menoetius' valiant son had wrought much harm, Apollo slew him in the forefront of the battle, and gave glory unto Hector. Therefore now come I a suppliant unto thy knees, if haply thou be willing to give my short-lived son shield and helmet, and goodly greaves fitted with ankle-pieces, and cuirass. For the armour that he had erst, his trusty comrade lost when he fell beneath the men of Troy; and my son lieth on the earth with anguish in his soul."

Then made answer unto her the lame god of great renown: "Be of good courage, let not these things trouble thy heart. Would that so might I avail to hide him far from dolorous death, when dread fate cometh upon him, as surely shall goodly armour be at his need, such as all men afterward shall marvel at, whosoever may behold."

Thus saying he left her there and went unto his bellows and turned them upon the fire and bade them work. And the bellows, twenty in all, blew on the crucibles, sending deft blasts on every side, now to aid his labour and now anon howsoever Hephaestus willed and the work went on. And he threw bronze that weareth not into the fire, and tin and precious gold and silver, and next he set on an anvil-stand a great anvil, and took in his hand a sturdy hammer, and in the other he took the tongs.

First fashioned he a shield great and strong, adorning it all over, and set thereto a shining rim, triple, bright-glancing, and therefrom a silver baldric. Five were the folds of the shield itself; and therein fashioned he much cunning work from his wise heart.

There wrought he the earth, and the heavens, and the sea, and the unwearying sun, and the moon waxing to the full, and the signs every one wherewith the heavens are crowned, Pleiads and Hyads and Orion's might, and the Bear that men call also the Wain, her that turneth in her place and watcheth Orion; and alone hath no part in the baths of Ocean.

Also he fashioned therein two fair cities of mortal men. In the one were espousals and marriage feasts, and beneath the blaze of torches they were leading the brides from their chambers through the city, and loud arose the bridal song. And young men were whirling in the dance, and among them flutes and viols sounded high; and the women standing each at her door were marvelling. But the folk were gathered in the assembly place; for there a strife was arisen, two men striving about the blood-price of a man slain; the one claimed to pay full atonement, expounding to the people, but the other denied him and would take naught; and both were fain to receive arbitrament at the hand of a referee. And the folk were cheering both, as they took part on either side. And heralds kept order among the folk, while the elders on polished stones were sitting in the sacred circle, and holding in their hands staves from the loud-voiced heralds. Then before the people they rose up and gave judgment each in turn. And in the midst lay two talents of gold, to be given unto him who should plead among them most righteously.

But around the other city were two armies in siege with glittering arms. And two counsels found favour among them, either to sack the town or to share all with the townsfolk even whatsoever substance the fair city held within. But the besieged were not yet yielding, but arming for an ambushment. On the wall there stood to guard it their dear wives and infant children, and with these the old men; but the rest went forth, and their leaders were Ares and Pallas Athene, both wrought in gold, and golden was the vesture they had on. Goodly and great were they in their armour, even as gods, far seen around, and the folk at their feet were smaller. And when they came where it seemed good to them to lay ambush, in a river bed where there was a common watering-place of herds, there they set them, clad in glittering bronze. And two scouts were posted by them afar off to spy the coming of flocks and of oxen with crooked horns. And presently came the cattle, and with them two herdsmen playing on pipes, that took no thought of the guile. Then the others when they beheld these ran upon them and quickly cut off the herds of oxen and fair flocks of white sheep, and slew the shepherds withal. But the besiegers, as they sat before the speech-places and heard much din among the oxen, mounted forthwith behind their high-stepping horses, and came up with speed. Then they arrayed their battle and fought beside the river banks, and smote one another with bronze-shod spears. And among them mingled Strife and Tumult, and fell Death, grasping one man alive fresh-wounded, another without wound, and dragging another dead through the melee by the feet; and the raiment on her shoulders was red with the blood of men. Like living mortals they hurled together and fought, and haled the corpses each of the other's slain.

Furthermore he set in the shield a soft fresh-ploughed field, rich tilth and wide, the third time ploughed; and many ploughers therein drove their yokes to and fro as they wheeled about. Whensoever they came to the boundary of the field and turned, then would a man come to each and give into his hands a goblet of sweet wine, while others would be turning back along the furrows, fain to reach the boundary of the deep tilth. And the field grew black behind and seemed as it were a-ploughing, albeit of gold, for this was the great marvel of the work.

Furthermore he set therein the demesne-land of a king, where hinds were reaping with sharp sickles in their hands. Some armfuls along the swathe were falling in rows to the earth, whilst others the sheaf-binders were binding in twisted bands of straw. Three sheaf-binders stood over them, while behind boys gathering corn and bearing it in their arms gave it constantly to the binders; and among them the king in silence was standing at the swathe with his staff, rejoicing in his heart. And henchmen apart beneath an oak were making ready a feast, and preparing a great ox they had sacrificed; while the women were strewing much white barley to be a supper for the hinds.

Also he set therein a vineyard teeming plenteously with clusters, wrought fair in gold; black were the grapes, but the vines hung throughout on silver poles. And around it he ran a ditch of blue enamel, and round that a fence of tin; and one single pathway led to it, whereby the vintagers might go when they should gather the vintage. And maidens and striplings in childish glee bare the sweet fruit in plaited baskets. And in the midst of them a boy made pleasant music on a clear-toned viol, and sang thereto a sweet song of Linus with delicate voice; while the rest with feet falling together kept time with the music and song.

Also he wrought therein a herd of kine with upright horns, and the kine were fashioned of gold and tin, and with lowing they hurried from the byre to pasture beside a murmuring river, beside the waving reed. And herdsmen of gold were following with the kine, four of them, and nine dogs fleet of foot came after them. But two terrible lions among the foremost kine had seized a loud-roaring bull that bellowed mightily as they haled him, and the dogs and the young men sped after him. The lions rending the great bull's hide were devouring his vitals and his black blood; while the herdsmen in vain incited their fleet dogs to set on, for they shrank from biting the lions but stood hard by and barked and swerved away.

Also the glorious lame god wrought therein a pasture in a fair glen, a great pasture of white sheep, and a steading, and roofed huts, and folds.

Also did the glorious lame god devise a dancing-place like unto that which once in wild Cnossus Daedalus wrought for Ariadne of the lovely tresses. There were youths dancing and maidens of costly wooing, their hands upon one another's wrists. Fine linen the maidens had on, and the youths well-woven doublets faintly glistening with oil. Fair wreaths had the maidens, and the youths daggers of gold

Thetis Receiving the Weapons for Achilles.

PAINTING FROM A KYLIX.
(BERLIN MUSEUM)

hanging from silver baldrics. And now would they run round
with deft feet exceeding lightly, as when a potter sitting by
his wheel that fitteth between his hands maketh trial of it
whether it run: and now anon they would run in lines to
meet each other. And a great company stood round the
lovely dance in joy; and among them a divine minstrel was
making music on his lyre, and through the midst of them,
leading the measure, two tumblers whirled.

Also he set therein the great might of the River of Ocean

around the uttermost rim of the cunningly-fashioned shield.

Now when he had wrought the shield great and strong, then wrought he him a corslet brighter than a flame of fire, and he wrought him a massive helmet to fit his brows, goodly and graven, and set thereon a crest of gold, and he wrought him greaves of pliant tin.

So when the renowned lame god had finished all the armour, he took and laid it before the mother of Achilles. Then she like a falcon sprang down from snowy Olympus, bearing from Hephaestus the glittering arms.

XIX

Achilles and Agamemnon Make Peace

❧ Thetis brings the arms to Achilles and tells him to make
his peace with Agamemnon. Agamemnon puts the blame for
their quarrel on Zeus and Ate, Infatuation. He sends the promised gifts to Achilles, who is so desirous of war that he does
not wish to delay for gifts or food. Zeus sends Athene to distill
nectar and ambrosia in his breast so that he can fight without
hunger until evening. Then Achilles puts on his armor.

HIS teeth gnashed together, and his eyes blazed as it were
the flame of a fire, for into his heart was intolerable
anguish entered in. . . .

And terribly he called upon the horses of his sire: "Xanthus and Balius, famed children of Podarge, in other sort
take heed to bring your charioteer safe back to the Danaan
host, when we have done with battle, and leave him not as
ye left Patroclus to lie there dead."

Then the horse Xanthus of glancing feet made answer
unto him from beneath the yoke;—and he bowed with his
head, and all his mane fell from the yoke-cushion beside
the yoke and touched the ground;—for the white-armed goddess Hera gave him speech: "Yea verily for this hour, dread
Achilles, we will still bear thee safe, yet is thy death-day nigh
at hand, neither shall we be cause thereof, but a mighty god,
and forceful Fate. For not through sloth or heedlessness of
ours did the men of Troy from Patroclus' shoulders strip his
arms, but the best of the gods, whom bright-haired Leto

bore, slew him in the forefront of the battle, and to Hector gave renown. We even with the wind of Zephyr, swiftest, they say, of all winds, well might run; nathless to thee thyself it is appointed to be slain in fight by a god and by a man."

Now when he had thus spoken the Erinyes stayed his voice. And sore troubled did fleet-footed Achilles answer him: "Xanthus, why prophesiest thou my death? nowise behoveth it thee. Well know I of myself that it is appointed me to perish here, far from my father dear and mother; howbeit anywise I will not refrain till I give the Trojans surfeit of war."

He said, and with a cry among the foremost held on his whole-hooved steeds.

Achilles climbs into his chariot; by his side is Phoenix.

PAINTING FROM AN AMPHORA.
(BRITISH MUSEUM)

XX

Aphrodite Arming Herself to Go and Fight.
PAINTING FROM AN OXYBAPHON WITH YELLOW FIGURES.
(LOUVRE MUSEUM)

The Gods Join the Fray

⟨ Zeus, summoning a council of the gods, bids them take part in the battle as they wish; he will watch the struggle from a peak on Olympus.

The gods sit on a great wall and watch the fray. Achilles and Aeneas fight, but Aeneas is snatched away by Poseidon, for his destiny is to escape the destruction of Troy in order that the Trojan race may not perish. Hector proclaims that he will fight Achilles, but is warned by Apollo not to seek single combat. Hector forgets himself when he sees Achilles kill his brother; he hurls a spear at Achilles, but is caught up in a cloud by Apollo. Achilles rages like a fire over the plain.

XXI

Achilles Fights the River

B^UT when now they came unto the ford of the fair-flowing
river, even eddying Xanthus,[1] whom immortal Zeus begat, there sundering them he chased the one part to the
plain toward the city, even where the Achaeans were flying
in affright the day before, when glorious Hector was in his
fury—thither poured some in flight, and Hera spread before
them thick mist to hinder them:—but half were pent into
the deep-flowing silver-eddied river, and fell therein with
a mighty noise, and the steep channel sounded, and the
banks around rang loudly; for with shouting they swam
therein hither and thither, whirled round the eddies. And
as when at the rush of fire locusts take wing to fly unto a
river, and the unwearying fire flameth forth on them with
sudden onset, and they huddle in the water; so before Achilles was the stream of deep-eddying Xanthus filled with the
roar and the throng of horses and men.

Then the seed of Zeus left behind him his spear upon the
bank, leant against tamarisk bushes, and leapt in, as it were
a god, keeping his sword alone, and devised grim work at
heart, and smote as he turned him every way about: and
their groaning went up ghastly as they were stricken by the
sword, and the water reddened with blood. As before a dol-
phin of huge maw fly other fish and fill the nooks of some
fair-havened bay, in terror, for he devoureth amain which-

---

[1] Another name for the Scamander River.

soever of them he may catch; so along the channels of that dread stream the Trojans crouched beneath the precipitous sides. And when his hands were weary of slaughter he chose twelve young men alive out of the river, an atonement for Patroclus that was dead. These brought he forth amazed like fawns, and bound behind them their hands with well-cut thongs, which they themselves wore on their pliant doublets, and gave them to his comrades to lead down to the hollow ships. Then again he made his onset, athirst for slaying.

There met he a son of Dardanian Priam, in flight out of the river, Lycaon, whom once himself he took and brought unwilling out of his father's orchard, in a night assault; he was cutting with keen bronze young shoots of a wild fig-tree, to be hand-rails of a chariot; but to him an unlooked-for bane came goodly Achilles. And at that time he sold him into well-peopled Lemnos, sending him on ship-board, and the son of Jason gave a price for him; and thence a guest friend freed him with a great ransom, Eëtion of Imbros, and sent him to goodly Arisbe; whence flying secretly he came to his father's house. Eleven days he rejoiced among his friends after he was come from Lemnos, but on the twelfth once more God brought him into the hands of Achilles, who was to send him to the house of Hades though nowise fain to go. Him when fleet-footed noble Achilles saw bare of helm and shield, neither had he a spear, but had thrown all to the ground; for he sweated grievously as he tried to flee out of the river, and his knees were failing him for weariness: then in wrath spake Achilles to his great heart: "Ha! verily great marvel is this that I behold with my eyes. Surely then will the proud Trojans whom I have slain rise up again from beneath the murky gloom, since thus hath this man come back escaped from his pitiless fate, though sold into goodly Lemnos, neither hath the deep of the hoary sea stayed him, that holdeth many against their will. But come then, of our spear's point shall he taste, that I may see and learn in my mind whether likewise he shall come back even from beneath, or whether the life-giving Earth shall hold him down, she that holdeth so even the strong."

Thus pondered he in his place; but the other came near amazed, fain to touch his knees, for his soul longed exceedingly to flee from evil death and black destruction. Then goodly Achilles lifted his long spear with intent to smite him, but he stooped and ran under it and caught his knees; and the spear went over his back and stood in the ground, hungering for flesh of men. Then Lycaon besought him, with one hand holding his knees, while with the other he held the sharp spear and loosed it not, and spake to him winged words: "I cry thee mercy, Achilles; have thou regard and pity for me: to thee, O fosterling of Zeus, am I in the bonds of suppliantship. For at thy table first I tasted meal of Demeter on the day when thou didst take me captive in the well-ordered orchard, and didst sell me away from my father and my friends unto goodly Lemnos, and I fetched thee the price of a hundred oxen. And now have I been ransomed for thrice that, and this is my twelfth morn since I came to Ilium after much pain. Now once again hath ruinous fate delivered me into thy hands; surely I must be hated of father Zeus, that he hath given me a second time unto thee; and to short life my mother bare me, Laothoe, old Altes' daughter—Altes who ruleth among the war-loving Leleges, holding steep Pedasus on the Satnioïs. His daughter Priam had to wife, with many others, and of her were we two born, and thou wilt butcher both. Him among the foremost of the foot-soldiers didst thou lay low, even godlike Polydorus, when thou smotest him with thy sharp spear: and now will it go hard with me here, for no hope have I to escape thy hands, since God hath delivered me thereunto. Yet one thing will I tell thee, and do thou lay it to heart: slay me not, since I am not of the same mother as Hector, who slew thy comrade the gentle and brave."

Thus spake to him the noble son of Priam, beseeching him with words, but he heard a voice implacable: "Fond fool, proffer me no ransom, nor these words. Until Patroclus met his fated day, then was it welcomer to my soul to spare the men of Troy, and many I took alive and sold beyond the sea: but now there is none shall escape death,

whomsoever before Ilium God shall deliver into my hands
—yea, even among all Trojans, but chiefest among Priam's
sons. Ay, friend, thou too must die: why thus lamentest
thou? Patroclus too is dead, who was better far than thou.
Seest thou not also what manner of man am I for might
and goodliness? and a good man was my father, and a goddess mother bare me. Yet over me too hang death and forceful fate. There cometh morn or eve or some noonday when
my life too some man shall take in battle, whether with spear
he smite or arrow from the string."

Thus spake he, and the other's knees and heart were unstrung. He let go Achilles' spear, and sat with both hands
outspread. But Achilles drew his sharp sword and smote on
the collar-bone beside the neck, and all the two-edged sword
sank into him, and he lay stretched prone upon the earth,
and blood flowed dark from him and soaked the earth. Him
seized Achilles by the foot and sent him down the stream,
and over him exulting spake winged words: "There lie thou
among the fishes, which shall lick off thy wound's blood
heedlessly, nor shall thy mother lay thee on a bed and
mourn for thee, but Scamander shall bear thee on his eddies
into the broad bosom of the sea. Leaping along the wave
shall many a fish dart up to the dark ripple to eat of the
white flesh of Lycaon. So perish all, until we reach the citadel
of sacred Ilium, ye flying and I behind destroying. Nor even
the River, fair-flowing, silver-eddied, shall avail you, to whom
long time forsooth ye sacrifice many bulls, and among his
eddies throw whole-hooved horses down alive. For all this
yet shall ye die the death, until ye pay all for Patroclus' slaying and the slaughter of Achaeans whom at the swift ships
ye slew while I tarried afar."

Thus spake he, but the River waxed ever more wroth in
his heart, and sought in his soul how he should stay goodly
Achilles from his work, and ward destruction from the Trojans. Meanwhile the son of Peleus with his far-shadowing
spear leapt, fain to slay him, upon Asteropaeus son of Pelegon, whom wide-flowing Axius begat of Periboea eldest of
the daughters of Acessamenus, for with her lay that deep-

eddying River. Upon him set Achilles, and Asteropaeus
stood against him from the river, holding two spears; for
Xanthus put courage into his heart, being angered for the
slaughtered youths whom Achilles was slaughtering along
the stream and had no pity on them. Then when the twain
were come nigh in onset on each other, unto him first spake
fleet-footed noble Achilles: "Who and whence art thou of
men, that darest to come against me? Ill-fated are they whose
children match them with my might."

And to him made answer Pelegon's noble son: "High-
hearted son of Peleus, why askest thou my lineage? I come
from deep-soiled Paeonia, a land far off, leading Paeonian
men with their long spears, and this now is the eleventh
morn since I am come to Ilium. My lineage is of wide-flowing Axius, who begat Pelegon famous with the spear, and he,
men say, was my father. Now fight we, noble Achilles!"

Thus spake he in defiance, and goodly Achilles lifted the
Pelian ash: but the warrior Asteropaeus hurled with both
spears together, for he could use both hands alike, and with
the one spear smote the shield, but pierced it not right
through, for the gold stayed it, the gift of a god; and with
the other he grazed the elbow of Achilles' right arm, and
there leapt forth dark blood, but the point beyond him fixed
itself in the earth, eager to batten on flesh. Then in his turn
Achilles hurled on Asteropaeus his straight-flying ash, fain to
have slain him, but missed the man and struck the high
bank, and quivering half its length in the bank he left the
ashen spear. Then the son of Peleus drew his sharp sword
from his thigh and leapt fiercely at him, and he availed not
to draw with his stout hand Achilles' ashen shaft from the
steep bank. Thrice shook he it striving to draw it forth, and
thrice gave up the strain, but the fourth time he was fain to
bend and break the ashen spear of the seed of Peleus, but
ere that Achilles closing on him reft him of life with his
sword. For in the belly he smote him beside the naval, and
all his bowels gushed out to the earth, and darkness covered
his eyes as he lay gasping. Then Achilles trampling on his
breast stripped off his armour and spake exultingly: "Lie

there! It is hard to strive against children of Cronos' mighty son, even though one be sprung from a River-god. Thou truly declarest thyself the seed of a wide-flowing River, but I avow me of the lineage of great Zeus. My sire is a man ruling many Myrmidons, Peleus the son of Aeacus, and Aeacus was begotten of Zeus. As Zeus is mightier than seaward-murmuring rivers, so is the seed of Zeus made mightier than the seed of a river. Nay, there is hard beside thee a great river, if he may anywise avail; but against Zeus the son of Cronos it is not possible to fight. For him not even king Achelous is match, nor yet the great strength of deep-flowing Ocean, from whom all rivers flow and every sea, and all springs and deep wells: yea, even he hath fear of the lightning of great Zeus and his dread thunder, when it pealeth out of heaven."

He said, and from the steep bank drew his bronze spear, and left there Asteropaeus whom he had slain, lying in the sands, and the dark water flooded him. Around him eels and fishes swarmed, tearing and gnawing the fat about his kidneys. But Achilles went on after the charioted Paeonians who still along the eddying river huddled in fear, when they saw their best man in the stress of battle slain violently by the hands and the sword of the son of Peleus. There slew he Thersilochus and Mydon and Astypylus and Mnesus and Thrasius and Aenius and Ophelestes; and more yet of the Paeonians would swift Achilles have slain, had not the deep-eddying River called unto him in wrath, in semblance of a man, and from an eddy's depth sent forth a voice: "O Achilles, thy might and thy evil work are beyond the measure of men; for gods themselves are ever helping thee. If indeed the son of Cronos hath delivered thee all the Trojans to destroy, at least drive them forth from me and do thy grim deeds on the plain, for filled with dead men is my pleasant bed, nor can I pour my stream to the great sea, being choked with dead, and thou slayest ruthlessly. Come then, let be; I am dismayed, O captain of hosts."

And to him answered Achilles fleet of foot: "So be it, heaven-sprung Scamander, even as thou biddest. But the proud Trojans I will not cease from slaying until I have driven them into their city, and have made trial with Hector face to face whether he is to vanquish me or I him."

Thus saying, he set upon the Trojans, like a god. Then unto Apollo spake the deep-eddying River: "Out on it, lord of the silver bow, child of Zeus, thou hast not kept the ordinance of Cronos' son, who charged thee straitly to stand by the Trojans and to help them, until eve come with light late-setting, and darken the deep-soiled earth."

He said, and spear-famed Achilles sprang from the bank and leapt into his midst; but he rushed on him in a furious wave, and stirred up all his streams in tumult, and swept down the many dead who lay thick in him, slain by Achilles; these on dry land he cast with bellowing like a bull, and saved the living under his fair streams, hiding them within eddies deep and wide. But terribly around Achilles arose his tumultuous wave, and the stream smote violently against his shield, nor availed he to stand firm upon his feet. Then he grasped a tall fair-grown elm, and it fell uprooted and tore away all the bank, and reached over the fair river bed with its thick shoots, and stemmed the River himself, bridging it from side to side: and Achilles, struggling out of the eddy, made haste to fly over the plain with his swift feet, for he was afraid. But the great god ceased not, but arose upon him with darkness on his crest, that he might stay noble Achilles from slaughter, and ward destruction from the men of Troy. And the son of Peleus rushed away a spear's throw, with the swoop of a black eagle, the mighty hunter, strongest at once and swiftest of winged birds. Like him he sped, and on his breast the bronze rang terribly as he fled from beneath the onset, and behind him the River rushed on with a mighty roar. As when a gardener from a dark spring leadeth water along a bed through crops and garden grounds, a mattock in his hands, casting forth hindrances from the ditch, and as it floweth all pebbles are swept down, and swiftly gliding it murmureth down a sloping place, and outrunneth him that is its guide:—thus ever the river wave caught up Achilles for all his speed; for gods are mightier than men. For when-

soever fleet-footed noble Achilles struggled to stand against
it, and know whether all Immortals who inhabit spacious
heaven were upon him, then would a great wave of the
heaven-sprung River beat upon his shoulders from above,
and he sprang upward with his feet, sore vexed at heart; and
the River was wearying his knees with violent rush beneath,
and devouring the earth from under his feet. Then the son
of Peleus cried aloud, looking up to the broad heaven:
"Zeus, Father, how doth none of the gods take it on him in
pity to save me from the River! after that let come to me
what may. None other of the inhabitants of Heaven is
blameworthy so as my dear mother, who beguiled me with
false words, saying that under the wall of the mail-clad men
of Troy I must die by the swift arrows of Apollo. Would that
Hector had slain me, the best of men bred here: then brave
had been the slayer, and a brave man had he slain. But now
by a sorry death am I doomed to die, pent in this mighty
river, like a swineherd boy whom a torrent sweepeth down
as he essayeth to cross it in a storm."

Thus spake he, and quickly Poseidon and Athene came
near and stood beside him, in the likeness of men, and taking his hands in theirs pledged him in words. And the
first that spake was Poseidon, Shaker of the earth: "Son of
Peleus, tremble not, neither be afraid; such helpers of thee
are we from the gods, approved of Zeus, even Pallas Athene
and I, for to be vanquished of a river is not appointed thee,
but he will soon give back, and thou wilt thyself perceive
it: but we will give thee wise counsel, if thou wilt obey it;
hold not thy hand from hazardous battle until within Ilium's
famous walls thou have pent the Trojan host, even all that
flee before thee. But do thou, when thou hast taken the life
of Hector, go back unto the ships; this glory we give unto
thee to win."

They having thus spoken departed to the Immortals, but
he toward the plain—for the bidding of gods was strong
upon him—went onward; and all the plain was filled with
water-flood, and many beautiful arms and corpses of slain
youths were drifting there. He stepped high as he rushed

right on against the stream, nor stayed him the wide-flowing River, for Athene put great strength in him. Neither did Scamander slacken his fierceness, but yet more raged against the son of Peleus, and he curled crestwise the billow of his stream, lifting himself on high, and on Simoïs he called with a shout: "Dear brother, the strength of this man let us both join to stay, since quickly he will lay waste the great city of king Priam, and the Trojans will not be left to fight. Help me with speed, and fill thy streams with water from thy springs, and urge on all thy torrents, and raise up a great wave, and stir huge roaring of tree-stumps and stones, that we may stay the fierce man who now is lording it, and deeming himself match for gods. For neither, I ween, will strength avail him, nor comeliness anywise, nor that armour beautiful, which deep beneath the flood shall be o'erlaid with slime, and himself I will wrap him in my sands and pour round him countless shingle without stint, nor shall the Achaeans know where to gather his bones, so vast a shroud of silt will I heap over them. Where he dieth there shall be his tomb, neither shall he have need of any barrow to be raised, when the Achaeans make his funeral."

He said, and rushed in tumult on Achilles, raging from on high, thundering with foam and blood and bodies of dead men. Then did a dark wave of the heaven-sprung River stand towering up and would overwhelm the son of Peleus. But Hera cried aloud in terror for Achilles, lest the great deep-eddying River sweep him away, and straightway she called to Hephaestus, her dear son: "Rise, lame god, O my son; it was against thee we thought that eddying Xanthus was matched in fight. Help with all speed, put forth large blast of flame. Then will I go to raise a strong storm out of the sea of the West Wind and the white South which shall utterly consume the dead Trojans and their armour, blowing the angry flame. Thou along Xanthus' banks burn up his trees and wrap himself in fire, nor let him anywise turn thee back by soft words or by threat, nor stay thy rage—only when I cry to thee with my voice, then hold the unwearying fire."

Thus spake she, and Hephaestus made ready fierce-blazing

fire. First on the plain fire blazed, and burnt the many dead who lay there thick, slain by Achilles; and all the plain was parched and the bright water stayed. And as when in late summer the North Wind swiftly parcheth a new watered orchard, and he that tilleth it is glad, thus was the whole plain parched, and Hephaestus consumed the dead; then against the river he turned his gleaming flame. Elms burnt and willow-trees and tamarisks, and lotos burnt and rush and galingale, which round the fair streams of the river grew in multitude. And the eels and fishes beneath the eddies were afflicted, which through the fair streams tumbled this way and that, in anguish at the blast of crafty Hephaestus. And the strong River burned, and spake and called to him by name: "Hephaestus, there is no god can match with thee, nor will I fight thee thus ablaze with fire. Cease strife, yea, let noble Achilles drive the Trojans forthwith out of their city; what have I to do with strife and succour?"

Thus spake he, burnt with fire, for his fair streams were bubbling. And as a caldron boileth within, beset with much fire, melting the lard of some fatted hog spurting up on all sides, and logs of firewood lie thereunder,—so burned his fair streams in the fire, and the water boiled. He had no mind to flow, but refrained him, for the breath of cunning Hephaestus violently afflicted him. Then unto Hera, earnestly beseeching her, he spake winged words: "Hera, wherefore hath thy son assailed my stream to vex it above others? I am less chargeable than all the rest that are helpers of the Trojans. But lo, I will give over, if thou wilt, and let thy son give over too. And I further will swear even this, that never will I ward the day of evil from the Trojans, not even when all Troy is burning in the blaze of hungry fire, and the warlike sons of Achaeans are the burners thereof."

Then when the white-armed goddess Hera heard his speech, straightway she spake unto Hephaestus her dear son: "Hephaestus, hold, famed son; it befitteth not thus for mortals' sake to do violence to an immortal god."

Thus said she and Hephaestus quenched the fierce-blazing fire, and the wave once more rolled down the fair river-bed.

So when the rage of Xanthus was overcome, both ceased, for Hera stayed them, though in wrath. But among the other gods fell grievous bitter strife, and their hearts were carried diverse in their breasts. And they clashed together with a great noise, and the wide earth groaned, and the clarion of great Heaven rang around. Zeus heard as he sate upon Olympus, and his heart within him laughed pleasantly when he beheld that strife of gods. Then no longer stood they asunder, for Ares piercer of shields began the battle and first made for Athene with his bronze spear, and spake a taunting word: "Wherefore, O dogfly, dost thou match gods with gods in strife, with stormy daring, as thy great spirit moveth thee? Rememberest thou not how thou movedst Diomedes Tydeus' son to wound me, and thyself didst take a visible spear and thrust it straight at me and pierce through my fair skin? Therefore deem I now that thou shalt pay me for all that thou hast done."

Thus saying he smote on the dread tasselled aegis that not even the lightning of Zeus can overcome—thereon smote bloodstained Ares with his long spear. But she, giving back, grasped with stout hand a stone that lay upon the plain, black, rugged, huge, which men of old time set to be the landmark of a field; this hurled she, and smote impetuous Ares on the neck, and unstrung his limbs. Seven roods he covered in his fall, and soiled his hair with dust, and his armour rang upon him. And Pallas Athene laughed, and spake to him winged words exultingly: "Fool, not even yet hast thou learnt how far better than thou I claim to be, that thus thou matchest thy might with mine. Thus shalt thou satisfy thy mother's curses, who deviseth mischief against thee in her wrath, for that thou hast left the Achaeans and givest the proud Trojans aid."

Thus having said she turned from him her shining eyes. Him did Aphrodite daughter of Zeus take by the hand and lead away, groaning continually, for scarce gathered he his spirit back to him. But when the white-armed goddess Hera was aware of them, straightway she spake unto Athene winged words: "Out on it, child of aegis-bearing Zeus, maiden invincible, lo there the dogfly is leading Ares destroyer of men out of the fray of battle down the throng—nay then, pursue her."

She said, and Athene sped after her with heart exultant, and made at her and smote her with stout hand upon the breast, and straightway her knees and heart were unstrung. So they twain lay on the bounteous earth, and Athene spake winged words exultingly: "Such let all be who give the Trojans aid when they fight against the mailed Argives. Be they even so bold and brave as Aphrodite when she came to succour Ares and defied my might. Then should we long ago have ceased from war, having laid waste the stablished citadel of Ilium."

She said, and the white-armed goddess Hera smiled. Then to Apollo spake the earth-shaking lord: "Phoebus, why stand we apart? It befitteth not after the rest have begun: that were the more shameful if without fighting we should go to Olympus to the bronze-thresholded house of Zeus. Begin, for thou art younger; it were not meet for me, since I was born first and know more. Fond god, how foolish is thy heart! Thou rememberest not all the ills we twain alone of gods endured at Ilium, when by ordinance of Zeus we came to proud Laomedon and served him through a year for promised recompense, and he laid on us his commands. I round their city built the Trojans a wall, wide and most fair, that the city might be unstormed, and thou, Phoebus, didst herd shambling crook-horned kine among the spurs of woody many-folded Ida. But when the joyous seasons were accomplishing the term of hire, then redoubtable Laomedon robbed us of all hire, and sent us off with threats. He threatened that he would bind together our feet and hands and sell us into far-off isles, and the ears of both of us he vowed to shear off with the sword. So we went home with angry hearts, wroth for the hire he promised and gave us not. To his folk now thou showest favour, nor essayest with us how the proud Trojans may be brought low and perish miserably with their children and noble wives."

Then to him answered King Apollo the Far-darter:

"Shaker of the earth, of no sound mind wouldst thou repute me if I should fight against thee for the sake of pitiful mortals, who like unto leaves now live in glowing life, consuming the fruit of the earth, and now again pine into death. Let us with all speed cease from combat, and let them do battle by themselves."

Thus saying he turned away, for he felt shame to deal in blows with his father's brother. But his sister upbraided him sore, the queen of wild beasts, huntress Artemis, and spake a taunting word: "So then thou fleest, Far-darter, and hast quite yielded to Poseidon the victory, and given him glory for naught! Fond god, why bearest thou an ineffectual bow in vain? Let me not hear thee again in the halls of our sire boast as before among the immortal gods that thou wouldst stand up to fight against Poseidon."

Thus spake she, but far-darting Apollo answered her not. But angrily the noble spouse of Zeus upbraided the Archer Queen with taunting words: "How now art thou fain, bold vixen, to set thy self against me? Hard were it for thee to match my might, bow-bearer though thou art, since against women Zeus made thee a lion, and giveth thee to slay whomso of them thou wilt. Truly it is better on the mountains to slay wild beasts and deer than to fight amain with mightier than thou. But if thou wilt, try war, that thou mayest know well how far stronger am I, since thou matchest thy might with mine."

She said, and with her left hand caught both the other's hands by the wrist, and with her right took the bow from off her shoulders, and therewith, smiling, beat her on the ears as she turned this way and that; and the swift arrows fell out of her quiver. And weeping from before her the goddess fled like a dove that from before a falcon flieth to a hollow rock, a cleft—for she was not fated to be caught;—thus Artemis fled weeping, and left her bow and arrows where they lay. Then to Leto [2] spake the Guide, the slayer

---

[2] Leto bore Artemis and Apollo to Zeus.

of Argus: "Leto, with thee will I nowise fight; a grievous thing it is to come to blows with wives of cloud-gathering Zeus; but boast to thy heart's content among the immortal gods that thou didst vanquish me by might and main."

Thus said he, and Leto gathered up the curved bow and arrows fallen hither and thither amid the whirl of dust: so taking her daughter's bow she went back. And Artemis came to Olympus, to the bronze-thresholded house of Zeus, and weeping set herself on her father's knee, while round her her divine vesture quivered: and her father, Cronos' son, took her to him and asked of her, laughing gently: "Who of the inhabitants of heaven, dear child, hath dealt with thee thus hastily, as though thou hadst been doing some wrong thing openly?"

And to him in answer spake the fair-crowned queen of the echoing chase: "It was thy wife that buffeted me, father, the white-armed Hera, from whom are strife and contention come upon the immortals."

Thus talked they unto one another. Then Phoebus Apollo entered into sacred Ilium, for he was troubled for the wall of the well-builded city, lest the Danaans waste it before its hour upon that day. But the other ever-living gods went to Olympus, some angry and some greatly triumphing, and sat down beside Zeus who hideth himself in dark clouds.

Now Achilles was still slaying the Trojans, both themselves and their whole-hooved horses. And as when a smoke goeth up to the broad heaven, when a city burneth, kindled by the wrath of gods, and causeth toil to all, and griefs to many, thus caused Achilles toil and griefs to the Trojans. And the old man Priam stood on the sacred tower, and was aware of dread Achilles, how before him the Trojans thronged in rout, nor was any succour found of them. Then with a cry he went down from the tower, to rouse the gallant warders along the walls: "Hold open the gates in your hands until the folk come to the city in their rout, for closely is Achilles chasing them—now trow I there will be deadly deeds. But when they are gathered within the wall and are taking breath, then again shut back the gate-wings firmly builded; for I fear lest that murderous man spring in within the wall."

Thus spake he, and they opened the gates and thrust back the bolts; and the gates flung back gave safety. Then Apollo leapt forth to the front that he might ward destruction from the Trojans. They straight for the city and the high wall were fleeing, parched with thirst and dust-grimed from the plain, and Achilles chased them vehemently with his spear, for strong frenzy possessed his heart continually, and he thirsted to win him renown. Then would the sons of the Achaeans have taken high-gated Troy, had not Phoebus Apollo aroused goodly Agenor, Antenor's son, a princely man and a strong. In his heart he put good courage, and himself stood by his side that he might ward off the grievous visitations of death, leaning against the oak, and he was shrouded in thick mist. So when Agenor was aware of Achilles waster of cities, he halted, and his heart much wavered as he stood; and in trouble he spake to his great heart: "Ay me, if I flee before mighty Achilles, there where the rest are driven terror-struck, nevertheless will he overtake me and slaughter me as a coward. Or what if I leave these to be driven before Achilles the son of Peleus, and flee upon my feet from the wall by another way to the Ileian plain, until I come to the spurs of Ida, and hide me in the underwood? So then at evening, having bathed in the river and refreshed me of sweat, I might return to Ilium. Nay, why doth my heart debate thus within me? Lest he might be aware of me as I get me from the city for the plain, and speeding after overtake me with swift feet; then will it no more be possible to avoid the visitation of death, for he is exceeding mighty above all mankind. What then if in front of the city I go forth to meet him? Surely his flesh too is penetrable by sharp bronze, and there is but one life within, and men say he is mortal, howbeit Zeus the son of Cronos giveth him renown."

Thus saying, he gathered himself to await Achilles, and within him his stout heart was set to strive and fight. As a leopardess goeth forth from a deep thicket to affront a huntsman, nor is afraid at heart, nor fleeth when she heareth the bay of hounds; for albeit the man first smite her with thrust or throw, yet even pierced through with the spear she ceaseth not from her courage until she either grapple or be slain, so noble Antenor's son, goodly Agenor, refused to flee till he should put Achilles to the proof, but held before him the circle of his shield, and aimed at him with his spear, and cried aloud: "Doubtless thou hopest in thy heart, noble Achilles, on this day to sack the city of the proud men of Troy. Fond man, there shall many woful things yet be wrought before it, for within it we are many men and staunch, who in front of our parents dear and wives and sons keep Ilium safe; but thou shalt here meet death, albeit so redoubtable and bold a man of war."

He said, and hurled his sharp spear with weighty hand, and smote him on the leg beneath the knee, nor missed his mark, and the greave of new-wrought tin rang terribly on him; but the bronze bounded back from him it smote, nor pierced him, for the god's gift drove it back. Then the son of Peleus in his turn made at godlike Agenor, but Apollo suffered him not to win renown, but caught away Agenor, and shrouded him in thick mist, and sent him in peace to be gone out of the war. Then by wile he kept the son of Peleus away from the folk, for in complete semblance of Agenor himself he stood before the feet of Achilles, who hasted to run upon him and chase him. And while he chased him over the wheat-bearing plain, edging him toward the deep-eddying river Scamander, as he ran but a little in front of him (for by wile Apollo beguiled him that he kept ever hoping to overtake him in the race), meantime the other Trojans in common rout came gladly unto their fastness, and the city was filled with the throng of them. Neither had they heart to await one another outside the city and wall, and to know who might have escaped and who had perished in the fight, but impetuously they poured into the city, whomsoever of them his feet and knees might save.

XXII

The Death of Hector

THUS they throughout the city, scared like fawns, were cooling their sweat and drinking and slaking their thirst, leaning on the fair battlements, while the Achaeans drew near the wall, setting shields to shoulders. But Hector deadly fate bound to abide in his place, in front of Ilium and the Scaean gates. Then to the son of Peleus spake Phoebus Apollo: "Wherefore, son of Peleus, pursuest thou me with swift feet, thyself being mortal and I a deathless god? Thou hast not even yet known me, that I am a god, but strivest vehemently. Truly thou regardest not thy task among the affliction of the Trojans whom thou affrightedst, who now are gathered into the city, while thou hast wandered hither. Me thou wilt never slay, for I am not subject unto death."

Then mightily moved spake unto him Achilles fleet of foot: "Thou hast baulked me, Far-darter, most mischievous of all the gods, in that thou hast turned me hither from the wall: else should full many yet have bitten the dust or ever within Ilium had they come. Now hast thou robbed me of great renown, and lightly hast saved them, because thou hadst no vengeance to fear thereafter. Verily I would avenge me on thee, had I but the power."

Thus saying toward the city he was gone in pride of heart, rushing like some victorious horse in a chariot, that runneth lightly at full speed over the plain; so swiftly plied Achilles in his feet and knees. Him the old man Priam first beheld as he sped across the plain, blazing as the star that cometh forth at harvest-time, and plain seen his rays shine forth amid the host of stars in the darkness of night, the star whose name men call Orion's Dog. Brightest of all is he, yet for an evil sign is he set, and bringeth much fever upon hapless men. Even so on Achilles' breast the bronze gleamed as he ran. And the old man cried aloud and beat upon his head with his hands, raising them on high, and with a cry called aloud beseeching his dear son; for he before the gates was standing, all hot for battle with Achilles.

And the old man spake piteously unto him, stretching forth his hands: "Hector, beloved son, I pray thee await not this man alone with none beside thee, lest thou quickly meet thy doom, slain by the son of Peleus, since he is mightier far, a merciless man. Would the gods loved him even as do I! then quickly would dogs and vultures devour him on the field—thereby would cruel pain go from my heart—the man who hath bereft me of many valiant sons, slaying them and selling them captive into far-off isles. Ay even now twain of my children, Lycaon and Polydorus, I cannot see among the Trojans that throng into the fastness, sons whom Laothoe bare me, a princess among women. If they be yet alive amid the enemy's host, then will we ransom them with bronze and gold, for there is store within, for much goods gave the old man famous Altes to his child. If they be dead, then even in the house of Hades shall they be a sorrow to my soul and to their mother, even to us who gave them birth, but to the rest of the folk a briefer sorrow, if but thou die not by Achilles' hand. Nay, come within the wall, my child, that thou preserve the men and women of Troy, neither give great triumph to the son of Peleus, and be thyself bereft of sweet life. Have compassion also on me, the helpless one, who still can feel, ill-fated; whom the father, Cronos' son, will bring to nought by a grievous doom in the path of old age, having seen full many ills, his sons perishing and his daughters carried away captive, and his chambers laid waste and infant children hurled to the ground in terrible war, and his sons' wives dragged away by the ruinous hands of the Achaeans. Myself then last of all at the street door will ravening dogs tear, when some one by stroke or throw of the sharp bronze hath bereft my limbs of life—even the dogs I reared in my halls about my table and to guard my door, which then having drunk my blood, maddened at heart shall lie in the gateway. A young man all befitteth, even to be slain in war, to be torn by the sharp bronze and lie on the field; though he be dead yet is all honourable to him, whate'er be seen: but when dogs defile the hoary head and hoary beard and the secret parts of an old man slain, this is the most piteous thing that cometh upon hapless men."

Thus spake the old man, and grasped his hoary hairs, plucking them from his head, but he persuaded not Hector's soul. Then his mother in her turn wailed tearfully, loosening the folds of her robe, while with the other hand she showed her breast; and through her tears spake to him winged words: "Hector, my child, have regard unto this bosom and pity me, if ever I gave thee consolation of my breast. Think of it, dear child, and from this side of the wall drive back the foe, nor stand in front to meet him. He is merciless; if he slay thee it will not be on a bed that I or thy wife wooed with many gifts shall bewail thee, my own dear child, but far away from us by the ships of the Argives will swift dogs devour thee."

Thus they with wailing spake to their dear son, beseeching him sore, yet they persuaded not Hector's soul, but he stood awaiting Achilles as he drew nigh in giant might. As a serpent of the mountains upon his den awaiteth a man, having fed on evil poisons, and fell wrath hath entered into him, and terribly he glareth as he coileth himself about his den, so Hector with courage unquenchable gave not back, leaning his shining shield against a jutting tower. Then sore troubled he spake to his great heart: "Ay me, if I go within the gates and walls, Polydamas will be first to bring reproach against me, since he bade me lead the Trojans to the city during this ruinous night, when noble Achilles arose. But I regarded him not, yet surely it had been better far. And now that I have undone the host by my wantonness, I am ashamed before the men of Troy and women of trailing robes, lest at any time some worse man than I shall say: 'Hector by trusting his own might undid the host.' So will they speak; then to me would it be better far to face Achilles and either slay him and go home, or myself die gloriously before the city. Or what if I lay down my bossy shield and my stout helm, and lean my spear against the wall, and go of myself to meet noble Achilles and promise him that Helen, and with her all possessions that Alexandros brought in hollow ships to Troy, the beginning of strife, we will give to the sons of Atreus to take away, and therewithal to divide in half with the Achaeans all else that this city holdeth: and if thereafter I obtain from the Trojans an oath of the Elders that they will hide nothing but divide all in twain whatever wealth the pleasant city hold within? But wherefore doth my heart debate thus? I might come unto him and he would not pity or regard me at all, but presently slay me unarmed as, it were but a woman, if I put off my armour. No time is it now to dally with him from oak-tree or from rock, like youth with maiden, as youth and maiden hold dalliance one with another. Better is it to join battle with all speed: let us know upon which of us twain the Olympian shall bestow renown."

Thus pondered he as he stood, but nigh on him came Achilles, peer of Ares warrior of the waving helm, brandishing from his right shoulder the Pelian ash, his terrible spear; and all around the bronze on him flashed like the gleam of blazing fire or of the Sun as he ariseth. And trembling seized Hector as he was aware of him, nor endured he to abide in his place, but left the gates behind him and fled in fear. And the son of Peleus darted after him, trusting in his swift feet. As a falcon upon the mountains, swiftest of winged things, swoopeth fleetly after a trembling dove; and she before him fleeth, while he with shrill screams hard at hand still darteth at her, for his heart urgeth him to seize her; so Achilles in hot haste flew straight for him, and Hector fled beneath the Trojans' wall, and plied swift knees. They past the watch-place and wind-waved wild fig-tree sped ever, away from under the wall, along the waggon-track, and came to the two fair-flowing springs, where two fountains rise that feed deep-eddying Scamander. The one floweth with warm water, and smoke goeth up therefrom around as it were from a blazing fire, while the other even in summer floweth forth like cold hail or snow or ice that water formeth. And there beside the springs are broad washing-troughs hard by, fair troughs of stone, where wives and fair daughters of the men of Troy were wont to wash bright raiment, in the old time of peace, before the sons of the Achaeans came. Thereby they ran, he flying, he pursuing. Valiant was the flier but far mightier he who fleetly pursued him. For not for beast of sacrifice or for

Achilles encouraged by Athene kills Hector. Apollo retires, showing the arrow that will one day kill Achilles.

PAINTING FROM A PELIKE.
(VATICAN MUSEUM)

an ox-hide were they striving, such as are prizes for men's speed of foot, but for the life of horse-taming Hector was their race. And as when victorious whole-hooved horses run rapidly round the turning-points, and some great prize lieth in sight, be it a tripod or a woman, in honour of a man that is dead, so thrice around Priam's city circled those twain with flying feet, and all the gods were gazing on them. Then among them spake first the father of gods and men: "Ay me, a man beloved I see pursued around the wall. My heart is woe for Hector, who hath burnt for me many thighs of oxen amid the crests of many-folded Ida, and other times on the city-height; but now is goodly Achilles pursuing him with swift feet round Priam's town. Come, give your counsel, gods, and devise whether we shall save him from death or now at last slay him, valiant though he be, by the hand of Achilles Peleus' son."

Then to him answered the bright-eyed goddess Athene: "O Father, Lord of the bright lightning and the dark cloud, what is this thou hast said? A man that is a mortal, doomed long ago by fate, wouldst thou redeem back from ill-boding death? Do it, but not all we other gods approve."

And unto her in answer spake cloud-gathering Zeus: "Be of good cheer, Trito-born, dear child: not in full earnest speak I, and I would fain be kind to thee. Do as seemeth good to thy mind, and draw not back."

Thus saying he roused Athene, that already was set thereon, and from the crests of Olympus she darted down.

But after Hector sped fleet Achilles chasing him vehemently. And as when on the mountains a hound hunteth the fawn of a deer, having started it from its covert, through glens and glades, and if it crouch to baffle him under a bush, yet scenting it out the hound runneth constantly until he find it; so Hector baffled not Peleus' fleet-footed son. Oft as he set himself to dart under the well-built walls over against the Dardanian gates, if haply from above they might succour him with darts, so oft would Achilles gain on him and turn him toward the plain, while himself he sped ever on the city-side. And as in a dream one faileth in chase of a flying man—the one faileth in his flight and the other in his chase —so failed Achilles to overtake him in the race, and Hector to escape. And thus would Hector have avoided the visitation of death, had not this time been utterly the last wherein Apollo came nigh to him, who nerved his strength and his swift knees. For to the host did noble Achilles sign with his head, and forbade them to hurl bitter darts against Hector, lest any smiting him should gain renown, and he himself come second. But when the fourth time they had reached the springs, then the Father hung his golden balances, and set therein two lots of dreary death, one of Achilles, one of horse-taming Hector, and held them by the midst and poised. Then Hector's fated day sank down, and fell to the house of Hades, and Phoebus Apollo left him. But to Peleus' son came the bright-eyed goddess Athene, and standing near spake to him winged words: "Now verily, glorious Achilles dear to Zeus, I have hope that we twain shall carry off great glory to the ships for the Achaeans, having slain Hector, for all his thirst for fight. No longer is it possible for him to escape us, not even though far-darting Apollo should travail sore, grovelling before the Father, aegis-bearing Zeus. But do thou now stand and take breath, and I will go and persuade this man to confront thee in fight."

Thus spake Athene, and he obeyed, and was glad at heart, and stood leaning on his bronze-pointed ashen-spear. And she left him and came to noble Hector, like unto Deiphobus in shape and in strong voice, and standing near spake to him winged words: "Dear brother, verily fleet Achilles doth thee violence, chasing thee round Priam's town with swift feet: but come let us make a stand and await him on our defence."

Then answered her great Hector of the glancing helm: "Deiphobus, verily aforetime wert thou far dearest of my brothers, whom Hecabe and Priam gendered, but now methinks I shall honour thee even more, in that thou hast dared for my sake, when thou sawest me, to come forth of the wall, while the others tarry within."

Then to him again spake the bright-eyed goddess Athene: "Dear brother, of a truth my father and lady mother and my comrades around besought me much, entreating me in turn, to tarry there, so greatly do they all tremble before him; but my heart within was sore with dismal grief. And now fight we with straight-set resolve and let there be no sparing of spears, that we may know whether Achilles is to slay us and carry our bloody spoils to the hollow ships, or whether he might be vanquished by thy spear."

Thus saying Athene in her subtlety led him on. And when they were come nigh in onset on one another, to Achilles first spake great Hector of the glancing helm: "No longer, son of Peleus, will I fly thee, as before I thrice ran round the great town of Priam, and endured not to await thy onset. Now my heart biddeth me stand up against thee; I will either slay or be slain. But come hither and let us pledge us by our gods, for they shall be best witnesses and beholders of covenants: I will treat thee in no outrageous sort, if Zeus grant me to outstay thee, and if I take thy life, but when I have despoiled thee of thy glorious armour, O Achilles, I will give back thy dead body to the Achaeans, and do thou the same."

But unto him with grim gaze spake Achilles fleet of foot: "Hector, talk not to me, thou madman, of covenants. As between men and lions there is no pledge of faith, nor wolves and sheep can be of one mind, but imagine evil continually against each other, so is it impossible for thee and me to be friends, neither shall be any pledge between us until one or other shall have fallen and glutted with blood Ares, the stubborn god of war. Bethink thee of all thy soldiership: now behoveth it thee to quit thee as a good spearman and valiant man of war. No longer is there way of escape for thee, but Pallas Athene will straightway subdue thee to my spear; and now in one hour shalt thou pay back for all my sorrows for my friends whom thou hast slain in the fury of thy spear."

He said, and poised his far-shadowing spear and hurled. And noble Hector watched the coming thereof and avoided it; for with his eye on it he crouched, and the bronze spear flew over him, and fixed itself in the earth; but Pallas Athene caught it up and gave it back to Achilles, unknown of Hector shepherd of hosts. Then Hector spake unto the noble son of Peleus: "Thou hast missed, so nowise yet, godlike Achilles, hast thou known from Zeus the hour of my doom, though thou thoughtest it. Cunning of tongue art thou and a deceiver in speech, that fearing thee I might forget my valour and strength. Not as I flee shalt thou plant thy spear in my back, but drive it straight through my breast as I set on thee, if God hath given thee to do it. Now in thy turn avoid my spear of bronze. O that thou mightst take it all into thy flesh! Then would the war be lighter to the Trojans, if but thou wert dead, for thou art their greatest bane."

He said, and poised his long-shadowed spear and hurled

it, and smote the midst of the shield of Peleus' son, and missed him not: but far from the shield the spear leapt back. And Hector was wroth that his swift weapon had left his hand in vain, and he stood downcast, for he had no second ashen spear. And he called with a loud shout to Deiphobus of the white shield, and asked of him a long spear, but he was nowise nigh. Then Hector knew the truth in his heart, and spake and said: "Ay me, now verily the gods have summoned me to death. I deemed the warrior Deiphobus was by my side, but he is within the wall, and it was Athene who played me false. Now therefore is evil death come very nigh me, not far off, nor is there way of escape. This then was from of old the pleasure of Zeus and of the far-darting son of Zeus, who yet before were fain to succour me: but now my fate hath found me. At least let me not die without a struggle or ingloriously, but in some great deed of arms whereof men yet to be born shall hear."

Thus saying he drew his sharp sword that by his flank hung great and strong, and gathered himself and swooped like a soaring eagle that darteth to the plain through the dark clouds to seize a tender lamb or crouching hare. So Hector swooped, brandishing his sharp sword. And Achilles made at him, for his heart was filled with wild fierceness, and before his breast he made a covering with his fair graven shield, and tossed his bright four-plated helm; and round it waved fair golden plumes that Hephaestus had set thick about the crest. As a star goeth among stars in the darkness of night, Hesperus, fairest of all stars set in heaven, so flashed there forth a light from the keen spear Achilles poised in his right hand, devising mischief against noble Hector, eyeing his fair flesh to find the fittest place. Now for the rest of him his flesh was covered by the fair bronze armour he stripped from strong Patroclus when he slew him, but there was an opening where the collar bones coming from the shoulders clasp the neck, even at the gullet, where destruction of life cometh quickliest; there, as he came on, noble Achilles drave at him with his spear, and right through the tender neck went the point. Yet the bronze-weighted ashen spear clave not the windpipe, so that he might yet speak words of answer to his foe. And he fell down in the dust, and noble Achilles spake exultingly: "Hector, thou thoughtest, whilst thou wert spoiling Patroclus, that thou wouldst be safe, and didst reck nothing of me who was afar, thou fool. But away among the hollow ships his comrade, a mightier far, even I, was left behind, who now have unstrung thy knees. Thee shall dogs and birds tear foully, but his funeral shall the Achaeans make."

Round the walls of Troy guarded by two archers, Achilles runs after Hector.

PAINTING FROM A KYLIX (RESTITUTION).
(DEPOLETTI COLL., BOSTON MUSEUM)

Then with faint breath spake unto him Hector of the glancing helm: "I pray thee by thy life and knees and parents leave me not for dogs of the Achaeans to devour by the ships, but take good store of bronze and gold, gifts that my father and lady mother shall give to thee, and give them home my body back again, that the Trojans and Trojans' wives give me my due of fire after my death."

But unto him with grim gaze spake Achilles fleet of foot: "Entreat me not, dog, by knees or parents. Would that my heart's desire could so bid me myself to carve and eat raw thy flesh, for the evil thou hast wrought me, as surely is there none that shall keep the dogs from thee, not even should they bring ten or twenty fold ransom and here weigh it out, and promise even more, not even were Priam Dardanus' son to bid pay thy weight in gold, not even so shall thy lady mother lay thee on a bed to mourn her son, but dogs and birds shall devour thee utterly."

Then dying spake unto him Hector of the glancing helm: "Verily I know thee and behold thee as thou art, nor was I destined to persuade thee; truly thy heart is iron in thy breast. Take heed now lest I draw upon thee wrath of gods, in the day when Paris and Phoebus Apollo slay thee, for all thy valour, at the Scaean gate."

He ended, and the shadow of death came down upon him, and his soul flew forth of his limbs and was gone to the house of Hades, wailing her fate, leaving her vigour and youth. Then to the dead man spake noble Achilles: "Die: for my death, I will accept it whensoever Zeus and the other immortal gods are minded to accomplish it."

He said, and from the corpse drew forth his bronze spear, and set it aside, and stripped the bloody armour from the shoulders. And other sons of Achaeans ran up around, who gazed upon the stature and marvellous goodliness of Hector. Nor did any stand by but wounded him, and thus would many a man say looking toward his neighbour: "Go to, of a truth far easier to handle is Hector now than when he burnt the ships with blazing fire." Thus would many a man say, and wound him as he stood hard by. And when fleet noble Achilles had despoiled him, he stood up among the Achaeans and spake winged words: "Friends, chiefs and counsellors of the Argives, since the gods have vouchsafed us to vanquish this man who hath done us more evil than all the rest together, come let us make trial in arms round about the city, that we may know somewhat of the Trojans' purpose, whether since he hath fallen they will forsake the citadel, or whether they are minded to abide, albeit Hector is no more. But wherefore doth my heart debate thus? There lieth by the ships a dead man unbewailed, unburied, Patroclus; him will I not forget, while I abide among the living and my knees can stir. Nay if even in the house of Hades the dead forget their dead, yet will I even there be mindful of my dear comrade. But come, ye sons of the Achaeans, let us now, singing our song of victory, go back to the hollow ships and take with us our foe. Great glory have we won; we have slain the noble Hector, unto whom the Trojans prayed throughout their city, as he had been a god."

He said, and devised foul entreatment of noble Hector. The tendons of both feet behind he slit from heel to ankle-joint, and thrust therethrough thongs of ox-hide, and bound him to his chariot, leaving his head to trail. And when he had mounted the chariot and lifted therein the famous armour, he lashed his horses to speed, and they nothing loth flew on. And dust rose around him that was dragged, and his dark hair flowed loose on either side, and in the dust lay all his once fair head, for now had Zeus given him over to his foes to treat foully in his own native land.

Thus was his head all grimed with dust. But his mother when she beheld her son, tore her hair and cast far from her her shining veil, and cried aloud with an exceeding bitter cry. And piteously moaned his father, and around them the folk fell to crying and moaning throughout the town. Most like it seemed as though all beetling Ilium were burning utterly in fire. Scarcely could the folk keep back the old man in his hot desire to get him forth of the Dardanian gates. For he besought them all, casting himself down in the mire, calling on each man by his name: "Hold, friends, and though you love me leave me to get me forth of the city alone and go unto the ships of the Achaeans. Let me pray this accursed horror-working man, if haply he may feel shame before his age-fellows and pity an old man. He also hath a father such as I am, Peleus, who begat and reared him to be a bane of Trojans—and most of all to me hath he brought woe. So many sons of mine hath he slain in their flower—yet for all my sorrow for the rest I mourn them all less than this one alone, for whom my sharp grief will bring me down to the house of Hades—even Hector. Would that he had died in my arms; then would we have wept and wailed our fill, his mother who bore him to her ill hap, and I myself."

Thus spake he wailing, and all the men of the city made

moan with him. And among the women of Troy, Hecabe led the wild lament: "My child, ah, woe is me! wherefore should I live in my pain, now thou art dead, who night and day wert my boast through the city, and blessing to all, both men and women of Troy throughout the town, who hailed thee as a god, for verily an exceeding glory to them wert thou in thy life:—now death and fate have overtaken thee."

Thus spake she wailing. But Hector's wife knew not as yet, for no true messenger had come to tell her how her husband abode without the gates, but in an inner chamber of the lofty house she was weaving a double purple web, and broidering therein manifold flowers. Then she called to her goodly-haired handmaids through the house to set a great tripod on the fire, that Hector might have warm washing when he came home out of the battle—fond heart, and was unaware how, far from all washings, bright-eyed Athene had slain him by the hand of Achilles. But she heard shrieks and groans from the battlements, and her limbs reeled, and the shuttle fell from her hands to earth. Then again among her goodly-haired maids she spake: "Come two of ye this way with me that I may see what deeds are done. It was the voice of my husband's noble mother that I heard, and in my own breast my heart leapeth to my mouth and my knees are numbed beneath me: surely some evil thing is at hand against the children of Priam. Would that such word might never reach my ear! yet terribly I dread lest noble Achilles have cut off bold Hector from the city by himself and chased him to the plain and ere this ended his perilous pride that possessed him, for never would Hector tarry among the throng of men but ran out before them far, yielding place to no man in his hardihood."

Thus saying she sped through the chamber like one mad, with beating heart, and with her went her handmaidens. But when she came to the battlements and the throng of men, she stood still upon the wall and gazed, and beheld him dragged before the city:—swift horses dragged him recklessly toward the hollow ships of the Achaeans. Then dark night came on her eyes and shrouded her, and she fell backward and gasped forth her spirit. From off her head she shook the bright attiring thereof, frontlet and net and woven band, and veil, the veil that golden Aphrodite gave her on the day when Hector of the glancing helm led her forth of the house of Eëtion, having given bride-gifts untold. And around her thronged her husband's sisters and his brothers' wives, who held her up among them, distraught even to death. But when at last she came to herself and her soul returned into her breast, then wailing with deep sobs she spake among the women of Troy:

"O Hector, woe is me! to one fate then were we both born, thou in Troy in the house of Priam, and I in Thebe under woody Placus, in the house of Eëtion, who reared me from a little one—ill-fated sire of cruel-fated child. Ah, would he had begotten me not. Now thou to the house of Hades beneath the secret places of the earth departest, and me in bitter mourning thou leavest a widow in thy halls: and thy son is but an infant child—son of unhappy parents, thee and me—nor shalt thou profit him, Hector, since thou art dead, neither he thee. For even if he escape the Achaeans' woful war, yet shall labour and sorrow cleave unto him hereafter, for other men shall seize his lands. The day of orphanage sundereth a child from his fellows, and his head is bowed down ever, and his cheeks are wet with tears. And in his need the child seeketh his father's friends, plucking this one by cloak and that by coat, and one of them that pity him holdeth his cup a little to his mouth, and moisteneth his lips, but his palate he moisteneth not. And some child un-orphaned thrusteth him from the feast with blows and taunting words, 'Out with thee! no father of thine is at our board.' Then weeping to his widowed mother shall he return, even Astyanax, who erst upon his father's knee ate only marrow and fat flesh of sheep; and when sleep fell on him and he ceased from childish play, then in bed in his nurse's arms he would slumber softly nested, having satisfied his heart with good things; but now that he hath lost his father he will suffer many ills, Astyanax—that name the Trojans gave him, because thou only wert the defence of their gates and their long walls. But now by the beaked ships, far from thy parents, shall coiling worms devour thee when the dogs have had their fill, as thou liest naked; yet in these halls lieth raiment of thine, delicate and fair, wrought by the hands of women. But verily all these will I consume with burning fire —to thee no profit, since thou wilt never lie therein, yet that this be honour to thee from the men and the women of Troy."

Thus spake she wailing, and the women joined their moan.

XXIII

Funeral Games for Patroclus.
PAINTING FROM AN HYDRIA.
(BERLIN MUSEUM)

The Funeral of Patroclus

❨ The Achaeans return to their ships. When the Myrmidons go to their tents, Achilles sleeps on the seashore. To him comes the shade of Patroclus begging for speedy rites and asking that his bones be buried with those of Achilles.

On a great pyre a hundred feet square the body of Patroclus is burned with sacrifice of sheep and oxen, dogs and horses, and twelve Trojan youths. Then the bones are gathered into an urn and a barrow is heaped. The funeral games follow—chariot racing, boxing, wrestling, running, fighting in armor, weight-throwing, and archery. All the winners are given magnificent prizes.

XXIV

Priam Ransoms Hector

THEN the assembly was broken up, and the tribes were scattered to betake them each to their own swift ships. The rest bethought them of supper and sweet sleep to have joy thereof; but Achilles wept, remembering his dear comrade, nor did sleep that conquereth all take hold on him, but he kept turning him to this side and to that, yearning for Patroclus' manhood and excellent valour, and all the toils he achieved with him and the woes he bare, cleaving the battles of men and the grievous waves. As he thought thereon he shed big tears, now lying on his side, now on his back, now on his face; and then anon he would arise upon his feet and roam wildly beside the beach of the salt sea. Nor would he be unaware of the Dawn when she arose over the sea and shores. But when he had yoked the swift steeds to his car he would bind Hector behind his chariot to drag him withal; and having thrice drawn him round the barrow of Patroclus he rested again in his hut, and left Hector lying stretched on his face in the dust. But Apollo kept away all defacement from his flesh, for he had pity on him even in death, and covered him all with his golden aegis, that Achilles might not tear him when he dragged him.

Thus Achilles in his anger treated noble Hector shamefully; but the blessed gods when they beheld him pitied him, and urged Hermes the clear-sighted slayer of Argus to steal the corpse away. So to all the others seemed it good, yet not to Hera or Poseidon or Athene the bright-eyed Maiden, but they continued as when at the beginning sacred Ilium became hateful to them, and Priam and his people, by reason of the sin of Alexandros in that he contemned those goddesses when they came to his steading, and preferred her who brought him deadly lustfulness. But when the twelfth morn from that day arose, then spake among the Immortals Phoebus Apollo: "Hard of heart are ye, O gods, and cruel. Hath Hector never burnt for you thigh-bones of unblemished bulls and goats? Now have ye not taken heart to rescue even his corpse for his wife to look upon and his mother and his child and his father Priam and his people, who speedily would burn him in the fire and make his funeral. But brutal Achilles, O gods, ye are fain to abet, whose mind is nowise just nor the purpose in his breast to be turned away, but he is cruelly minded as a lion that in great strength and at the bidding of his proud heart goeth forth against men's flocks to make his meal; even thus Achilles hath cast out pity, neither hath he shame, that doth both harm and profit men greatly. It must be that many a man lose even some dearer one than was this, a brother of the same womb born or perchance a son; yet bringeth he his wailing and lamentation to an end, for an enduring soul have the Fates given unto men. But Achilles after bereaving noble Hector of his life bindeth him behind his horses and draggeth him around the tomb of his dear comrade: not, verily, is that more honourable or better for him. Let him take heed lest we wax wroth with him, good man though he be, for in his fury he is treating shamefully the senseless clay."

Then in anger spake unto him white-armed Hera: "Even thus mightest thou speak, O Lord of the silver bow, if ye are to give equal honour to Achilles and to Hector. Hector is but a mortal and was suckled at a woman's breast, but Achilles is child of a goddess whom I myself bred up and reared and gave to a man to be his wife, even to Peleus who was dearest of all men to the Immortals' heart. And all ye gods came to her bridal, and thou among them wert feasting with thy lyre, O lover of ill company, faithless ever."

Then to her in answer spake Zeus who gathereth the

clouds: "Hera, be not wroth utterly with the gods: for these men's honour is not to be the same, yet Hector also was dearest to the gods of all mortals that are in Ilium. So was he to me at least, for nowise failed he in the gifts I loved. Never did my altar lack seemly feast, drink-offering and the steam of sacrifice, even the honour that falleth to our due. But verily we will say no more of stealing away brave Hector, for it cannot be hidden from Achilles, for his mother abideth ever nigh to him night and day. But I were fain that some one of the gods would call Thetis to come near to me, that I may speak unto her a wise word, so that Achilles may take gifts from Priam and give Hector back."

Thus spake he, and airy-footed Iris sped forth upon the errand and between Samothrace and rocky Imbros leapt into the black sea, and the waters closed above her with a noise. And she sped to the bottom like a weight of lead that mounted on horn of a field-ox goeth down bearing death to ravenous fishes. And she found Thetis in a hollow cave; about her sat gathered other goddesses of the sea, and she in their midst was wailing for the fate of her noble son who must perish in deep-soiled Troy, far from his native land. And standing near, fleet-footed Iris spake to her: "Rise, Thetis; Zeus of immortal counsels calleth thee."

And to her made answer Thetis the silver-footed goddess: "Wherefore biddeth me that mighty god? I shrink from mingling among the Immortals, for I have countless woes at heart. Yet go I, nor shall his word be in vain, whatsoever he saith."

Thus having said the noble goddess took to her a dark-hued robe, no blacker raiment was there found than that. Then she went forth, and wind-footed swift Iris led the way before her, and around them the surge of the sea was sundered. And when they had come forth upon the shore they sped up to Heaven, and found the far-seeing son of Cronos, and round him sat gathered all the other blessed gods that are for ever. Then she sat down beside father Zeus, and Athene gave her place. And Hera set a fair golden cup in her hand and cheered her with words, and Thetis drank,

and gave back the cup. Then began speech to them the father of gods and men: "Thou art come to Olympus, divine
Thetis, in thy sorrow, with violent grief at thy heart; I know
it of myself. Nevertheless will I tell thee wherefore I called
thee hither. Nine days hath dispute arisen among the Immortals concerning the corpse of Hector and Achilles waster
of cities. Fain are they to send clear-sighted Hermes to steal
the body away, but now hear what glory I accord herein to
Achilles, that I may keep through times to come thy honour
and good will. Go with all speed to the host and bear to thy
son my bidding. Say to him that the gods are displeased at
him, and that I above all Immortals am wroth, because with
furious heart he holdeth Hector at the beaked ships and hath
not given him back, so that haply he may fear me and give
Hector back. But I will send Iris to great-hearted Priam to
bid him go to the ships of the Achaeans to ransom his dear
son, and carry gifts to Achilles that may gladden his heart."

Thus spake he, and Thetis the silver-footed goddess was
not disobedient to his word, and sped darting upon her way
down from the peaks of Olympus. And she came to her
son's hut; there found she him making grievous moan, and
his dear comrades round were swiftly making ready and fur-
nishing their early meal, and a sheep great and fleecy was
being sacrificed in the hut. Then his lady-mother sate her
down close beside him, and stroked him with her hand and
spake to him by his name: "My child, how long with lamentation and woe wilt thou devour thine heart, taking thought
of neither food nor rest? good were even a woman's embrace,
for not long shalt thou be left alive to me; already death and
forceful fate are standing nigh thee. But hearken forthwith
unto me, for I am the messenger of Zeus to thee. He saith
that the gods are displeased at thee, and that himself above
all Immortals is wroth, because with furious heart thou hold-
est Hector at the beaked ships and hast not given him back.
But come restore him, and take ransom for the dead."

Then to her in answer spake fleet-footed Achilles: "So be
it: whoso bringeth ransom let him take back the dead, if
verily with heart's intent the Olympian biddeth it himself."

So they in the assembly of the ships, mother and son, spake to each other many winged words. But the son of Cronos thus bade Iris go to holy Ilium: "Go forth, fleet Iris, leave the abode of Olympus and bear my message within Ilium to great-hearted Priam that he go to the ships of the Achaeans and ransom his dear son and carry gifts to Achilles that may gladden his heart; let him go alone, and no other man of the Trojans go with him. Only let some elder herald

Thetis orders Achilles to give back to Priam the corpse of Hector.

PAINTING FROM AN AMPHORA OF RUVA.
(ERMITAGE MUSEUM)

attend on him to guide the mules and smooth-wheeled waggon and carry back to the city the dead man whom noble Achilles slew. Let not death be in his thought nor any fear; such guide will we give unto him, even the slayer of Argus, who shall lead him until his leading bring him to Achilles. And when he shall have led him within the hut, neither shall Achilles himself slay him nor suffer any other herein, for not senseless is he or unforeseeing or wicked, but with all courtesy he will spare a suppliant man."

Thus spake he, and airy-footed Iris sped forth upon the errand. And she came to the house of Priam, and found therein crying and moan. His children sitting around their

father within the court were bedewing their raiment with
their tears, and the old man in their midst was close wrapped
all over in his cloak; and on his head and neck was much
mire that he had gathered in his hands as he grovelled upon
the earth. And his daughters and his sons' wives were wailing
throughout the house, bethinking them of all those valiant
men who had lost their lives at the hands of the Argives and
were lying low. And the messenger of Zeus stood beside
Priam and spake softly unto him, and trembling came upon
his limbs: "Be of good cheer in thy heart, O Priam son of
Dardanus, and be not dismayed for anything, for no evil
come I hither to foretell to thee, but with good will. I am
the messenger of Zeus to thee, who, though he be afar off,
hath great care and pity for thee. The Olympian biddeth
thee ransom noble Hector and carry gifts to Achilles that
may gladden his heart: go thou alone, let none other of the
Trojans go with thee. Only let some elder herald attend on
thee to guide the mules and the smooth-wheeled waggon to
carry back to the city the dead man whom noble Achilles
slew. Let not death be in thy thought, nor any fear; such
guide shall go with thee, even the slayer of Argus, who shall
lead thee until his leading bring thee to Achilles. And when
he shall have led thee into the hut, neither shall Achilles himself slay thee nor suffer any other herein, for not senseless is
he or unforeseeing or wicked, but with all courtesy he will
spare a suppliant man."

Thus having spoken fleet Iris departed from him; and he
bade his sons make ready the smooth-wheeled mule waggon,
and bind the wicker carriage thereon. And himself he went
down to his fragrant chamber, of cedar wood, high-roofed,
that held full· many jewels: and to Hecabe his wife he called
and spake: "Lady, from Zeus hath an Olympian messenger
come to me, that I go to the ships of the Achaeans and ransom my dear son, and carry gifts to Achilles that may gladden his heart. Come tell me how seemeth it to thy mind, for
of myself at least my desire and heart bid me mightily to
go thither to the ships and enter the wide camp of the
Achaeans."

Thus spake he, but his wife lamented aloud and made answer unto him: "Woe is me, whither is gone thy mind whereby aforetime thou wert famous among stranger men and among them thou rulest? How art thou fain to go alone to the ships of the Achaeans, to meet the eyes of the man who hath slain full many of thy brave sons? of iron verily is thy heart. For if he light on thee and behold thee with his eyes, a savage and ill-trusted man is this, and he will not pity thee, neither reverence thee at all. Nay, now let us sit in the hall and make lament afar off. Even thus did forceful Fate erst spin for Hector with her thread at his beginning, when I bare him, even I that he should glut fleet-footed dogs, far from his parents, in the dwelling of a violent man whose inmost vitals I were fain to fasten and feed upon; then would his deeds against my son be paid again to him, for not playing the coward was he slain of him, but championing the men and deep-bosomed women of Troy, neither bethought he him of shelter or of flight."

Then to her in answer spake the old man godlike Priam: "Stay me not, for I am fain to go, neither be thyself a bird of ill boding in my halls, for thou wilt not change my mind. Were it some other and a child of earth that bade me this, whether some seer or of the priests that divine from sacrifice, then would we declare it false and have no part therein; but now, since I have heard the voice of the goddess myself and looked upon her face, I will go forth, and her word shall not be void. And if it be my fate to die by the ships of the mail-clad Achaeans, so would I have it; let Achilles slay me with all speed, when once I have taken in my arms my son, and have satisfied my desire with moan."

He spake, and opened fair lids of chests wherefrom he chose twelve very goodly women's robes and twelve cloaks of single fold and of coverlets a like number and of fair sheets, and of doublets thereupon. And he weighed and brought forth talents of gold ten in all, and two shining tripods and four caldrons, and a goblet exceeding fair that men of Thrace had given him when he went thither on an embassy, a chattel of great price, yet not that even did the old man grudge from his halls, for he was exceeding fain at heart to ransom his dear son. Then he drove out all the Trojans from the colonnade, chiding them with words of rebuke: "Begone, ye that dishonour and do me shame! Have ye no mourning of your own at home that ye come to vex me here? Think ye it a small thing that Zeus Cronos' son hath given me this sorrow, to lose him that was the best man of my sons? Nay, but ye too shall feel it, for easier far shall ye be to the Achaeans to slay now he is dead. But for me, ere I behold with mine eyes the city sacked and wasted, let me go down into the house of Hades."

He said, and with his staff chased forth the men, and they went forth before the old man in his haste. Then he called unto his sons, chiding Helenos and Paris and noble Agathon and Pammon and Antiphonus, and Polites of the loud warcry, and Deiphobus and Hippothous and proud Dius; nine were they whom the old man called and bade unto him: "Haste ye, ill sons, my shame; would that ye all in Hector's stead had been slain at the swift ships! Woe is me all unblest, since I begat sons the best men in wide Troy-land, but none of them is left for me to claim, neither godlike Mestor, nor Troilus with his chariot of war, nor Hector who was a god among men, neither seemed he as the son of a mortal man but of a god:—all these hath Ares slain, and here are my shames all left to me, false-tongued, light-heeled, the heroes of the dance, plunderers of your own people's sheep and kids. Will ye not make me ready a wain with all speed, and lay all these thereon, that we get us forward on our way?"

Thus spake he, and they fearing their father's voice brought forth the smooth-running mule chariot, fair and new, and bound the body thereof on the frame; and from its peg they took down the mule yoke, a boxwood yoke with knob well fitted with guiding-rings; and they brought forth the yoke-band of nine cubits with the yoke. The yoke they set firmly on the polished pole on the rest at the end thereof, and slipped the ring over the upright pin, which with three turns of the band they lashed to the knob, and then wound the band close round the pole and tucked the loose end in. Then they brought from the chamber and heaped on the polished wain the countless ransom of Hector's head, and yoked strong-hooved harness mules, which on a time the Mysians gave to Priam, a splendid gift. But to Priam's car they yoked the horses that the old man kept for his use and reared at the polished crib.

Thus in the high palace were Priam and the herald letting yoke their cars, with wise thoughts at their hearts, when nigh them came Hecabe sore at heart, with honey-sweet wine in her right hand in a golden cup that they might make libation ere they went. And she stood before the horses and spake a word to Priam by name: "Lo now make libation to father Zeus and pray that thou mayest come back home from among the enemy, since thy heart speedeth thee forth to the ships, though fain were I thou wentest not. And next pray to Zeus of the Storm-cloud, the god of Ida, that beholdeth all Troy-land beneath, and ask of him a bird of omen, even the swift messenger that is dearest of all birds to him and of mightiest strength, to appear upon thy right, that seeing the sign with thine own eyes thou mayest go in trust thereto unto the ships of the fleet-horsed Danaans. But if far-seeing Zeus shall not grant unto thee his messenger, I at least shall not bid thee on to go among the ships of the Achaeans how fain soever thou mayest be."

Then answered and spake unto her godlike Priam: "Lady, I will not disregard this behest of thine, for good it is to lift up hands to Zeus, if haply he will have pity."

Thus spake the old man, and bade a house-dame that served him pour pure water on his hands; and she came near to serve him with water in a ewer to wash withal. And when he had washed his hands he took a goblet from his wife: then he stood in the midst of the court and prayed and poured forth wine as he looked up to heaven, and spake a word aloud: "Father Zeus that bearest sway from Ida, most glorious and most great, grant that I find welcome and pity under Achilles' roof, and send a bird of omen, even the swift messenger that is dearest of all birds to thee and of mightiest strength, to appear upon the right, that seeing this sign with mine own eyes I may go trusting therein unto the ships of the fleet-horsed Danaans."

Thus spake he praying, and Zeus of wise counsels hearkened unto him, and straightway sent forth an eagle, surest omen of winged birds, the dusky hunter called of men the Black Eagle. Wide as the door, well locking, fitted close, of some rich man's high-roofed hall, so wide were his spread wings; and he appeared to them speeding on the right hand above the city. And when they saw the eagle they rejoiced and all their hearts were glad within their breasts.

Then the old man made haste to go up into his car, and drove forth from the doorway and the echoing portico. In front the mules drew the four-wheeled wain, and wise Idaeus drove them; behind came the horses which the old man urged with the lash at speed along the city: and his friends all followed lamenting loud as though he were faring to his death. And when they were come down from the city and were now on the plain, then went back again to Ilium his sons and marriage kin. But the two coming forth upon the plain were not unbeheld of far-seeing Zeus. But he looked upon the old man and had compassion on him, and straightway spake unto Hermes his dear son: "Hermes, since unto thee especially is it dear to companion men, and thou hearest whomsoever thou wilt, go forth and so guide Priam to the hollow ships of the Achaeans that no man behold or be aware of him, among all the Danaans' host, until he come to the son of Peleus."

Thus spake he, and the Messenger, the slayer of Argus, was not disobedient unto his word. Straightway beneath his feet he bound on his fair sandals, golden, divine, that bare him over the wet sea and over the boundless land with the breathings of the wind. And he took up his wand wherewith he entranceth the eyes of such men as he will, and others he likewise waketh out of sleep: this did the strong slayer of Argus take in his hand, and flew. And quickly came he to Troy-land and the Hellespont, and went on his way

in semblance as a young man that is a prince, with the new
down on his chin, as when the youth of men is the comeliest.

Now the others, when they had driven beyond the great
barrow of Ilium, halted the mules and horses at the river to
drink; for darkness was come down over the earth. Then
the herald beheld Hermes from hard by, and marked him,
and spake and said to Priam: "Consider, son of Dardanus;
this is matter of prudent thought. I see a man, methinks we
shall full soon be rent in pieces. Come, let us flee in our
chariot, or else at least touch his knees and entreat him that
he have mercy on us."

Thus spake he, and the old man was confounded, and he
was dismayed exceedingly, and the hair on his pliant limbs
stood up, and he stood still amazed. But Hermes the Helper
came nigh of himself and took the old man's hand, and
spake and questioned him: "Whether, father, dost thou thus
guide these horses and mules through the divine night, when
other mortals are asleep? Hadst thou no fear of the fierce-
breathing Achaeans, thy bitter foes that are hard anigh
thee? If one of them should espy thee carrying such treasures
through the swift black night, what then would be thy
thought? Neither art thou young thyself, and thy companion
here is old, that ye should make defence against a man that
should assail thee first. But I will nowise harm thee, yea I
will keep any other from thy hurt: for the similitude of my
dear father I see in thee."

And to him in answer spake the old man, godlike Priam:
"Even so, kind son, are all these things as thou sayest.
Nevertheless hath some god stretched forth his hand even
over me in that he hath sent a wayfarer such as thou to meet
me, a bearer of good luck, by the nobleness of thy form and
semblance; and thou art wise of heart and of blessed parents art thou sprung."

And to him again spake the Messenger, the slayer of
Argus: "All this, old sire, hast thou verily spoken aright. But
come say this and tell me truly whether thou art taking forth
a great and goodly treasure unto alien men, where it may

abide for thee in safety, or whether by this ye are all forsaking holy Ilium in fear; so far the best man among you hath perished, even thy son; for of battle with the Achaeans abated he never a jot."

And to him in answer spake the old man, godlike Priam: "Who art thou, noble sir, and of whom art born? For meetly hast thou spoken of the fate of my hapless son."

And to him again spake the Messenger, the slayer of Argus: "Thou art proving me, old sire, in asking me of noble Hector. Him have I full oft seen with mine eyes in glorious battle, and when at the ships he was slaying the Argives he drave thither, piercing them with the keen bronze, and we stood still and marvelled thereat, for Achilles suffered us not to fight, being wroth against Atreus' son. His squire am I, and came in the same well-wrought ship. From the Myrmidons I come, and my father is Polyctor. Wealthy is he, and an old man even as thou, and six other sons hath he, and I am his seventh. With the others I cast lots, and it fell to me to fare hither with the host. And now am I come from the ships to the plain, for at day-break the glancing-eyed Achaeans will set the battle in array around the town. For it chafeth them to be sitting here, nor can the Achaean lords hold in their fury for the fray."

And the old man, godlike Priam, answered him, saying: "If verily thou art a squire of Achilles Peleus' son, come tell me all the truth, whether still my son is by the ships, or whether ere now Achilles hath riven him limb from limb and cast him to the dogs."

Then to him again spake the Messenger the slayer of Argus: "Old sire, not yet have dogs or birds devoured him, but there lieth he still by Achilles' ship, even as he fell, among the huts, and the twelfth morn now hath risen upon him, nor doth his flesh corrupt at all, neither worms consume it, such as devour men slain in war. Truly Achilles draggeth him recklessly around the barrow of his dear comrade so oft as divine day dawneth, yet marreth he him not; thou wouldst marvel if thou couldst go see thyself how dewy fresh he lieth, and is washed clean of blood, nor anywhere defiled; and all his wounds wherewith he was stricken are closed; howbeit many plunged their points in him. So careful are the blessed gods of thy son, though he be but a dead corpse, for they held him dear at heart."

Thus spake he, and the old man rejoiced, and answered him, saying: "My son, it is verily a good thing to give due offerings withal to the Immortals, for never did my child—if that child indeed I had—forget in our halls the gods who inhabit Olympus. Therefore have they remembered this for him, albeit his portion is death. But come now take from me this goodly goblet, and guard me myself and guide me, under Heaven, that I may come unto the hut of Peleus' son."

Then spake unto him again the Messenger the slayer of Argus: "Thou art proving me, old sire, who am younger than thou, but thou wilt not prevail upon me, in that thou biddest me take gifts from thee without Achilles' knowledge. I were afraid and shamed at heart to defraud him, lest some evil come to pass on me hereafter. But as thy guide I would go even unto famous Argos, accompanying thee courteously in swift ship or on foot. Not from scorn of thy guide would any assail thee then."

Thus spake the Helper, and leaping on the chariot behind the horses he swiftly took lash and reins into his hands, and breathed brave spirit into horses and mules. But when they were come to the towers and trench of the ships, there were the sentinels just busying them about their supper. Then the Messenger, the slayer of Argus, shed sleep upon them all, and straightway opened the gates and thrust back the bars, and brought within Priam and the splendid gifts upon his wain. And they came to the lofty hut of the son of Peleus, which the Myrmidons made for their king and hewed therefor timber of the pine, and thatched it with downy thatching-rush that they mowed in the meadows, and around it made for him their lord a great court with close-set palisades; and the door was barred by a single bolt of pine that three Achaeans wont to drive home, and three drew back that mighty bar—three ordinary men, but Achilles by himself would drive it home. Then opened the Helper Hermes the door for the old man, and brought in the splendid gifts for Peleus' fleet-footed son, and descended from the chariot to the earth and spake aloud: "Old sire, I that have come to thee am an immortal god, even Hermes, for my father sent me to companion thee on thy way. But now will I depart from thee nor come within Achilles' sight; it were cause of wrath that an immortal god should thus show favour openly unto mortals. But thou go in and clasp the knees of Peleus' son and entreat him for his father's sake and his mother's of the lovely hair and for his child's sake that thou mayest move his soul."

Thus Hermes spake, and departed unto high Olympus. But Priam leapt from the car to the earth, and left Idaeus in his place; he stayed to mind the horses and mules; but the old man made straight for the house where Achilles, dear to Zeus, was wont to sit. And therein he found the man himself, and his comrades sate apart: two only, the hero Automedon and Alcimus, of the stock of Ares, were busy in attendance; and he was lately ceased from meat, even from eating and drinking: and still the table stood beside him. But they were unaware of great Priam as he came in, and so stood he anigh and clasped in his hands the knees of Achilles, and kissed his hands, terrible, man-slaying, that slew many of Priam's sons. And as when a grievous curse cometh upon a man who in his own country hath slain another and escapeth to a land of strangers, to the house of some rich man, and wonder possesseth them that look on him—so Achilles wondered when he saw godlike Priam, and the rest wondered likewise, and looked upon one another. Then Priam spake and entreated him, saying: "Bethink thee, O Achilles like to gods, of thy father that is of like years with me, on the grievous pathway of old age. Him haply are the dwellers round about entreating evilly, nor is there any to ward from him ruin and bane. Nevertheless while he heareth of thee as yet alive he rejoiceth in his heart, and hopeth withal day after day that he shall see his dear son returning from Troy-land. But I, I am utterly unblest, since I begat sons the best men in wide Troy-land, but declare unto thee that none of them is left. Fifty I had, when the sons of the Achaeans came; nineteen were born to me of one mother, and concubines bare the rest within my halls. Now of the more part had impetuous Ares unstrung the knees, and he who was yet left and guarded city and men, him slewest thou but now as he fought for his country, even Hector. For his sake come I unto the ships of the Achaeans that I may win him back from thee, and I bring with me untold ransom. Yea, fear thou the gods,

Priam followed by men carrying presents, goes to Achilles
to give him the ransom of Hector's corpse.

PAINTING FROM A SKYPHOS.
(AUSTRIAN MUSEUM, VIENNA)

Achilles, and have compassion on me, even me, bethinking thee of thy father. Lo, I am yet more piteous than he, and have braved what none other man on earth hath braved before, to stretch forth my hand toward the face of the slayer of my sons."

Thus spake he, and stirred within Achilles desire to make lament for his father. And he touched the old man's hand and gently moved him back. And as they both bethought them of their dead, so Priam for man-slaying Hector wept sore as he was fallen before Achilles' feet, and Achilles wept for his own father, and now again for Patroclus, and their moan went up throughout the house. But when noble Achilles had satisfied him with lament, and the desire thereof

departed from his heart and limbs, straightway he sprang
from his seat and raised the old man by his hand, pitying
his hoary head and hoary beard, and spake unto him winged
words and said: "Ah hapless! many ill things verily thou
hast endured in thy heart. How durst thou come alone to
the ships of the Achaeans and to meet the eyes of the man
who hath slain full many of thy brave sons? of iron verily is
thy heart. But come then set thee on a seat, and we will
let our sorrows lie quiet in our hearts, for all our pain, for
no avail cometh of chill lament. This is the lot the gods
have spun for miserable men, that they should live in pain;
yet themselves are sorrowless. For two urns stand upon the
floor of Zeus filled with his evil gifts, and one with blessings.
To whomsoever Zeus whose joy is in the lightning dealeth
a mingled lot, that man chanceth now upon ill and now
again on good, but to whom he giveth but of the bad kind
him he bringeth to scorn, and evil famine chaseth him over
the goodly earth, and he is a wanderer honoured of neither
gods nor men. Even thus to Peleus gave the gods splendid
gifts from his birth, for he excelled all men in good fortune
and wealth, and was king of the Myrmidons, and mortal
though he was the gods gave him a goddess to be his bride.
Yet even on him God brought evil, seeing that there arose
to him no offspring of princely sons in his halls, save that
he begat one son to an untimely death. Neither may I tend
him as he groweth old, since very far from my country I
am dwelling in Troy-land, to vex thee and thy children. And
of thee, old sire, we have heard how of old time thou wert
happy, even how of all that Lesbos, seat of Macar, boundeth
to the north thereof and Phrygia farther up and the vast
Hellespont—of all these folk, men say, thou wert the richest
in wealth and in sons, but after that the Powers of Heaven
brought this bane on thee, ever are battles and man-slayings
around thy city. Keep courage, and lament not unabatingly
in thy heart. For nothing wilt thou avail by grieving for thy
son, neither shalt thou bring him back to life or ever some
new evil come upon thee."

Then made answer unto him the old man, godlike Priam:

"Bid me not to a seat, O fosterling of Zeus, so long as Hector lieth uncared for at the huts, but straightway give him back that I may behold him with mine eyes; and accept thou the great ransom that we bring. So mayest thou have pleasure thereof, and come unto thy native land, since thou hast spared me from the first."

Then fleet-footed Achilles looked sternly upon him and said: "No further drive me, old sire; of myself am I minded to give Hector back to thee, for there came to me a messenger from Zeus, even my mother who bare me, daughter of the Ancient One of the Sea. And I know, O Priam, in my mind, nor am unaware that some god it is that hath guided thee to the swift ships of the Achaeans. For no mortal man, even though in prime of youth, would dare to come among the host, for neither could he escape the watch, nor easily thrust back the bolt of our doors. Therefore now stir my heart no more amid my troubles, lest I leave not even thee in peace, old sire, within my hut, albeit thou art my suppliant, and lest I transgress the commandment of Zeus."

Thus spake he, and the old man feared, and obeyed his word. And the son of Peleus leapt like a lion through the door of the house, not alone, for with him went two squires, the hero Automedon and Alcimus, they whom above all his comrades Achilles honoured, save only Patroclus that was dead. They then loosed from under the yoke the horses and mules, and led in the old man's crier-herald and set him on a chair, and from the wain of goodly felloes [1] they took the countless ransom set on Hector's head. But they left two robes and a well-spun doublet, that Achilles might wrap the dead therein when he gave him to be carried home. And he called forth handmaids and bade them wash and anoint him when they had borne him apart, so that Priam should not look upon his son, lest he should not refrain the wrath at his sorrowing heart when he should look upon his son, and lest Achilles' heart be vexed thereat and he slay him and transgress the commandment of Zeus. So when the

---

[1] The circular rim of a wheel, supported by the spokes.

handmaids had washed the body and anointed it with oil, and had thrown over it a fair robe and a doublet, then Achilles himself lifted it and laid it on a bier, and his comrades with him lifted it onto the polished waggon. Then he groaned aloud and called on his dear comrade by his name: "Patroclus, be not vexed with me if thou hear even in the house of Hades that I have given back noble Hector unto his dear father, for not unworthy is the ransom he hath given me, whereof I will deal to thee again thy rightful share."

Thus spake noble Achilles, and went back into the hut, and sate him down on the cunningly-wrought couch whence he had arisen by the opposite wall, and spake a word to Priam: "Thy son, old sire, is given back as thou wouldest and lieth on a bier, and with the break of day thou shalt see him thyself as thou carriest him. But now bethink we us of supper. For even fair-haired Niobe bethought her of meat, she whose twelve children perished in her halls,. six daughters and six lusty sons. The sons Apollo, in his anger against Niobe, slew with arrows from his silver bow, and the daughters archer Artemis, for that Niobe matched herself against fair-cheeked Leto, saying that the goddess bare but twain but herself many children: so they though they were but twain destroyed the others all. Nine days they lay in their blood, nor was there any to bury them, for Zeus turned the folk to stones. Yet on the tenth day the gods of heaven buried them, and she then bethought her of meat, when she was wearied out with weeping tears. And somewhere now among the cliffs, on the lonely mountains, even on Sipylus, where they say are the couching-places of nymphs that dance around Achelous, there she, in marble, broodeth still over her troubles from the gods. But come let us too, noble father, take thought of meat, and afterward thou shalt mourn over thy dear son as thou carriest him to Ilium; and many tears shall be his due."

Thus spake fleet Achilles, and sprang up, and slew a pure white sheep, and his comrades skinned and made it ready in seemly fashion, and divided it cunningly and pierced it with spits, and roasted it carefully and drew all off. And Automedon took bread and served it on a table in fair baskets, while Achilles dealt out the flesh. And they stretched forth their hands to the good cheer lying ready before them. But when they had put off the desire of meat and drink, then Priam son of Dardanus marvelled at Achilles to see how great he was and how goodly, for he was like a god to look upon. And Achilles marvelled at Priam son of Dardanus, beholding his noble aspect and hearkening to his words. But when they had gazed their fill upon one another, then first spake the old man, godlike Priam, to Achilles: "Now presently give me whereon to lie, fosterling of Zeus, that of sweet sleep also we may now take our fill at rest: for never yet have mine eyes closed beneath their lids since at thy hands my son lost his life, but I continually mourn and brood over countless griefs, grovelling in the courtyard-close amid the mire. Now at last have I tasted bread and poured bright wine down my throat, but till now I had tasted nought."

He said, and Achilles bade his comrades and handmaids to set a bedstead beneath the portico, and to cast thereon fair shining rugs and spread coverlets above and thereon to lay thick mantles to be a clothing over all. And the maids went forth from the inner hall with torches in their hands, and quickly spread two beds in haste. Then with bitter meaning said fleet-footed Achilles unto Priam: "Lie thou without, dear sire, lest there come hither one of the counsellors of the Achaeans, such as ever take counsel with me by my side, as custom is. If any of such should behold thee through the swift black night, forthwith he might haply tell it to Agamemnon, shepherd of the host, and thus would there be delay in giving back the dead. But come say this to me and tell it true, how many days' space thou art fain to make funeral for noble Hector, so that for so long I may myself abide and may keep back the host."

And the old man, godlike Priam, answered him saying: "If thou art verily willing that I accomplish noble Hector's funeral, by doing as thou sayest, O Achilles, thou wilt do me grace. For thou knowest how we are pent within the city, and wood from the mountain is far to fetch, and the Trojans are much in fear. Nine days will we make moan for him in our halls, and on the tenth we will hold funeral and the folk shall feast, and on the eleventh we will make a barrow over him, and on the twelfth we will do battle if need be."

Then again spake the fleet noble Achilles unto him saying: "All this, O ancient Priam, shall be as thou biddest; for I will hold back the battle even so long a time as thou tellest me."

Thus speaking he clasped the old man's right hand at the wrist, lest he should be anywise afraid at heart. So they in the forepart of the house laid them down, Priam and the herald, with wise thoughts at their hearts, but Achilles slept in a recess of the firm-wrought hut, and beside him lay fair-cheeked Briseis.

Now all other gods and warriors lords of chariots slumbered all night, by soft sleep overcome. But not on the Helper Hermes did sleep take hold as he sought within his heart how he should guide forth king Priam from the ships unespied of the trusty sentinels. And he stood above his head and spake a word to him: "Old sire, no thought then hast thou of any evil, seeing thou yet sleepest among men that are thine enemies, for that Achilles spared thee. Truly now hast thou won back thy dear son, and at great price. But for thy life will thy sons thou hast left behind be offering threefold ransom, if but Agamemnon Atreus' son be aware of thee, and aware be all the Achaeans."

Thus spake he, and the old man feared, and roused the herald. And Hermes yoked the horses and mules for them, and himself drove them lightly through the camp, and none was aware of them.

But when they came to the ford of the fair-flowing river, even eddying Xanthus, begotten of immortal Zeus, then Hermes departed up to high Olympus, and Morning of the saffron robe spread over all the earth. And they with wail and moan drove the horses to the city, and the mules drew the dead. Nor marked them any man or fair-girdled woman until Cassandra, peer of golden Aphrodite, having gone up upon Pergamus,[2] was aware of her dear father as he stood in the car, and the herald that was crier to the town. Then beheld she him that lay upon the bier behind the mules, and thereat she wailed and cried aloud throughout all the town: "O men and women of Troy, come ye hither and look upon Hector, if ever while he was alive ye rejoiced when he came back from battle, since great joy was he to the city and all the folk."

Thus spake she, nor was man or woman left within the city, for upon all came unendurable grief. And near the gates they met Priam bringing home the dead. First bewailed him his dear wife and lady mother, as they cast them on the fair-wheeled wain and touched his head; and around them stood the throng and wept. So all day long unto the setting of the sun they had lamented Hector in tears without the gate, had not the old man spoken from the car among the folk: "Give me place for the mules to pass through; hereafter ye shall have your fill of wailing, when I have brought him unto his home."

Thus spake he, and they parted asunder and gave place to the wain. And the others when they had brought him to the famous house, laid him on a fretted bed, and set beside him minstrels leaders of the dirge, who wailed a mournful lay, while the women made moan with them. And among the women white-armed Andromache led the lamentation, while in her hands she held the head of Hector slayer of men: "Husband, thou art gone young from life, and leavest me a widow in thy halls. And the child is yet but a little one, child of ill-fated parents, thee and me; nor methinks shall he grow up to manhood, for ere then shall this city be utterly destroyed. For thou art verily perished who didst watch over it, who guardedst it and keptest safe its noble wives and infant little ones. These soon shall be voyaging in the hollow ships, yea and I too with them, and thou, my child, shalt either go with me unto a place where thou shalt toil at unseemly tasks, labouring before the face of some

---

[2] A height near the town where there was a temple to Apollo.

harsh lord, or else some Achaean will take thee by the arm and hurl thee from the battlement, a grievous death, for that he is wroth because Hector slew his brother or father or son, since full many of the Achaeans at Hector's hands have bitten the firm earth. For no light hand had thy father in the grievous fray. Therefore the folk lament him throughout the city, and woe unspeakable and mourning hast thou left to thy parents, Hector, but with me chiefliest shall grievous pain abide. For neither didst thou stretch thy hands to me from a bed in thy death, neither didst speak to me some memorable word that I might have thought on evermore as my tears fall night and day."

Thus spake she wailing, and the women joined their moan. And among them Hecabe again led the loud lament: "Hector, of all my children far dearest to my heart, verily while thou wert alive dear wert thou to the gods, and even in thy doom of death have they had care for thee. For other sons of mine whom he took captive would fleet Achilles sell beyond the barren sea unto Samos and Imbros and smoking Lemnos, but when with keen-edged bronze he had bereft thee of thy life he was fain to drag thee oft around the tomb of his comrade, even Patroclus whom thou slewest, yet might he not raise him up thereby. But now all dewy and fresh thou liest in our halls, like one on whom Apollo, lord of the silver bow, hath descended and slain him with his gentle darts."

Thus spake she wailing, and stirred unending moan. Then, thirdly, Helen led their sore lament: "Hector, of all my brethren of Troy far dearest to my heart! Truly my lord is godlike Alexandros who brought me to Troy-land—would I had died ere then. For this is now the twentieth year since I went thence and am gone from my own native land, but never yet heard I evil or despiteful word from thee; nay, if any other haply upbraided me in the palace-halls, whether brother or sister of thine or brother's fair-robed wife, or thy mother—but thy father is ever kind to me as he were my own—then wouldst thou soothe such with words and refrain them, by the gentleness of thy spirit and by thy gentle words. Therefore bewail I thee with pain at heart, and my hapless self with thee, for no more is any left in wide Troyland to be my friend and kind to me, but all men shudder at me."

Thus spake she wailing, and therewith the great multitude of the people groaned. But the old man Priam spake a word among the folk: "Bring wood, men of Troy, unto the city, and be not anywise afraid at heart of a crafty ambush of the Achaeans; for this message Achilles gave me when he sent me from the black ships, that they should do us no hurt until the twelfth morn arise."

Thus spake he, and they yoked oxen and mules to wains, and quickly then they flocked before the city. So nine days they gathered great store of wood. But when the tenth morn rose with light for men, then bare they forth brave Hector, weeping tears, and on a lofty pyre they laid the dead man, and thereon cast fire.

But when the daughter of Dawn, rosy-fingered Morning, shone forth, then gathered the folk around glorious Hector's pyre. First quenched they with bright wine all the burning, so far as the fire's strength went, and then his brethren and comrades gathered his white bones lamenting, and big tears flowed down their cheeks. And the bones they took and laid in a golden urn, shrouding them in soft purple robes, and straightway laid the urn in a hollow grave and piled thereon great close-set stones, and heaped with speed a barrow, while watchers were set everywhere around, lest the well-greaved Achaeans should make onset before the time. And when they had heaped the barrow they went back, and gathered them together and feasted right well in noble feast at the palace of Priam, Zeus-fostered king.

Thus held they funeral for Hector tamer of horses.

THE ODYSSEY

OF HOMER

TRANSLATED BY

ANDREW LANG, WALTER LEAF AND ERNEST MYERS

I

Athena Intervenes

Tᴇʟʟ me, Muse, of that man, so ready at need, who wandered far and wide, after he had sacked the sacred citadel of Troy, and many were the men whose towns he saw and whose mind he learnt, yea, and many the woes he suffered in his heart upon the deep, striving to win his own life and the return of his company. Nay, but even so he saved not his company, though he desired it sore. For through the blindness of their own hearts they perished, fools, who devoured the oxen of Helios Hyperion: [1] but the

---
[1] The Sun.

god took from them their day of returning. Of these things, goddess, daughter of Zeus, whencesoever thou hast heard thereof, declare thou even unto us.

Now all the rest, as many as fled from sheer destruction, were at home, and had escaped both war and sea, but Odysseus only, craving for his wife and for his homeward path, the lady nymph Calypso held, that fair goddess, in her hollow caves, longing to have him for her lord. But when now the year had come in the courses of the seasons,

Murder of Aegisthus.

PAINTING FROM A VULCI AMPHORA.
(BERLIN MUSEUM)

wherein the gods had ordained that he should return home to Ithaca, not even there was he quit of labours, not even among his own; but all the gods had pity on him save Poseidon, who raged continually against godlike Odysseus, till he came to his own country. Howbeit Poseidon had now departed for the distant Ethiopians, the Ethiopians that are sundered in twain, the farthest distant of men, abiding some where Hyperion sinks and some where he rises. There he looked to receive his hecatomb of bulls and dams, there he made merry sitting at the feast, but the other gods were gathered in the halls of Olympian Zeus. Then among them the father of gods and men began to speak, for he bethought him in his heart of noble Aegisthus, whom the son of Agamemnon, far-famed Orestes, slew. Thinking upon him he spake out among the Immortals:

"Lo you now, how vainly mortal men do blame the gods! For of us they say comes evil, whereas they even of themselves, through the blindness of their own hearts, have sorrows beyond that which is ordained. Even as of late Aegisthus, beyond that which was ordained, took to him the wedded wife of the son of Atreus and killed her lord on his return, and that with sheer doom before his eyes, since we had warned him by the embassy of Hermes the keen-sighted, the slayer of Argus, that he should neither kill the man, nor woo his wife. For the son of Atreus shall be avenged at the hand of Orestes, so soon as he shall come to man's estate and long for his own country. So spake Hermes, yet he prevailed not on the heart of Aegisthus, for all his good will; but now hath he paid one price for all."

And the goddess, grey-eyed Athene, answered him, saying: "O father, our father Zeus, throned in the highest, that man assuredly lies in a death that is his due; so perish likewise all who work such deeds! But my heart is rent for wise Odysseus, the hapless one, who far from his friends this long while suffereth affliction in a sea-girt isle, in the middle of the sea, a woodland isle, and therein a goddess hath her habitation, the daughter of the malevolent Atlas, who knows the depths of every sea, and himself upholds the tall pillars which keep earth and sky asunder. His daughter it is that holds the hapless man in sorrow: and ever with soft and guileful tales she is wooing him to forgetfulness of Ithaca. But Odysseus yearning to see if it were but the smoke leap upwards from his own land, hath a desire to die. As for thee, thine heart regardeth it not at all, Olympian! What! did not Odysseus by the ships of the Argives make thee free offering of sacrifice in the wide Trojan land? Wherefore wast thou then so wroth with him, O Zeus?"

And Zeus the cloud-gatherer answered her, and said: "My child, what word hath escaped the door of thy lips? Yea, how should I forget divine Odysseus, who in understanding is beyond mortals and beyond all men hath done sacrifice to the deathless gods, who keep the wide heaven? Nay, but it is Poseidon, the girdler of the earth, that hath been wroth continually with quenchless anger for the Cyclops' sake whom he blinded of his eye, even godlike Polyphemus whose power is mightiest amongst all the Cyclopes.[2] His mother was the nymph Thoösa, daughter of Phorcys, lord of the unharvested sea, and in the hollow caves she lay with Poseidon. From that day forth Poseidon the earth-shaker doth not indeed slay Odysseus, but driveth him wandering from his own country. But come, let us here one and all take good counsel as touching his returning, that he may be got home; so shall Poseidon let go his displeasure, for he will in nowise be able to strive alone against all, in despite of all the deathless gods."

Then the goddess, grey-eyed Athene, answered him, and said: "O father, our father Zeus, throned in the highest, if indeed this thing is now well pleasing to the blessed gods, that wise Odysseus should return to his own home, let us then speed Hermes the Messenger, the slayer of Argos, to the island of Ogygia. There with all speed let him declare to the lady of the braided tresses our unerring counsel, even the return of the patient Odysseus, that so he may come to his home. But as for me I will go to Ithaca that I may rouse his son yet the more, planting might in his heart, to call an assembly of the long-haired Achaeans and speak out to all the wooers who slaughter continually the sheep of his thronging flocks, and his kine with trailing feet and shambling gait. And I will guide him to Sparta and to sandy Pylos to seek tidings of his dear father's return, if peradventure he may hear thereof and that so he may be had in good report among men."

She spake and bound beneath her feet her lovely golden sandals, that wax not old, and bare her alike over the wet sea and over the limitless land, swift as the breath of the wind. And she seized her doughty spear, shod with sharp

---

[2] Singular, Cyclops; plural, Cyclopes.

bronze, weighty and huge and strong, wherewith she quells the ranks of heroes with whomsoever she is wroth, the daughter of the mighty sire. Then from the heights of Olympus she came glancing down, and she stood in the land of Ithaca, at the entry of the gate of Odysseus, on the threshold of the courtyard, holding in her hand the spear of bronze, in the semblance of a stranger, Mentes the captain of the Taphians. And there she found the lordly wooers: now they were taking their pleasure at draughts in front of the doors, sitting on hides of oxen, which themselves had slain. And of the henchmen and the ready squires, some were mixing for them wine and water in bowls, and some again were washing the tables with porous sponges and were setting them forth, and others were carving flesh in plenty.

And godlike Telemachus was far the first to descry her, for he was sitting with a heavy heart among the wooers dreaming on his good father, if haply he might come somewhence, and make a scattering of the wooers there throughout the palace, and himself get honour and bear rule among his own possessions. Thinking thereupon, as he sat among wooers, he saw Athene—and he went straight to the outer porch, for he thought it blame in his heart that a stranger should stand long at the gates: and halting nigh her he clasped her right hand and took from her the spear of bronze, and uttered his voice and spake unto her winged words:

"Hail, stranger, with us thou shalt be kindly treated, and thereafter, when thou hast tasted meat, thou shalt tell us that whereof thou hast need."

Therewith he led the way, and Pallas Athene followed. And when they were now within the lofty house, he set her spear that he bore against a tall pillar, within the polished spear-stand, where stood many spears besides, even those of Odysseus of the hardy heart; and he led the goddess and seated her on a goodly carven chair, and spread a linen cloth thereunder, and beneath was a footstool for the feet. For himself he placed an inlaid seat hard by, apart from the company of the wooers, lest the stranger should be disquieted by the noise and should have a loathing for the meal, being come among arrogant men, and also that he might ask him about his father that was gone from his home.

Then a handmaid bare water for the washing of hands in a goodly golden ewer, and poured it forth over a silver basin to wash withal, and drew to their side a polished table. And a grave dame bare wheaten bread and set it by them, and laid on the board many dainties, giving freely of such things as she had by her. And a carver lifted and placed by them platters of divers kinds of flesh, and nigh them he set golden bowls, and a henchman walked to and fro pouring out to them the wine.

Then in came the lordly wooers; and they sat them down in rows on chairs and on high seats, and henchmen poured water on their hands, and maidservants piled wheaten bread by them in baskets, and pages crowned the bowls with drink; and they stretched forth their hands upon the good cheer spread before them. Now when the wooers had put from them the desire of meat and drink, they minded them of other things, even of the song and dance: for these are crown of the feast. And a henchman placed a beauteous lyre in the hands of Phemius, who was minstrel to the wooers despite his will. Yea, and as he touched the lyre he lifted up his voice in sweet song.

But Telemachus spake unto grey-eyed Athene, holding his head close to her that those others might not hear: "Dear stranger, wilt thou of a truth be wroth at the word that I shall say? Yonder men verily care for such things as these, the lyre and song, lightly, as they that devour the livelihood of another without atonement, of that man whose white bones, it may be, lie wasting in the rain upon the mainland, or the billow rolls them in the brine. Were but these men to see him returned to Ithaca, they all would pray rather for greater speed of foot than for gain of gold and raiment. But now he hath perished, even so, an evil doom, and for us is no comfort, no, not though any of earthly men should say that he will come again. Gone is the day of his re-

not as in realistic dialogue.

turning! But come, declare me this, and tell me all plainly: Who art thou of the sons of men, and whence? Where is thy city, where are they that begat thee? Say, on what manner of ship didst thou come, and how did sailors bring thee to Ithaca, and who did they avow themselves to be, for in no wise do I deem that thou camest hither by land. And herein tell me true, that I may know for a surety whether thou art a newcomer, or whether thou art a guest of the house, seeing that many were the strangers that came to our home, for that *he* too had voyaged much among men."

Then the goddess, grey-eyed Athene, answered him: "Yea now, I will plainly tell thee all. I avow me to be Mentes, son of wise Anchialus, and I bear rule among the Taphians, lovers of the oar. And now am I come to shore, as thou seest, with ship and crew, sailing over the wine-dark sea, unto men of strange speech, even to Temesa, in quest of copper, and my cargo is shining iron. And there my ship is lying toward the upland, away from the city, in the harbour of Rheithron beneath wooded Neïon: and we declare ourselves to be friends one of the other, and of houses friendly, from of old. Nay, if thou wouldest be assured, go ask the old man, the hero Laertes, who they say no more comes to the city, but far away toward the upland suffers affliction, with an ancient woman for his handmaid, who sets by him meat and drink, whensoever weariness takes hold of his limbs, as he creeps along the knoll of his vineyard plot. And now am I come; for verily they said that *he*, thy father, was among his people; but lo, the gods withhold him from his way. For goodly Odysseus hath not yet perished on the earth; but still, methinks, he lives and is kept on the wide deep in a sea-girt isle, and hard men constrain him, wild folk that hold him, it may be, sore against his will. But now of a truth will I utter my word of prophecy, as the Immortals bring it into my heart and as I deem it will be accomplished, though no soothsayer am I, nor skilled in the signs of birds. Henceforth indeed for no long while shall he be far from his own dear country, not though bonds of iron bind him; he will advise him of a way to return, for he is a man of many devices. But

this will encourage Telemachus

come, declare me this, and tell me all plainly, whether indeed, so tall as thou art, thou art sprung from the loins of Odysseus. Thy head surely and thy beauteous eyes are wondrous like to his, since full many a time have we held converse together ere he embarked for Troy, whither the others, aye the bravest of the Argives, went in hollow ships. From that day forth neither have I seen Odysseus, nor he me."

Then wise Telemachus answered her, and said: "Yea, sir, now will I plainly tell thee all. My mother verily saith that I am his; for myself I know not, for never man yet knew of himself his own descent. O that I had been the son of some blessed man, whom old age overtook among his own possessions! But now of him that is the most hapless of mortal men, his son they say that I am, since thou dost question me hereof."

Then the goddess, grey-eyed Athene, spake unto him, and said: "Surely no nameless lineage have the gods ordained for thee in days to come, since Penelope bore thee so goodly a man. But come, declare me this, and tell it all plainly. What feast, nay, what rout is this? What hast thou to do therewith? Is it a clan drinking, or a wedding feast, for here we have no banquet where each man brings his share? In such wise, flooded with insolence, do they seem to me to revel wantonly through the house: and well might any man be wroth to see so many deeds of shame, whatever wise man came among them."

Then wise Telemachus answered her, and said: "Sir, forasmuch as thou questionest me of these things and inquirest thereof, our house was once like to have been rich and honourable, while yet that man was among his people. But now the gods willed it otherwise, in evil purpose, who have made him pass utterly out of sight as no man ever before. Truly I would not even for his death make so great sorrow, had he fallen among his fellows in the land of the Trojans, or in the arms of his friends when all his fighting was done. Then would the whole Achaean host have builded him a barrow, and even for his son would he have won great glory in the after days. But now the spirits of the storm have swept him away inglorious. He is gone, lost to sight and hearsay, but for me hath he left anguish and lamentation; nor henceforth is it for him alone that I mourn and weep, since the gods have wrought for me other sore distress. For all the noblest that are princes in the isles, in Dulichium and Same and wooded Zacynthus, and as many as lord it in rocky Ithaca, all these woo my mother and waste my house. But as for her she neither refuseth the hated bridal, nor hath the heart to make an end: so they devour and diminish my house, and ere long will they make havoc likewise of myself."

Then in heavy displeasure spake unto him Pallas Athene: "God help thee! thou art surely sore in need of Odysseus that is afar, to stretch forth his hands upon the shameless wooers. If he could but come now and stand at the entering in of the gate, with helmet and shield and lances twain, as mighty a man as when first I marked him in our house drinking and making merry what time he came up out of Ephyra from Ilus son of Mermerus! For even thither had Odysseus gone on his swift ship to seek a deadly drug, that he might have wherewithal to smear his bronze-shod arrows: but Ilus would in no wise give it him, for he had in awe the everliving gods. But my father gave it him, for he bare him wondrous love. O that Odysseus might in such strength consort with the wooers: so should they all have swift fate and bitter wedlock! Howbeit these things surely lie on the knees of the gods, whether he shall return or not, and take vengeance in his halls. But I charge thee to take counsel how thou mayest thrust forth the wooers from the hall. Come now, mark and take heed unto my words. On the morrow call the Achaean lords to the assembly, and declare thy saying to all, and take the gods to witness. As for the wooers bid them scatter them each one to his own, and for thy mother, if her heart is moved to marriage, let her go back to the hall of that mighty man her father, and her kinsfolk will furnish a wedding feast, and array the gifts of wooing exceeding many, all that should go back with a daughter dearly beloved. And to thyself I will give a word of wise counsel, if perchance thou wilt hearken. Fit out a ship, the best thou hast, with twenty oarsmen, and go to inquire concerning thy father that is long afar, if perchance any man shall tell thee aught, or if thou mayest hear the voice from Zeus, which chiefly brings tidings to men. Get thee first to Pylos and inquire of goodly Nestor, and from thence to Sparta to Menelaus of the fair hair, for he came home the last of the mailcoated Achaeans. If thou shalt hear news of the life and the returning of thy father, then verily thou mayest endure the wasting for yet a year. But if thou shalt hear that he is dead and gone, return then to thine own dear country and pile his mound, and over it pay burial rites, full many as is due, and give thy mother to a husband. But when thou hast done this and made an end, thereafter take counsel in thy mind and heart, how thou mayest slay the wooers in thy halls, whether by guile or openly; for thou shouldest not carry childish thoughts, being no longer of years thereto. Or hast thou not heard what renown the goodly Orestes gat him among all men in that he slew the slayer of his father, guileful Aegisthus, who killed his famous sire? And thou, too, my friend, for I see that thou art very comely and tall, be valiant, that even men unborn may praise thee. But I will now go down to the swift ship and to my men, who methinks chafe much at tarrying for me; and do thou thyself take heed and give ear unto my words."

Then wise Telemachus answered her, saying: "Sir, verily thou speakest these things out of a friendly heart, as a father to his son, and never will I forget them. But now I pray thee abide here, though eager to be gone, to the end that after thou hast bathed and had all thy heart's desire, thou mayst wend to the ship joyful in spirit, with a costly gift and very goodly, to be an heirloom of my giving, such as dear friends give to friends."

Then the goddess, grey-eyed Athene, answered him: "Hold me now no longer, that am eager for the way. But whatsoever gift thine heart shall bid thee give me, when I am on my way back let it be mine to carry home: bear from thy stores a gift right goodly, and it shall bring thee the worth thereof in return."

The renowned minstrel, Phemius, was Singing
to the wooers.

So spake she and departed, the grey-eyed Athene, and like an eagle of the sea she flew away, but in his spirit she planted might and courage, and put him in mind of his father yet more than heretofore. And he marked the thing and was amazed, for he deemed that it was a god: and anon he went among the wooers, a godlike man.

Now the renowned minstrel was singing to the wooers, and they sat listening in silence; and his song was of the pitiful return of the Achaeans, that Pallas Athene laid on them as they came forth from Troy. And from her upper chamber the daughter of Icarius, wise Penelope, caught the glorious strain, and she went down the high stairs from her chamber, not alone, for two of her handmaids bare her company. Now when the fair lady had come unto the wooers, she stood by the pillar of the well-builded roof holding glistening attire before her face; and a faithful maiden stood on either side her. Then she fell a-weeping, and spake unto the divine minstrel:

"Phemius, since thou knowest many other charms for mortals, deeds of men and gods, which bards rehearse, some one of these do thou sing as thou sittest by them, and let them drink their wine in silence; but cease from this pitiful strain, that ever wastes my heart within my breast, since to me above all women hath come a sorrow comfortless. So dear a head do I long for in constant memory, namely, that man whose fame is noised abroad from Hellas to mid Argos."

Then wise Telemachus answered her, and said: "O my mother, why then dost thou grudge the sweet minstrel to gladden us as his spirit moves him? It is not minstrels who are in fault, but Zeus, methinks, is in fault, who gives to men, that live by bread, to each one as he will. As for Phemius it is no blame if he sings the ill-faring of the Danaans; for men always prize that song the most, which rings newest in their ears. But let thy heart and mind endure to listen, for not Odysseus only lost in Troy the day of his returning, but many another likewise perished. So go to thy chamber and mind thine own housewiferies, the loom and distaff, and bid thy handmaids ply their tasks. But speech shall be for men, for all, but for me in chief; for mine is the lordship in the house."

Then in amaze she went back to her chamber, for she laid up the wise saying of her son in her heart. She ascended to her upper chamber with the women her handmaids, and then was bewailing Odysseus, her dear lord, till grey-eyed Athene cast sweet sleep upon her eyelids.

Now the wooers clamoured throughout the shadowy halls, and each one uttered a prayer to be her bedfellow. And wise Telemachus first spake among them:

"Wooers of my mother, men despiteful out of measure, let us feast now and make merry and let there be no brawling; for, lo, it is a good thing to list to a minstrel such as him, like to the gods in voice. But in the morning let us all go to the assembly and sit us down, that I may declare my saying outright, to wit that ye leave these halls: and busy yourselves with other feasts, eating your own substance, going in turn from house to house. But if ye deem this a likelier and a better thing, that one man's goods should perish without atonement, then waste ye as ye will; and I will call upon the everlasting gods, if haply Zeus may grant that acts of recompense be made: so should ye hereafter perish within the halls without atonement."

So spake he, and all that heard him bit their lips and marvelled at Telemachus, in that he spake boldly.

Then Antinous, son of Eupeithes, answered him: "Telemachus, in very truth the gods themselves instruct thee to be proud of speech and boldly to harangue. Never may Zeus make thee king in sea-girt Ithaca, which thing is of inheritance thy right!"

Then wise Telemachus answered him, and said: "Antinous, wilt thou indeed be wroth at the word that I shall say? Yea, at the hand of Zeus would I be fain to take even this thing upon me. Sayest thou that this is the worst hap that can befall a man? Nay, verily, it is no ill thing to be a king: the house of such an one quickly waxeth rich and himself is held in greater honour. Howsoever there are many other kings of the Achaeans in sea-girt Ithaca, kings young and old; some one of them shall surely have this kingship since goodly Odysseus is dead. But as for me, I will be lord of our own house and thralls, that goodly Odysseus won me with his spear."

Then Eurymachus, son of Polybus, answered him, saying: "Telemachus, on the knees of the gods it surely lies, what man is to be king over the Achaeans in sea-girt Ithaca. But mayest thou keep thine own possessions and be lord in thine own house! Never may that man come, who shall wrest from thee thy substance violently in thine own despite, while Ithaca yet stands. But I would ask thee, friend, concerning the stranger—whence he is, and of what land he avows him to be? Where are his kin and his native fields? Doth he bear some tidings of thy father on his road, or cometh he thus to speed some matter of his own? In such wise did he start up, and lo, he was gone, nor tarried he that we should know him;—and yet he seemed no mean man to look upon."

Then wise Telemachus answered him, and said: "Eurymachus, surely the day of my father's returning hath gone by. Therefore no more do I put faith in tidings, whencesoever they may come, neither have I regard unto any divination, whereof my mother may inquire at the lips of a diviner, when she hath bidden him to the hall. But as for that man, he is a friend of my house from Taphos, and he avows him to be Mentes, son of wise Anchialus, and he hath lordship among the Taphians, lovers of the oar."

So spake Telemachus, but in his heart he knew the deathless goddess. Now the wooers turned them to the dance and the delightsome song, and made merry, and waited till evening should come on. And as they made merry, dusk evening came upon them. Then they went each one to his own house to lie down to rest.

But Telemachus, where his chamber was builded high up in the fair court, in a place with wide prospect, thither betook him to his bed, pondering many thoughts in his mind; and with him went trusty Eurycleia, and bare for him torches burning. She was the daughter of Ops, son of Peisenor, and Laertes bought her on a time with his wealth, while as yet she was in her first youth, and gave for her the worth of twenty oxen. And he honoured her even as he honoured his dear wife in the halls, but he never lay with her, for he shunned the wrath of his lady. She went with Telemachus and bare for him the burning torches: and of all the women of the household she loved him most, and she had nursed him when a little one. Then he opened the doors of the well-builded chamber and sat down on the bed and took off his soft doublet, and put it in the wise old woman's hands. So she folded the doublet and smoothed it, and hung it on a pin by the jointed bedstead, and went forth on her way from the room, and pulled to the door with the silver handle, and drew home the bar with the thong. There, all night through, wrapt in a fleece of wool, he meditated in his heart upon the journey that Athene had showed him.

II

Telemachus Calls a Council

Now so soon as early Dawn shone forth, the rosy-fingered, the dear son of Odysseus gat him up from his bed, and put on his raiment and cast his sharp sword about his shoulder, and beneath his smooth feet he bound his goodly sandals, and stept forth from his chamber in presence like a god. And straightway he bade the clear-voiced heralds to call the long-haired Achaeans to the assembly. And the heralds called the gathering, and the Achaeans were assembled quickly. Now when they were gathered and come together, he went on his way to the assembly holding in his hand a spear of bronze,—not alone he went, for two swift hounds bare him company. Then Athene shed on him a wondrous grace, and all the people marvelled at him as he came. And he sat him in his father's seat and the elders gave place to him.

Then the lord Aegyptus spake among them first; bowed was he with age, and skilled in things past number. Now for this reason he spake that his dear son, the warrior Antiphus, had gone in the hollow ships to Ilium of the goodly steeds; but the savage Cyclops slew him in his hollow cave, and made of him then his latest meal. Three other sons Aegyptus had, and one consorted with the wooers, namely Eurynomus, but two continued in their father's fields; yet even so forgat he not Antiphus, still mourning and sorrowing. So weeping for his sake he made harangue and spake among them:

"Hearken now to me, ye men of Ithaca, to the word that I shall say. Never hath our assembly or session been since the day that goodly Odysseus departed in the hollow ships. And now who was minded thus to assemble us? On what man hath such sore need come, of the young men or of the elder born? Hath he heard some tidings of the host now returning, which he might plainly declare to us, for that he first learned thereof, or doth he show forth and tell some other matter of the common weal? Methinks he is a true man—good luck be with him! Zeus vouchsafe him some good thing in his turn, even all his heart's desire!"

So spake he, and the dear son of Odysseus was glad at the omen of the word; nor sat he now much longer, but he burned to speak, and he stood in mid assembly; and the herald Peisenor, skilled in sage counsels, placed the staff in his hands. Then he spake, accosting the old man first:

"Old man, he is not far off, and soon shalt thou know it for thyself, he who called the folk together, even I: for sorrow hath come to me in chief. Neither have I heard any tidings of the host now returning, which I may plainly declare to you, for that I first learned thereof; neither do I show forth or tell any other matter of the common weal, but mine own need, for that evil hath befallen my house, a double woe. First, I have lost my noble sire, who sometime was king among you here, and was gentle as a father; and now is there an evil yet greater far, which surely shall soon make grievous havoc of my whole house and ruin all my livelihood. My mother did certain wooers beset sore against her will, even the sons of those men that here are the noblest. They are too craven to go to the house of her father Icarius, that he may himself set the bride-price for his daughter, and bestow her on whom he will, even on him who finds favour in his sight. But they resorting to our house day by day sacrifice oxen and sheep and fat goats, and keep revel, and drink the dark wine recklessly, and lo, our great wealth is wasted, for there is no man now alive such as Odysseus was, to keep ruin from the house. As for me I am no wise strong like him to ward mine own; verily to the end of my days shall I be a weakling and all unskilled in prowess. Truly I would defend me if but strength were mine; for deeds past sufferance have now been wrought, and now my house is wasted utterly beyond pretence of right. Resent it in your own hearts, and have regard to your neighbours who dwell around, and tremble ye at the anger of the gods, lest haply they turn upon you in wrath at your evil deeds. I pray you by Olympian Zeus and by Themis, who looseth and gathereth the meetings of men, let be, my friends, and leave me alone to waste in bitter grief;—unless it so be that my father, the good Odysseus, out of evil heart wrought harm to the goodly-greaved Achaeans, in quittance whereof ye now work me harm out of evil hearts, and spur on these men. Better for me that ye yourselves should eat up my treasures and my flocks. Were *ye* so to devour them, ere long would some recompense be made, for we would urge our plea throughout the town, begging back our substance, until all should be restored. But now without remedy are the pains that ye lay up in my heart."

So spake he in wrath, and dashed the staff to the ground, and brake forth in tears; and pity fell on all the people. Then all the others held their peace, and none had the heart to answer Telemachus with hard words, but Antinous alone made answer, saying:

"Telemachus, proud of speech and unrestrained in fury, what is this thou hast said to put us to shame, and wouldest fasten on us reproach? Behold the fault is not in the Achaean wooers, but in thine own mother, for she is the craftiest of women. For it is now the third year, and the fourth is fast going by, since she began to deceive the minds of the Achaeans in their breasts. She gives hope to all, and makes promises to every man, and sends them messages, but her mind is set on other things. And she hath devised in her heart this wile besides; she set up in her halls a mighty web, fine of woof and very wide, whereat she would weave, and anon she spake among us:

" 'Ye princely youths, my wooers, now that the goodly Odysseus is dead, do ye abide patiently, how eager soever to

Penelope's famous web. She is a good mate for the crafty Ody.

II · *Telemachus Calls a Council* 221

speed on this marriage of mine, till I finish the robe. I would not that the threads perish to no avail, even this shroud for the hero Laertes, against the day when the ruinous doom shall bring him low, of death that lays men at their length. So shall none of the Achaean women in the land count it blame in me, as well might be, were he to lie without a winding-sheet, a man that had gotten great possessions.'

Penelope in Front of her Loom, Talking with Antinous,
One of her Young Wooers.

PAINTING FROM A SCYPHUS OF CHIUSI.
(CHIUSI MUSEUM)

"So spake she, and our high hearts consented thereto. So then in the day time she would weave the mighty web, and in the night unravel the same, when she had let place the torches by her. Thus for the space of three years she hid the thing by craft and beguiled the minds of the Achaeans; but when the fourth year arrived and the seasons came round, then at the last one of her women who knew all declared it, and we found her unravelling the splendid web. Thus she finished it perforce and sore against her will. But as for thee, the wooers make thee answer thus, that thou mayest know it in thine own heart, thou and all the Achaeans! Send away thy mother, and bid her be married to whosoever her father commands, and whoso is well pleasing unto her. But if she will continue for long to vex the sons of the Achaeans, pondering in her heart those things that Athene hath given her beyond women, knowledge of all fair handiwork, yea, and cunning wit, and wiles—so be it! Such wiles as hers we have never yet heard that any even of the women of old did know, of those that aforetime were fair-tressed Achaean ladies, Tyro, and Alcmene, and Mycene with the bright crown. Not one of these in the imaginations of their hearts was like unto Penelope, yet herein at least her imagining was not good. For in despite of her the wooers will devour thy living and thy substance, so long as she is steadfast in such purpose as the gods now put within her breast: great renown for herself she winneth, but for thee regret for thy great riches. But we will neither go to our own lands, nor otherwhere, till she marry that man whom she will of the Achaeans."

Then wise Telemachus answered him, saying: "Antinous, I may in no wise thrust forth from the house, against her will, the woman that bare me, that reared me: while as for my father he is abroad on the earth, whether he be alive or dead. Moreover it is hard for me to make heavy restitution to Icarius, as needs I must, if of mine own will I send my mother away. For I shall have evil at his hand, at the hand of her father, and some god will give me more besides, for my mother will call down the dire Avengers [1] as she departs from the house, and I shall have blame of men; surely then I will never speak this word. Nay, if your own heart, even yours, is indignant, quit ye my halls, and busy yourselves with other feasts, eating your own substance, and going in turn from house to house. But if ye deem this a likelier and a better thing, that one man's goods should perish without atonement, then waste ye as ye will: and I will call upon the everlasting gods, if haply Zeus may grant that acts of rec-

---

[1] The Furies, avengers of crime, especially crimes against the ties of kinship.

ompense be made: so should ye hereafter perish in the halls without atonement."

So spake Telemachus, and in answer to his prayer did Zeus, of the far-borne voice, send forth two eagles in flight, from on high, from the mountain-crest. Awhile they flew as fleet as the blasts of the wind, side by side, with straining of their pinions. But when they had now reached the mid assembly, the place of many voices, there they wheeled about and flapped their strong wings, and looked down upon the heads of all, and destruction was in their gaze. Then tore they with their talons each the other's cheeks and neck on every side, and so sped to the right across the dwellings and the city of the people. And the men marvelled at the birds when they had sight of them, and pondered in their hearts the things that should come to pass. Yea and the old man, the lord Halitherses son of Mastor, spake among them, for he excelled his peers in knowledge of birds, and in uttering words of fate. With good will he made harangue and spake among them:

"Hearken to me now, ye men of Ithaca, to the word that I shall say: and mainly to the wooers do I show forth and tell these things, seeing that a mighty woe is rolling upon them. For Odysseus shall not long be away from his friends, nay, even now, it may be, he is near, and sowing the seeds of death and fate for these men, every one; and he will be a bane to many another likewise of us who dwell in clearseen Ithaca. But long ere that falls out let us advise us how we may make an end of their mischief; yea, let them of their own selves make an end, for this is the better way for them, as will soon be seen. For I prophesy not as one unproved, but with sure knowledge; verily, I say, that for him all things now are come to pass, even as I told him, what time the Argives embarked for Ilium, and with them went the wise Odysseus. I said that after sore affliction, with the loss of all his company, unknown to all, in the twentieth year he should come home. And behold, all these things now have an end."

And Eurymachus, son of Polybus, answered him, saying: "Go now, old man, get thee home and prophesy to thine own children, lest haply they suffer harm hereafter: but herein am I a far better prophet than thou. There be many birds that fly to and fro under the sun's rays, but all are not birds of fate. Now as for Odysseus, he hath perished far away, as would that thou too with him hadst been cut off: so wouldst thou not have babbled thus much prophecy, nor wouldst thou hound on Telemachus that is already angered, expecting a gift for thy house, if perchance he may vouchsafe thee aught. But now will I speak out, and my word shall surely be accomplished. If thou, that knowest much lore from of old, shalt beguile with words a younger man, and rouse him to indignation, first it shall be a great grief to him:—and yet he can count on no aid from these who hear him;—while upon thee, old man, we will lay a fine, that thou mayest pay it and chafe at heart, and sore pain shall be thine. And I myself will give a word of counsel to Telemachus in presence of you all. Let him command his mother to return to her father's house; and her kinsfolk will furnish a wedding feast, and array the gifts of wooing, exceeding many, all that should go back with a daughter dearly beloved. For ere that, I trow, we sons of the Achaeans will not cease from our rough wooing, since, come what may, we fear not any man, no, not Telemachus, full of words though he be, nor soothsaying do we heed, whereof thou, old man, pratest idly, and art hated yet the more. His substance too shall be woefully devoured, nor shall recompense ever be made, so long as she shall put off the Achaeans in the matter of her marriage; while we in expectation, from day to day, vie one with another for the prize of her perfection, nor go we after other women whom it were meet that we should each one wed."

Then wise Telemachus answered him, saying: "Eurymachus, and ye others, that are lordly wooers, I entreat you no more concerning this nor speak thereof, for the gods have knowledge of it now and all the Achaeans. But come, give me a swift ship and twenty men, who shall accomplish for me my voyage to and fro. For I will go to Sparta and to sandy Pylos to inquire concerning the return of my father that is long afar, if perchance any man shall tell me aught, or if I may hear the voice from Zeus, that chiefly brings tidings to men. If I shall hear news of the life and the returning of my father, then verily I may endure the wasting for yet a year; but if I shall hear that he is dead and gone, let me then return to my own dear country, and pile his mound, and over it pay burial rites full many as is due, and I will give my mother to a husband."

So with that word he sat him down; then in the midst uprose Mentor, the companion of noble Odysseus. He it was to whom Odysseus, as he departed in the fleet, had given the charge over all his house, that it should obey the old man, and that he should keep all things safe. With good will he now made harangue and spake among them:

"Hearken to me now, ye men of Ithaca, to the word that I shall say. Henceforth let not any sceptred king be kind and gentle with all his heart, nor minded to do righteousness: for behold, there is none that remembereth divine Odysseus of the people whose lord he was, and was gentle as a father. Howsoever, it is not that I grudge the lordly wooers their deeds of violence in the evil devices of their heart. For at the hazard of their own heads they violently devour the household of Odysseus, and say of him that he will come no more again. But I am indeed wroth with the rest of the people, to see how ye all sit thus speechless, and do not cry shame upon the wooers, and put them down, ye that are so many and they so few."

And Leocritus, son of Euenor, answered him, saying: "Mentor infatuate, with thy wandering wits, what word hast thou spoken, that callest upon them to put us down? Nay, it is a hard thing to fight about a feast, and that with men who are even more in number than you. Though Odysseus of Ithaca himself should come and were eager of heart to drive forth from the hall the lordly wooers that feast throughout his house, yet should his wife have no joy of his coming, though she yearns for him;—but even there should he meet foul doom, if he fought with those that outnumbered him; so thou hast not spoken aright. But as for the people, come now, scatter yourselves each one to his own lands, but Mentor and Halitherses will speed this man's voyage, for they are friends of his house from of old. Yet after all, methinks, that long time he will abide and seek tidings in Ithaca, and never accomplish this voyage."

Thus he spake, and in haste they broke up the assembly. So they were scattered each one to his own dwelling, while the wooers departed to the house of divine Odysseus.

Then Telemachus, going far apart to the shore of the sea, laved his hands in the grey sea water, and prayed unto Athene, saying: "Hear me, thou who yesterday didst come in thy godhead to our house, and badst me go in a ship across the misty seas, to seek tidings of the return of my father that is long gone: but all this my purpose do the Achaeans delay, and mainly the wooers in the naughtiness of their pride."

So spake he in prayer, and Athene drew nigh him in the likeness of Mentor, in fashion and in voice, and she spake and hailed him in winged words:

"Telemachus, even hereafter thou shalt not be craven or witless, if indeed thou hast a drop of thy father's blood and a portion of his spirit; such an one was he to fulfil both word and work. Nor, if this be so, shall thy voyage be vain or unfulfilled. But if thou art not the very seed of him and of Penelope, then have I no hope that thou wilt accomplish thy desire. For few children, truly, are like their father; lo, the more part are worse, yet a few are better than the sire. But since thou shalt not even hereafter be craven or witless, nor hath the wisdom of Odysseus failed thee quite, so is there good hope of thine accomplishing this work. Wherefore now take no heed of the counsel or the purpose of the senseless wooers, for they are in no way wise or just: neither know they aught of death and of black fate, which already is close upon them, that they are all to perish in one day. But the voyage on which thy heart is set shall not long be lacking to thee—so faithful a friend of thy father am I, who will furnish thee a swift ship and myself be thy companion. But go thou to the house, and consort with the wooers, and make ready corn, and bestow all in vessels, the wine in jars and barley-flour, the marrow of men, in well-sewn skins; and I will lightly gather in the township a crew that offer themselves willingly. There are many ships, new and old, in sea-girt Ithaca; of these I will choose out the best for thee, and we will quickly rig her and launch her on the broad deep."

So spake Athene, daughter of Zeus, and Telemachus made no long tarrying, when he had heard the voice of the goddess. He went on his way towards the house, heavy at heart, and there he found the noble wooers in the halls, flaying goats and singeing swine in the court. And Antinous laughed out and went straight to Telemachus, clasped his hand and spake and hailed him:

"Telemachus, proud of speech and unrestrained in fury, let no evil word any more be in thy heart, nor evil work, but let me see thee eat and drink as of old. And the Achaeans will make thee ready all things without fail, a ship and chosen oarsmen, that thou mayest come the quicker to fair Pylos, to seek tidings of thy noble father."

Then wise Telemachus answered him, saying: "Antinous, in no wise in your proud company can I sup in peace, and make merry with a quiet mind. Is it a little thing, ye wooers, that in time past ye wasted many good things of my getting, while as yet I was a child? But now that I am a man grown, and learn the story from the lips of others, and my spirit waxeth within me, I will seek to let loose upon you evil fates, as I may, going either to Pylos for help, or abiding here in this township. Yea, I will go, nor vain shall the voyage be whereof I speak; a passenger on another's ship go I, for I am not to have a ship nor oarsmen of mine own; so in your wisdom ye have thought it for the better."

He spake and snatched his hand from out the hand of Antinous, lightly, and all the while the wooers were busy feasting through the house; and they mocked him and sharply taunted him, and thus would some proud youth speak:

"In very truth Telemachus planneth our destruction. He will bring a rescue either from sandy Pylos, or even it may be from Sparta, so terribly is he set on slaying us. Or else he will go to Ephyra, a fruitful land, to fetch a poisonous drug that he may cast it into the bowl and make an end of all of us."

And again another proud youth would say: "Who knows but that he himself, if he goes hence on the hollow ship, may perish wandering far from his friends, even as Odysseus? So should we have yet more ado, for then must we divide among us all his substance, and moreover give the house to his mother to possess it, and to him whosoever should wed her."

So spake they; but he stepped down into the vaulted treasure-chamber of his father, a spacious room, where gold and bronze lay piled, and raiment in coffers, and fragrant olive oil in plenty. And there stood casks of sweet wine and old, full of the unmixed drink divine, all orderly ranged by the wall, ready if ever Odysseus should come home, albeit after travail and much pain. And the close-fitted doors, the folding doors, were shut, and night and day there abode within a dame in charge, who guarded all in the fulness of her wisdom, Eurycleia, daughter of Ops son of Peisenor. Telemachus now called her into the chamber and spake unto her, saying:

"Mother, come draw off for me sweet wine in jars, the choicest next to that thou keepest mindful ever of that ill-fated one, Odysseus, of the seed of Zeus, if perchance he may come I know not whence, having avoided death and the fates. So fill twelve jars, and close each with his lid, and pour me barley-meal into well-sewn skins, and let there be twenty measures of the grain of bruised barley-meal. Let none know this but thyself! As for these things let them all be got together; for in the evening I will take them with me, at the time that my mother hath gone to her upper chamber and turned her thoughts to sleep. Lo, to Sparta I go and to sandy Pylos to seek tidings of my dear father's return, if haply I may hear thereof."

So spake he, and the good nurse Eurycleia wailed aloud,

and making lament spake to him winged words: "Ah, where-fore, dear child, hath such a thought arisen in thine heart? How shouldst thou fare over wide lands, thou that art an only child and well-beloved? As for him he hath perished, Odysseus of the seed of Zeus, far from his own country in the land of strangers. And yonder men, so soon as thou art gone, will devise mischief against thee thereafter, that thou mayest perish by guile, and they will share among them all this wealth of thine. Nay, abide here, settled on thine own lands: thou hast no need upon the deep unharvested to suf-fer evil and go wandering."

Then wise Telemachus answered her, saying: "Take heart, nurse, for lo, this my purpose came not but of a god. But swear to tell no word thereof to my dear mother, till at least it shall be the eleventh or twelfth day from hence, or till she miss me of herself, and hear of my departure, that so she may not mar her fair face with her tears."

Thus he spake, and the old woman sware a great oath by the gods not to reveal it. But when she had sworn and done that oath, straightway she drew off the wine for him in jars, and poured barley-meal into well-sewn skins, and Telema-chus departed to the house and consorted with the wooers.

Then the goddess, grey-eyed Athene, turned to other thoughts. In the likeness of Telemachus she went all through the city, and stood by each one of the men and spake her saying, and bade them gather at even by the swift ship. Fur-thermore, she craved a swift ship of Noemon, famous son of Phromius, and right gladly he promised it.

Now the sun sank and all the ways were darkened. Then at length she let drag the swift ship to the sea and stored within it all such tackling as decked ships carry. And she moored it at the far end of the harbour and the good com-pany were gathered together, and the goddess cheered on all.

Then the goddess, grey-eyed Athene, turned to other thoughts. She went on her way to the house of divine Odys-seus; and there she shed sweet sleep upon the wooers and made them distraught in their drinking, and cast the cups from their hands. And they arose up to go to rest through-out the city, nor sat they yet a long while, for slumber was falling on their eyelids. Now grey-eyed Athene spake unto Telemachus, and called him from out the fair-lying halls, taking the likeness of Mentor, both in fashion and in voice:

"Telemachus, thy goodly-greaved companions are sitting already at their oars, it is thy despatch they are awaiting. Nay then, let us go, that we delay them not long from the way."

Therewith Pallas Athene led the way quickly, and he followed hard in the steps of the goddess. Now when they had come down to the ship and to the sea, they found the long-haired youths of the company on the shore; and the mighty prince Telemachus spake among them:

"Come hither, friends, let us carry the corn on board, for all is now together in the room, and my mother knows nought thereof, nor any of the maidens of the house: one woman only heard my saying."

Thus he spake and led the way, and they went with him. So they brought all and stowed it in the decked ship, according to the word of the dear son of Odysseus. Then Telemachus climbed the ship, and Athene went before him, and behold, she sat her down in the stern, and near her sat Telemachus. And the men loosed the hawsers and climbed on board themselves, and sat down upon the benches. And grey-eyed Athene sent them a favourable gale, a fresh West Wind, singing over the wine-dark sea.

And Telemachus called unto his company and bade them lay hands on the tackling, and they hearkened to his call. So they raised the mast of pine tree and set it in the hole of the cross plank, and made it fast with forestays, and hauled up the white sails with twisted ropes of oxhide. And the wind filled the belly of the sail, and the dark wave seethed loudly round the stem of the running ship, and she fleeted over the wave, accomplishing her path. Then they made all fast in the swift black ship, and set mixing bowls brimmed with wine, and poured drink offering to the deathless gods that are from everlasting, and in chief to the grey-eyed daughter of Zeus. So all night long and through the dawn the ship cleft her way.

III

Fights Around Troy.

PAINTING FROM AN HYDRIA.
(TYSZKIEWICZ COLL.)

Telemachus Visits Nestor

❨ Telemachus with his shipmates arrives in Pylos and states his mission with grace and dignity. Nestor praises Odysseus as supreme in fighting and council. He knows nothing of the fate of Odysseus, however, because the Achaeans did not all follow the same road home. He tells stories of the homecoming of some of the heroes, particularly the grievous tale of Agamemnon. Athena returns to Olympus. Nestor sends Telemachus to Sparta with his own son Peisistratus as guide to learn what Menelaus knows of the fate of Odysseus.

IV

LASS-A-DEE-MON

Telemachus Visits Menelaus

AND they came to Lacedaemon lying low among the caverned hills, and drave to the dwelling of renowned Menelaus. Him they found giving a feast in his house to many friends of his kin, a feast for the wedding of his noble son and daughter. His daughter he was sending to the son of Achilles, cleaver of the ranks of men, for in Troy he first had promised and covenanted to give her, and now the gods were bringing about their marriage. So now he was speeding her on her way with chariot and horses, to the famous city of the Myrmidons, among whom her lord bare rule. And for his son he was bringing to his home the daughter of Alector out of Sparta, for his well-beloved son, strong Megapenthes, born of a slave woman, for the gods no more showed promise of seed to Helen, from the day that she bare a lovely child, Hermione, as fair as golden Aphrodite. So they were feasting through the great vaulted hall, the neighbours and the kinsmen of renowned Menelaus, making merry; and among them a divine minstrel was singing to the lyre, and as he began the song two tumblers in the company whirled through the midst of them.

Meanwhile those twain, the hero Telemachus and the splendid son of Nestor, made halt at the entry of the gate, they and their horses. And the lord Eteoneus came forth and saw them, the ready squire of renowned Menelaus; and he went through the palace to bear the tidings to the shepherd of the people, and standing near spake to him winged words:

Duty of hospitality again (handwritten)

"Menelaus, fosterling of Zeus, here are two strangers, whosoever they be, two men like to the lineage of great Zeus. Say, shall we loose their swift horses from under the yoke, or send them onward to some other host who shall receive them kindly?"

Then in sore displeasure spake to him Menelaus of the fair hair: "Eteoneus son of Boethous, truly thou wert not a fool aforetime, but now for this once, like a child thou talkest folly. Surely ourselves ate much hospitable cheer of other men, ere we twain came hither and could expect in time to come Zeus would haply give us rest from affliction. Nay go, unyoke the horses of the strangers, and as for the men, lead them forward to the house to feast with us."

So spake he, and Eteoneus hasted from the hall, and called the other ready squires to follow with him. So they loosed the sweating horses from beneath the yoke, and fastened them at the stalls of the horses, and threw beside them spelt, and therewith mixed white barley, and tilted the chariot against the shining faces of the gateway, and led the men into the hall divine. And they beheld and marvelled as they gazed throughout the palace of the king, the fosterling of Zeus; for there was a gleam as it were of sun or moon through the lofty palace of renowned Menelaus. But after they had gazed their fill, they went to the polished baths and bathed them. Now when the maidens had bathed them and anointed them with olive oil, and cast about them thick cloaks and doublets, they sat on chairs by Menelaus, son of Atreus. And a handmaid bare water for the hands in a goodly golden ewer and poured it forth over a silver basin to wash withal; and to their side she drew a polished table, and a grave dame bare food and set it by them, and laid upon the board many dainties, giving freely of such things as she had by her, and a carver lifted and placed by them platters of divers kinds of flesh, and nigh them he set golden bowls. So Menelaus of the fair hair greeted the twain and spake:

"Taste ye food and be glad, and thereafter when ye have supped, we will ask what men ye are; for the blood of your parents is not lost in you, but ye are of the line of men that are sceptred kings, the fosterlings of Zeus; for no churls could beget sons like you."

So spake he, and took and set before them the fat oxchine roasted, which they had given him as his own mess by way of honour. And they stretched forth their hands upon the good cheer set before them. Now when they had put from them the desire of meat and drink Telemachus spake to the son of Nestor, holding his head close to him, that those others might not hear:

"Son of Nestor, delight of my heart, mark the flashing of bronze through the echoing halls, and the flashing of gold and of amber and of silver and of ivory. Such like, methinks, is the court of Olympian Zeus within, for the world of things that are here; wonder comes over me as I look thereon."

And as he spake Menelaus of the fair hair was ware of him, and uttering his voice spake to them winged words:

"Children dear, of a truth no one of mortal men may contend with Zeus, for his mansions and his treasures are everlasting: but of men there may be who will vie with me in treasure, or there may be none. Yea, for after many a woe and wanderings manifold, I brought my wealth home in ships, and in the eighth year came hither. I roamed over Cyprus and Phoenicia and Egypt, and reached the Ethiopians and Sidonians and Erembi and Libya, where lambs are horned from the birth. For there the ewes yean thrice within the full circle of a year; there neither lord nor shepherd lacketh aught of cheese or flesh or of sweet milk, but ever the flocks yield store of milk continual. While I was yet roaming in those lands, gathering much livelihood, meantime another slew my brother privily, at unawares, by the guile of his accursed wife. Thus, look you, I have no joy of my lordship among these my possessions; and ye are like to have heard hereof from your fathers, whosoever they be, for I have suffered much and let a house go to ruin that was stablished fair, and had in it much choice substance. I would that I had but a third part of those my riches, and dwelt in my halls, and that those men were yet safe, who perished of old in the wide land of Troy, far from Argos, the pasture-land of horses. Howbeit, though I bewail them all and sorrow oftentimes as I sit in our halls,—awhile indeed I satisfy my soul with lamentation, and then again I cease; for soon hath man enough of chill lamentation—yet for them all I make no such dole, despite my grief, as for one only, who causes me to loathe both sleep and meat, when I think upon him. For no one of the Achaeans toiled so greatly as Odysseus toiled and adventured himself: but to him it was to be but labour and trouble, and to me grief ever comfortless for his sake, so long he is afar, nor know we aught, whether he be alive or dead. Yea methinks they lament him, even that old Laertes and the constant Penelope and Telemachus, whom he left a child new-born in his house."

So spake he, and in the heart of Telemachus he stirred a yearning to lament his father; and at his father's name he let a tear fall from his eyelids to the ground, and held up his purple mantle with both his hands before his eyes. And Menelaus marked him and mused in his mind and his heart whether he should leave him to speak of his father, or first question him and prove him in every word.

While yet he pondered these things in his mind and in his heart, Helen came forth from her fragrant vaulted chamber, like Artemis of the golden arrows; and with her came Adraste and set for her the well-wrought chair, and Alcippe bare a rug of soft wool, and Phylo bare a silver basket which Alcandre gave her, the wife of Polybus, who dwelt in Thebes of Egypt, where is the chiefest store of wealth in the houses. He gave two silver baths to Menelaus, and tripods twain, and ten talents of gold. And besides all this, his wife bestowed on Helen lovely gifts; a golden distaff did she give, and a silver basket with wheels beneath, and the rims thereof were finished with gold. This it was that the handmaid Phylo bare and set beside her, filled with dressed yarn, and across it was laid a distaff charged with wool of violet blue. So Helen sat her down in the chair, and beneath was a footstool for the feet. And anon she spake to her lord and questioned him of each thing:

"Menelaus, fosterling of Zeus, know we now who these

Helen has apparently reformed.

men avow themselves to be that have come under our roof? Shall I dissemble or shall I speak the truth? Nay, I am minded to tell it. None, I say, have I ever yet seen so like another, man nor woman—wonder comes over me as I look on him—as this man is like the son of great-hearted Odysseus, Telemachus, whom he left a new-born child in his house, when for the sake of me, shameless woman that I was, ye Achaeans came up under Troy with bold war in your hearts."

And Menelaus of the fair hair answered her, saying: "Now I too, lady, mark the likeness even as thou tracest it. For such as these were his feet, such his hands, and the glances of his eyes, and his head, and his hair withal. Yea, and even now I was speaking of Odysseus, as I remembered him, of all his woeful travail for my sake; when, lo, he let fall a bitter tear beneath his brows, and held his purple cloak up before his eyes."

And Peisistratus, son of Nestor, answered him, saying: "Menelaus, son of Atreus, fosterling of Zeus, leader of the host, assuredly this is the son of that very man, even as thou sayest. But he is of a sober wit, and thinketh it shame in his heart as on this his first coming to make show of presumptuous words in the presence of thee, in whose voice we twain delight as in the voice of a god. Now Nestor of Gerenia, lord of chariots, sent me forth to be his guide on the way: for he desired to see thee that thou mightest put into his heart some word or work. For a son hath many griefs in his halls when his father is away, if perchance he hath none to stand by him. Even so it is now with Telemachus; his father is away, nor hath he others in the township to defend him from distress."

And Menelaus of the fair hair answered him, and said: "Lo now, in good truth there has come unto my house the son of a friend indeed, who for my sake endured many adventures. And I thought to welcome him on his coming more nobly than all the other Argives, if but Olympian Zeus, of the far-borne voice, had vouchsafed us a return over the sea in our swift ships,—that such a thing should be. And in

Argos I would have given him a city to dwell in, and established for him a house, and brought him forth from Ithaca with his substance and his son and all his people, making one city desolate of those that lie around, and are in mine own domain. Then ofttimes would we have held converse here, and naught would have parted us, the welcoming and the welcomed, ere the black cloud of death overshadowed us. Howsoever, the god himself, methinks, must have been jealous hereof, who from that hapless man alone cut off his returning."

So spake he, and in the hearts of all he stirred the desire of lamentation. She wept, even Argive Helen the daughter of Zeus, and Telemachus wept, and Menelaus the son of Atreus; nay, nor did the son of Nestor keep tearless eyes. For he bethought him in his heart of noble Antilochus, whom the glorious son of the bright Dawn had slain. Thinking upon him he spake winged words:

"Son of Atreus, the ancient Nestor in his own halls was ever wont to say that thou wert wise beyond man's wisdom, whensoever we made mention of thee and asked one another concerning thee. And now, if it be possible, be persuaded by me, who for one have no pleasure in weeping at supper time—the new-born day will right soon be upon us. Not indeed that I deem it blame at all to weep for any mortal who hath died and met his fate. Lo, this is now the only due we pay to miserable men, to cut the hair and let the tear fall from the cheek. For I too have a brother dead, nowise the meanest of the Argives, and thou art like to have known him, for as for me I never encountered him, never beheld him. But men say that Antilochus outdid all, being excellent in speed of foot and in the fight."

And Menelaus of the fair hair answered him, and said: "My friend, lo, thou hast said all that a wise man might say or do, yea, and an elder than thou;—for from such a sire too thou art sprung, wherefore thou dost even speak wisely. Right easily known is that man's seed, for whom Zeus weaves the skein of luck at bridal and at birth: even as now hath he granted prosperity to Nestor for ever for all his days, that he himself should grow into a smooth old age in his halls, and his sons moreover should be wise and the best of spearmen. But we will cease now the weeping which was erewhile made, and let us once more bethink us of our supper, and let them pour water over our hands. And again in the morning there will be tales for Telemachus and me to tell one to the other, even to the end."

So spake he, and Asphalion poured water over their hands, the ready squire of renowned Menelaus. And they put forth their hands upon the good cheer spread before them.

Then Helen, daughter of Zeus, turned to new thoughts. Presently she cast a drug into the wine whereof they drank, a drug to lull all pain and anger, and bring forgetfulness of every sorrow. Whoso should drink a draught thereof, when it is mingled in the bowl, on that day he would let no tear fall down his cheeks, not though his mother and his father died, not though men slew his brother or dear son with the sword before his face, and his own eyes beheld it. Medicines of such virtue and so helpful had the daughter of Zeus, which Polydamna, the wife of Thon, had given her, a woman of Egypt, where earth the grain-giver yields herbs in greatest plenty, many that are healing in the cup, and many baneful. There each man is a leech skilled beyond all human kind; yea, for they are of the race of Paeëon. Now after she had cast in the drug and bidden pour forth of the wine, she made answer once again, and spake unto her lord:

"Son of Atreus, Menelaus, fosterling of Zeus, and lo, ye sons of noble men, forasmuch as now to one and now to another Zeus gives good and evil, for to him all things are possible,—now, verily, sit ye down and feast in the halls, and take ye joy in the telling of tales, and I will tell you one that fits the time. Now all of them I could not tell or number, so many as were the adventures of Odysseus of the hardy heart; but, ah, what a deed was this he wrought and dared in his hardiness in the land of the Trojans, where ye Achaeans suffered affliction. He subdued his body with unseemly stripes, and a sorry covering he cast about his shoulders, and in the fashion of a servant he went down into the wide-

wayed city of the foemen, and he did himself in the guise of
another, a beggar, though in no wise such an one was he at
the ships of the Achaeans. In this semblance he passed into
the city of the Trojans, and they wist not who he was, and I
alone knew him in that guise, and I kept questioning him,
but in his subtlety he avoided me. But when at last I was
about washing him and anointing him with olive oil, and
had put on him raiment, and sworn a great oath not to reveal Odysseus amid the Trojans, ere he reached the swift
ships and the huts, even then he told me all the purpose of
the Achaeans. And after slaying many of the Trojans with
the long sword, he returned to the Argives and brought
back word again of all. Then the other Trojan women wept
aloud, but my soul was glad, for already my heart was turned
to go back again even to my home: and now at the last I
groaned for the blindness that Aphrodite gave me, when she
led me thither away from mine own country, forsaking my
child and my bridal chamber and my lord, that lacked not
aught whether for wisdom or yet for beauty."

And Menelaus of the fair hair answered her, saying: "All
this tale, lady, thou hast well and truly told. Ere now have I
learned the counsel and the thought of many heroes, and
travelled over many a land, but never yet have mine eyes beheld any such man of heart as was Odysseus; such another
deed as he wrought and dared in his hardiness even in the
shapen horse,[1] wherein sat all we chiefs of the Argives, bearing to the Trojans death and doom. Anon thou camest
thither, and sure some god must have bidden thee, who
wished to bring glory to the Trojans. Yea and godlike
Deiphobus went with thee on thy way. Thrice thou didst go
round about the hollow ambush and handle it, calling aloud
on the chiefs of the Argives by name, and making thy voice
like the voices of the wives of all the Argives. Now I and the
son of Tydeus and goodly Odysseus sat in the midst and

---

[1] This was the hollow wooden horse which the Achaeans had filled
with armed men and trapped the Trojans into dragging within the
city walls. At the appointed time, the Achaeans leaped from the horse
and the last fight began.

heard thy call; and verily we twain had a desire to start up and come forth or presently to answer from within; but Odysseus stayed and held us there, despite our eagerness. Then all the other sons of the Achaeans held their peace, but Anticlus alone was still minded to answer thee. Howbeit Odysseus firmly closed his mouth with strong hands, and so saved all the Achaeans, and held him until such time as Pallas Athene led thee back."

Then wise Telemachus answered him, and said: "Menelaus, son of Atreus, fosterling of Zeus, leader of the host, all the more grievous it is! for in no way did this courage ward from him pitiful destruction, not though his heart within him had been very iron. But come, bid us to bed, that forthwith we may take our joy of rest beneath the spell of sleep."

So spake he, and Argive Helen bade her handmaids set out bedsteads beneath the gallery, and fling on them fair purple blankets and spread coverlets above, and thereon lay thick mantles to be a clothing over all. So they went from the hall with torch in hand, and spread the beds, and the henchman led forth the guests. Thus they slept there in the vestibule of the house, the hero Telemachus and the splendid son of Nestor. But the son of Atreus slept, as his custom was, in the inmost chamber of the lofty house, and by him lay long-robed Helen, that fair lady.

Soon as early Dawn shone forth, the rosy-fingered, Menelaus of the loud war-shout gat him up from his bed and put on his raiment, and cast his sharp sword about his shoulder, and beneath his smooth feet bound his goodly sandals, and stept forth from his chamber, in presence like a god, and sat by Telemachus, and spake and hailed him:

"To what end hath thy need brought thee hither, hero Telemachus, unto fair Lacedaemon, over the broad back of the sea? Is it a matter of the common weal or of thine own? Herein tell me the plain truth."

Then wise Telemachus answered him, and said: "Menelaus, son of Atreus, fosterling of Zeus, leader of the host, I have come if perchance thou mayest tell me some tidings of my father. My dwelling is being devoured and my fat lands are ruined, and of unfriendly men my house is full,—who slaughter continually my thronging flocks, and my kine with trailing feet and shambling gait,—none other than the wooers of my mother, despiteful out of measure. So now am I come hither to thy knees, if haply thou art willing to tell me of his pitiful death, as one that saw it perchance with thine own eyes, or heard the story from some other wanderer; for his mother bare him to exceeding sorrow. And speak me no soft words in ruth or pity, but tell me plainly how thou didst get sight of him. Ah, I pray thee, if ever at all my father, good Odysseus, made promise to thee of word or work and fulfilled the same in the land of the Trojans, where ye Achaeans suffered affliction, these things, I pray thee, now remember and tell me truth."

Then in heavy displeasure spake to him Menelaus of the fair hair: "Out upon them, for truly in the bed of a brave-hearted man were they minded to lie, very cravens as they are! Even as when a hind hath couched her newborn fawns unweaned in a strong lion's lair, and searcheth out the mountain-knees and grassy hollows, seeking pasture, and afterward the lion cometh back to his bed, and sendeth forth unsightly death upon that pair, even so shall Odysseus send forth unsightly death upon the wooers. Would to our father Zeus and Athene and Apollo, would that in such might as when of old in stablished Lesbos he rose up and wrestled a match with Philomeleides and threw him mightily, and all the Achaeans rejoiced; would that in such strength Odysseus might consort with the wooers: then should they all have swift fate, and bitter wedlock! But for that whereof thou askest and entreatest me, be sure I will not swerve from the truth in aught that I say, nor deceive thee; but of all that the ancient one of the sea, whose speech is sooth, declared to me, not a word will I hide or keep from thee.

"In the river Aegyptus, though eager I was to press onward home, the gods they stayed me, for that I had not offered them the acceptable sacrifice of hecatombs, and the gods ever desired that men should be mindful of their commandments. Now there is an island in the wash of the waves over against Aegyptus, and men call it Pharos, within one day's voyage of a hollow ship, when shrill winds blow fair in her wake. And therein is a good haven, whence men launch the gallant ships into the deep when they have drawn a store of deep black water. There the gods held me twenty days, nor did the sea-winds ever show their breath, they that serve to waft ships over the broad back of the sea. And now would all our corn have been spent, and likewise the strength of the men, except some goddess had taken pity on me and saved me, Eidotheë, daughter of mighty Proteus, the ancient one of the sea. For most of all I moved her heart, when she met me wandering alone apart from my company, who were ever roaming round the isle, fishing with bent hooks, for hunger was gnawing at their belly. So she stood by, and spake and uttered her voice, saying:

" 'Art thou so very foolish, stranger, and feeble-witted, or art thou wilfully remiss, and hast pleasure in suffering? So long time art thou holden in the isle and canst find no issue therefrom, while the heart of thy company faileth within them?'

"Even so she spake, and I answered her saying: 'I will speak forth, what goddess soever thou art, and tell thee that in no wise am I holden here by mine own will, but it needs must be that I have sinned against the deathless gods, who keep the wide heaven. Howbeit, do thou tell me—for the gods know all things—which of the immortals it is that binds me here and hath hindered me from my way, and declare as touching my returning how I may go over the teeming deep.'

"So I spake, and straightway the fair goddess made answer: 'Yea now, sir, I will plainly tell thee all. Hither resorteth that ancient one of the sea, whose speech is sooth, the deathless Egyptian Proteus, who knows the depths of every sea, and is the thrall of Poseidon, and who, they say, is my father that begat me. If thou couldst but lay an ambush and catch him, he will surely declare to thee the way and the measure of thy path, and will tell thee of thy returning, how thou mayest go over the teeming deep. Yea, and he will show thee, O fosterling of Zeus, if thou wilt, what good thing and what evil hath been wrought in thy halls, whilst thou hast been faring this long and grievous way.'

"So she spake, but I answered and said unto her: 'Devise now thyself the ambush to take this ancient one divine, lest by any chance he see me first, or know of my coming, and avoid me. For a god is hard for mortal man to quell.'

"So spake I, and straightway the fair goddess made answer: 'Yea now, sir, I will plainly tell thee all. So often as the sun in his course stands high in mid heaven, then forth from the brine comes the ancient one of the sea, whose speech is sooth, before the breath of the West Wind he comes, and the sea's dark ripple covers him. And when he is got forth, he lies down to sleep in the hollow of the caves. And around him the seals, the brood of the fair daughter of the brine, sleep all in a flock, stolen forth from the grey sea water, and bitter is the scent they breathe of the deeps of the salt sea. There will I lead thee at the breaking of the day, and couch you all orderly; so do thou choose diligently three of thy company, the best thou hast in thy decked ships. And I will tell thee all the magic arts of that old man. First, he will number the seals and go over them; but when he has told their tale and beheld them, he will lay him down in the midst, as a shepherd 'mid the sheep of his flock. So soon as ever ye shall see him couched, even then mind you of your might and strength, and hold him there, despite his eagerness and striving to be free. And he will make assay, and take all manner of shapes of things that creep upon the earth, of water likewise, and of fierce fire burning. But do ye grasp him steadfastly and press him yet the more, and at length when he questions thee in his proper shape, as he was when first ye saw him laid to rest, then, hero, hold thy strong hands, and let the ancient one go free, and ask him which of the gods is hard upon thee, and as touching thy returning, how thou mayest go over the teeming deep.'

"Therewith she dived beneath the heaving sea, but I betook me to the ships where they stood in the sand, and my heart was darkly troubled as I went. But after I had come down to the ship and to the sea, and we had made ready our supper and immortal night had come on, then did we lay us to rest upon the sea-beach. So soon as early Dawn shone forth, the rosy-fingered, in that hour I walked by the shore of the wide-wayed sea, praying instantly to the gods; and I took with me three of my company, in whom I trusted most for every enterprise.

"Meanwhile, so it was that she had plunged into the broad bosom of the sea, and had brought from the deep the skins of four sea-calves, and all were newly flayed, for she was minded to lay a snare for her father. She scooped lairs on the sea-sand, and sat awaiting us, and we drew very nigh her, and she made us all lie down in order, and cast a skin over each. There would our ambush have been most terrible, for the deadly stench of the sea-bred seals distressed us sore: nay, who would lay him down by a beast of the sea? But herself she wrought deliverance, and devised a great comfort. She took ambrosia of a very sweet savour, and set it beneath each man's nostril, and did away with the stench of the beast. So all the morning we waited with steadfast heart, and the seals came forth in troops from the brine, and then they couched them all orderly by the sea-beach. And at high day the ancient one came forth from out of the brine, and found his fatted seals, yea and he went along their line and numbered them; and first among the sea-beasts he reckoned us, and guessed not that there was guile, and afterward he too laid him down. Then we rushed upon him with a cry, and cast our hands about him, nor did that ancient one forget his cunning. Now behold, at the first he turned into a bearded lion, and thereafter into a snake, and a pard, and a huge boar; then he took the shape of running water, and of a tall and flowering tree. We the while held him close with steadfast heart. But when now that ancient one of the magic arts was aweary, then at last he questioned me and spake unto me, saying:

" 'Which of the gods was it, son of Atreus, that aided thee with his counsel, that thou mightest waylay and take me perforce? What wouldest thou thereby?'

"Even so he spake, but I answered him saying: 'Old man,

thou knowest all, wherefore dost thou question me thereof with crooked words? For lo, I am holden long time in this isle, neither can I find any issue therefrom, and my heart faileth within me. Howbeit do thou tell me—for the gods know all things—which of the immortals it is that bindeth me here, and hath hindered me from my way; and declare as touching my returning, how I may go over the teeming deep.'

"Even so I spake, and he straightway answered me saying: 'Nay, surely thou shouldest have done goodly sacrifice to Zeus and the other gods ere thine embarking, that with most speed thou mightest reach thy country, sailing over the wine-dark deep. For it is not thy fate to see thy friends, and come to thy stablished house and thine own country, till thou hast passed yet again within the waters of Aegyptus, the heaven-fed stream, and offered holy hecatombs to the deathless gods who keep the wide heaven. So shall the gods grant thee the path which thou desirest.'

"So spake he, but my spirit within me was broken, for that he bade me again to go to Aegyptus over the misty deep, a long and grievous way.

"Yet even so I answered him saying: 'Old man, all this will I do, according to thy word. But come, declare me this, and tell it all plainly. Did all those Achaeans return safe with their ships, all whom Nestor and I left as we went from Troy, or perished any by a shameful death aboard his own ship, or in the arms of his friends, after he had wound up the clew of war?'

"So spake I, and anon he answered me saying: 'Son of Atreus, why dost thou straitly question me hereof? Nay, it is not for thy good to know or learn my thought; for I tell thee thou shalt not long be tearless, when thou hast heard it all aright. For many of these were taken, and many were left; but two only of the leaders of the mail-coated Achaeans perished in returning; as for the battle, thou thyself wast there. And one methinks is yet alive, and is holden on the wide deep. Aias in truth was smitten in the midst of his ships of the long oars. Poseidon at first brought him nigh to

Gyrae, to the mighty rocks, and delivered him from the sea. And so would he have fled his doom, albeit hated by Athene, had he not let a proud word fall in the fatal darkening of his heart. He said that in the gods' despite he had escaped the great gulf of the sea; and Poseidon heard his loud boasting, and presently caught up his trident into his strong hands, and smote the rock Gyraean and cleft it in twain. And the one part abode in his place, but the other fell into the sea, the broken piece whereon Aias sat at the first, when his heart was darkened. And the rock bore him down into the vast and heaving deep; so there he perished when he had drunk of the salt sea water. But thy brother verily escaped the fates and avoided them in his hollow ships, for queen Hera saved him. But now when he was like soon to reach the steep mount of Malea, lo, the storm wind snatched him away and bore him over the teeming deep, making great moan, to the border of the country where of old Thyestes dwelt, but now Aegisthus abode there, the son of Thyestes. But when thence too there showed a good prospect of safe returning, and the gods changed the wind to a fair gale, and they had reached home, then verily did Agamemnon set foot with joy upon his country's soil, and as he touched his own land he kissed it, and many were the hot tears he let fall, for he saw his land and was glad. And it was so that the watchman spied him from his tower, the watchman whom crafty Aegisthus had led and posted there, promising him for a reward two talents of gold. Now he kept watch for the space of a year, lest Agamemnon should pass by him when he looked not, and mind him of his wild prowess. So he went to the house to bear the tidings to the shepherd of the people. And straightway Aegisthus contrived a cunning treason. He chose out twenty of the best men in the township, and set an ambush, and on the further side of the hall he commanded to prepare a feast. Then with chariot and horse he went to bid to the feast Agamemnon, shepherd of the people; but caitiff thoughts were in his heart. He brought him up to his house, all unwitting of his doom, and when he had feasted him slew him, as one slayeth an ox at the stall.

And none of the company of Atreides that were of his following were left, nor any of the men of Aegisthus, but they were all killed in the halls.'

"So spake he, and my spirit within me was broken, and I wept as I sat upon the sand, nor was I minded any more to live and to see the light of the sun. But when I had taken my fill of weeping and grovelling on the ground, then spake the ancient one of the sea, whose speech is sooth:

Murder of Agamemnon by Aegisthus,
assisted by Clytemnestra.

PAINTING FROM AN HYDRIA.
(BOLOGNA MUSEUM)

" 'No more, son of Atreus, hold this long weeping without cease, for we shall find no help therein. Rather with all haste make essay that so thou mayest come to thine own country. For either thou shalt find Aegisthus yet alive, or it may be Orestes was beforehand with thee and slew him; so mayest thou chance upon his funeral feast.'

"So he spake, and my heart and lordly soul again were comforted for all my sorrows, and I uttered my voice and I spake to him winged words:

" 'Their fate I now know; but tell me of the third; who is it that is yet living and holden on the wide deep, or perchance is dead? and fain would I hear despite my sorrow.'

"So spake I, and straightway he answered, and said: 'It is the son of Laertes, whose dwelling is in Ithaca; and I saw him in an island shedding big tears in the halls of the nymph Calypso, who holds him there perforce; so he may not come to his own country, for he has by him no ships with oars, and no companions to send him on his way over the broad back of the sea. But thou, Menelaus, son of Zeus, art not ordained to die and meet thy fate in Argos, the pasture-land of horses, but the deathless gods will convey thee to the Elysian plain [2] and the world's end, where is Rhadamanthus of the fair hair, where life is easiest for men. No snow is there, nor yet great storm, nor any rain; but always ocean sendeth forth the breeze of the shrill West to blow cool on men: yea, for thou hast Helen to wife, and thereby they deem thee to be son of Zeus.'

"So spake he, and plunged into the heaving sea; but I betook me to the ships with my godlike company, and my heart was darkly troubled as I went. Now after I had come down to the ship and to the sea, and had made ready our supper, and immortal night had come on, then did we lay us to rest upon the sea-beach. So soon as early Dawn shone forth, the rosy-fingered, first of all we drew down our ships to the fair salt sea and placed the masts and the sails in the gallant ships, and the crew too climbed on board, and sat upon the benches and smote the grey sea water with their oars. Then back I went to the waters of Aegyptus, the heaven-fed stream, and there I moored the ships and offered the acceptable sacrifice of hecatombs. So when I had appeased the anger of the everlasting gods, I piled a barrow to Agamemnon, that his fame might never be quenched. So having fulfilled all, I set out for home, and the deathless gods gave me a fair wind, and brought me swiftly to mine own

---

[2] Also known as the Islands of the Blest, or Elysium, located vaguely in the West. Rhadamanthus, son of Zeus and Europa, became a judge of the dead and ruler of Elysium.

dear country. But lo, now tarry in my halls till it shall be the eleventh day hence or the twelfth. Then will I send thee with all honour on thy way, and give thee splendid gifts, three horses and a polished car; and moreover I will give thee a goodly chalice, that thou mayest pour forth before the deathless gods, and be mindful of me all the days of thy life."

Then wise Telemachus answered him, saying: "Son of Atreus, nay, hold me not long time here. Yea even for a year would I be content to sit by thee, and no desire for home or parents would come upon me; for I take wondrous pleasure in thy tales and talk. But already my company wearieth in fair Pylos, and yet thou art keeping me long time here. And whatsoever gift thou wouldest give me, let it be a thing to treasure; but horses I will take none to Ithaca, but leave them here to grace thine own house, for thou art lord of a wide plain wherein is lotus great plenty, and therein is spear-reed and wheat and rye, and white and spreading barley. In Ithaca there are no wide courses, nor meadow land at all. It is a pasture-land of goats, and more pleasant in my sight than one that pastureth horses; for of the isles that lie and lean upon the sea, none are fit for the driving of horses, or rich in meadow land, and least of all is Ithaca."

So spake he, and Menelaus of the loud war-cry smiled, and caressed him with his hand, and spake and hailed him:

"Thou art of gentle blood, dear child, so gentle the words thou speakest. Therefore I will make exchange of the presents, as I may. Of the gifts, such as are treasures stored in my house, I will give thee the goodliest and greatest of price. I will give thee a mixing bowl beautifully wrought; it is all of silver, and the lips thereof are finished with gold, the work of Hephaestus; and the hero Phaedimus, the king of the Sidonians, gave it me, when his house sheltered me on my coming thither, and to thee now would I give it."

Even so they spake one to another, while the guests came to the palace of the divine king. They drave their sheep, and brought wine that maketh glad the heart of man; and their wives with fair attire sent them wheaten bread. Thus were these men preparing the feast in the halls.

❡ *Meantime, in Ithaca, the suitors hear with anger of the departure of Telemachus and send a ship and twenty men to lie in wait in the strait between Ithaca and Samos to kill him on his way home.*

Penelope, learning of her son's departure and the suitors' plan, mourns for Telemachus until comforted by a dream sent by Athena.

V

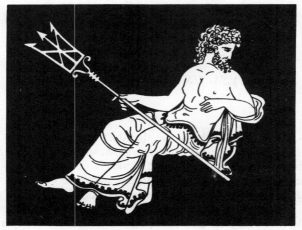

Poseidon Threatening Odysseus with his Wrath.

Calypso's Island

❰ Hermes is sent to Calypso to bid her aid Odysseus escape from her island and make his way to his home and wife, for whom he ceaselessly mourns. Calypso, though unwilling, bows to the commands of Zeus and helps Odysseus to build and equip a raft. On the eighteenth day after leaving her island, he comes in sight of the land of the Phaeacians, but Poseidon, returning from the Ethiopians, looses the winds upon him and wrecks his raft. The goddess Ino rises from the sea to give Odysseus her veil, which he winds around his breast. For two days and nights it upholds him as he swims, until finally Poseidon wearies of tormenting him. Athena brings a calm, and with great difficulty Odysseus gains the shore. He seeks safety by hiding himself under some dry leaves in a little wood. There he sleeps.

VI

The Phaeacians (handwritten annotation)

Odysseus Meets Nausicaa

S O THERE he lay asleep, the steadfast goodly Odysseus, fordone with toil and drowsiness. Meanwhile Athene went to the land and the city of the Phaeacians, who of old, upon a time, dwelt in spacious Hypereia; near the Cyclopes they dwelt, men exceeding proud, who harried them continually, being mightier than they. Thence the godlike Nausithous made them depart, and he carried them away, and planted them in Scheria, far off from men that live by bread. And he drew a wall around the town, and builded houses and made temples for the gods and meted out the fields. Howbeit ere this had he been stricken by fate, and had gone down to the house of Hades, and now Alcinous was reigning, with wisdom granted by the gods. To his house went the goddess, grey-eyed Athene, devising a return for the great-hearted Odysseus. She betook her to the rich-wrought bower, wherein was sleeping a maiden like to the gods in form and comeliness, Nausicaa, the daughter of Alcinous, high of heart. Beside her on either hand of the pillars of the door were two handmaids, dowered with beauty from the Graces, and the shining doors were shut.

But the goddess, fleet as the breath of the wind, swept towards the couch of the maiden, and stood above her head, and spake to her in the semblance of the daughter of a famous seafarer, Dymas, a girl of like age with Nausicaa, who had found grace in her sight. In her shape the greyeyed Athene spake to the princess, saying:

"Nausicaa, how hath thy mother so heedless a maiden to her daughter? Lo, thou hast shining raiment that lies by thee uncared for, and thy marriage-day is near at hand, when thou thyself must needs go beautifully clad, and have garments to give to them who shall lead thee to the house of the bride-groom! And, behold, these are the things whence a good report goes abroad among men, wherein a father and lady

Nausicaa Leaving to Wash her Linen in the River.
PAINTING FROM AN AMPHORA.
(MUNICH PINAKOTHEK)

mother take delight. But come, let us arise and go a-washing with the breaking of the day, and I will follow with thee to be thy mate in the toil, that without delay thou mayst get thee ready, since truly thou art not long to be a maiden. Lo, already they are wooing thee, the noblest youths of all the Phaeacians, among that people whence thou thyself dost draw thy lineage. So come, beseech thy noble father betimes in the morning to furnish thee with mules and a wain to carry the men's raiment, and the robes, and the shining cov-erlets. Yea and for thyself it is seemlier far to go thus than on foot, for the places where we must wash are a great way off the town."

So spake the grey-eyed Athene, and departed to Olympus, where, as they say, is the seat of the gods that standeth fast for ever. Not by winds is it shaken, nor ever wet with rain, nor doth the snow come nigh thereto, but most clear air is spread about it cloudless, and the white light floats over it. Therein the blessed gods are glad for all their days, and thither Athene went when she had shown forth all to the maiden.

Anon came the throned Dawn, and awakened Nausicaa of the fair robes, who straightway marvelled on the dream, and went through the halls to tell her parents, her father dear and her mother. And she found them within, her mother sitting by the hearth with the women her handmaids, spinning yarn of sea-purple stain, but her father she met as he was going forth to the renowned kings in their council, whither the noble Phaeacians called him. Standing close by her dear father she spake, saying: "Father, dear, couldst thou not lend me a high waggon with strong wheels, that I may take the goodly raiment to the river to wash, so much as I have lying soiled? Yea and it is seemly that thou thyself, when thou art with the princes in council, shouldest have fresh raiment to wear. Also, there are five dear sons of thine in the halls, two married, but three are lusty bachelors, and these are always eager for new-washen garments wherein to go to the dances: for all these things have I taken thought."

This she said, because she was ashamed to speak of glad marriage to her father; but he saw all and answered, saying:

"Neither the mules nor aught else do I grudge thee, my child. Go thy ways, and the thralls shall get thee ready a high waggon with good wheels, and fitted with an upper frame."

Therewith he called to his men, and they gave ear, and without the palace they made ready the smooth-running mule-wain, and led the mules beneath the yoke, and harnessed them under the car, while the maiden brought forth from her bower the shining raiment. This she stored in the polished car, and her mother filled a basket with all manner of food to the heart's desire, dainties too she set therein, and she poured wine into a goat-skin bottle, while Nausicaa climbed into the wain. And her mother gave her soft olive oil also in a golden cruse, that she and her maidens might anoint themselves after the bath. Then Nausicaa took the whip and the shining reins, and touched the mules to start them; then there was a clatter of hoofs, and on they strained without flagging, with their load of the raiment and the maiden. Not alone did she go, for her attendants followed with her.

Now when they were come to the beautiful stream of the river, where truly were the unfailing cisterns, and bright water welled up free from beneath, and flowed past, enough to wash the foulest garments clean, there the girls unharnessed the mules from under the chariot, and turning them loose they drove them along the banks of the eddying river to graze on the honey-sweet clover. Then they took the garments from the wain, in their hands, and bore them to the black water, and briskly trod them down in the trenches, in busy rivalry. Now when they had washed and cleansed all the stains, they spread all out in order along the shore of the deep, even where the sea, in beating on the coast, washed the pebbles clean. Then having bathed and anointed them well with olive oil, they took their mid-day meal on the river's banks, waiting till the clothes should dry in the brightness of the sun. Anon, when they were satisfied with food, the maidens and the princess, they fell to playing at ball, casting away their headgear, and among them Nausicaa of the white arms began the song. And even as Artemis, the archer, moveth down the mountain, either along the ridges of lofty Taygetus or Erymanthus, taking her pastime in the chase of boars and swift deer, and with her the wild wood-nymphs disport themselves, the daughters of Zeus, lord of the aegis, and Artemis is glad at heart, while high over all she rears her head and brows, and easily may she be known,—but all are fair; even so the girl unwed outshone her maiden company.

But when now she was about going homewards, after yoking the mules and folding up the goodly raiment, then grey-eyed Athene turned to other thoughts, that so Odysseus might awake, and see the lovely maiden, who should be his guide to the city of the Phaeacian men. So then the princess threw the ball at one of her company; she missed the girl, and cast the ball into the deep eddying current, whereat they all raised a piercing cry. Then the goodly Odysseus awoke and sat up, pondering in his heart and spirit:

"Woe is me! to what men's land am I come now? say, are they froward, and wild, and unjust, or are they hospitable, and of God-fearing mind? How shrill a cry of maidens rings round me, of the nymphs that hold the steep hill-tops, and the river-springs, and the grassy water-meadows! It must be, methinks, that I am near men of human speech. Go to, I myself will make trial and see."

Therewith the goodly Odysseus crept out from under the coppice, having broken with his strong hand a leafy bough from the thick wood, to hold athwart his body, that it might hide his nakedness withal. And forth he sallied like a lion mountain-bred, trusting in his strength, who fares out blown and rained upon, with flaming eyes; amid the kine he goes or amid the sheep or in the track of the wild deer; yea, his belly bids him go even to the good homestead to make assay upon the flocks. Even so Odysseus was fain to draw nigh to the fair-tressed maidens, all naked as he was, such need had come upon him. But he was terrible in their eyes, being marred with the salt sea foam, and they fled cowering here and there about the jutting spits of shore. And the daughter of Alcinous alone stood firm, for Athene gave her courage of heart, and took all trembling from her limbs. So she halted and confronted him, and Odysseus considered whether he should clasp the knees of the lovely maiden, and so make his prayer, or should stand as he was, apart, and beseech her with smooth words, if haply she might show him the town, and give him raiment. And as he thought within himself, it seemed better to stand apart, and beseech her with smooth words, lest the maiden should be angered with him if he touched her knees: so straightway he spake a sweet and cunning word:

"I supplicate thee, O queen, whether thou art a goddess or a mortal! If indeed thou art a goddess of them that keep the wide heaven; to Artemis, then, the daughter of great Zeus, I mainly liken thee, for beauty and stature and shapeliness. But if thou art one of the daughters of men who dwell on earth, thrice blessed are thy father and thy lady mother, and thrice blessed thy brethren. Surely their souls ever glow with gladness for thy sake, each time they see thee entering the dance, so fair a flower of maidens. But he is of heart the most blessed beyond all other who shall prevail with gifts of wooing, and lead thee to his home. Never have mine eyes beheld such an one among mortals, neither man nor woman; great awe comes upon me as I look on thee. Yet in Delos once I saw as goodly a thing: a young sapling of a palm tree springing by the altar of Apollo. For thither too I went, and much people with me, on that path where my sore troubles were to be. Yea, and when I looked thereupon, long time I marvelled in spirit,—for never grew there yet so goodly a shoot from ground,—even in such wise as I wonder at thee, lady, and am astonied and do greatly fear to touch thy knees, though grievous sorrow is upon me. Yesterday, on the twentieth day, I escaped from the wine-dark deep, but all that time continually the wave bare me, and the vehement winds drave, from the isle Ogygia. And now some god has cast me on this shore, that here too, methinks, some evil may betide me; for I trow not that trouble will cease; the gods ere that time will yet bring many a thing to pass. But, queen, have pity on me, for after many trials and sore to thee first of all am I come, and of the other folk, who hold this city and land, I know no man. Nay show me the town, give me an old garment to cast about me, if thou hadst, when thou camest here, any wrapper for the linen. And may the gods grant thee all thy heart's desire: a husband and a home, and a mind at one with his may they give—a good gift, for there is nothing mightier and nobler than when man and wife are of one heart and mind in a house, a grief to their foes, and to their friends great joy, but their own hearts know it best."

Then Nausicaa of the white arms answered him, and said: "Stranger, forasmuch as thou seemest no evil man nor foolish

—and it is Olympian Zeus himself that giveth weal to men, to the good and to the evil, to each one as he will, and this thy lot doubtless is of him, and so thou must in anywise endure it:—and now, since thou hast come to our city and our land, thou shalt not lack raiment, nor aught else that is the due of a hapless suppliant, when he has met them who can befriend him. And I will show thee the town, and name the name of the people. The Phaeacians hold this city and land, and I am the daughter of Alcinous, great of heart, on whom all the might and force of the Phaeacians depend."

Thus she spake, and called to her maidens of the fair tresses: "Halt, my maidens, whither flee ye at the sight of a man? Ye surely do not take him for an enemy? That mortal breathes not, and never will be born, who shall come with war to the land of the Phaeacians, for they are very dear to the gods. Far apart we live in the wash of the waves, the outermost of men, and no other mortals are conversant with us. Nay, but this man is some helpless one come hither in his wanderings, whom now we must kindly entreat, for all strangers and beggars are from Zeus, and a little gift is dear to them. So, my maidens, give the stranger meat and drink, and bathe him in the river, where withal is a shelter from the winds."

So she spake, but they had halted and called each to the other, and they brought Odysseus to the sheltered place, and made him sit down, as Nausicaa bade them, the daughter of Alcinous, high of heart. Beside him they laid a mantle, and a doublet for raiment, and gave him soft olive oil in the golden cruse, and bade him wash in the streams of the river. Then goodly Odysseus spake among the maidens, saying: "I pray you stand thus apart, while I myself wash the brine from my shoulders, and anoint me with olive oil, for truly oil is long a stranger to my skin. But in your sight I will not bathe, for I am ashamed to make me naked in the company of fair-tressed maidens."

Then they went apart and told all to their lady. But with the river water the goodly Odysseus washed from his skin the salt scurf that covered his back and broad shoulders, and from his head he wiped the crusted brine of the barren sea. But when he had washed his whole body, and anointed him with olive oil, and had clad himself in the raiment that the unwedded maiden gave him, then Athene, the daughter of Zeus, made him greater and more mighty to behold, and from his head caused deep curling locks to flow, like the hyacinth flower. And as when some skilful man overlays gold upon silver—one that Hephaestus and Pallas Athene have taught all manner of craft, and full of grace is his handiwork —even so did Athene shed grace about his head and shoulders.

Then to the shore of the sea went Odysseus apart, and sat down, glowing in beauty and grace, and the princess marvelled at him, and spake among her fair-tressed maidens, saying:

"Listen, my white-armed maidens, and I will say somewhat. Not without the will of all the gods who hold Olympus hath this man come among the godlike Phaeacians. Erewhile he seemed to me uncomely, but now he is like the gods that keep the wide heaven. Would that such an one might be called my husband, dwelling here, and that it might please him here to abide! But come, my maidens, give the stranger meat and drink."

Thus she spake, and they gave ready ear and hearkened, and set beside Odysseus meat and drink, and the steadfast goodly Odysseus did eat and drink eagerly, for it was long since he had tasted food.

Now Nausicaa of the white arms had another thought. She folded the raiment and stored it in the goodly wain, and yoked the mules strong of hoof, and herself climbed into the car. Then she called on Odysseus, and spake and hailed him: "Up now, stranger, and rouse thee to go to the city, that I may convey thee to the house of my wise father, where, I promise thee, thou shalt get knowledge of all the noblest of the Phaeacians. But do thou even as I tell thee, and thou seemest a discreet man enough. So long as we are passing along the fields and farms of men, do thou fare quickly with the maidens behind the mules and the chariot, and I

will lead the way. But when we set foot within the city,—
whereby goes a high wall with towers, and there is a fair
haven on either side of the town, and narrow is the entrance,
and curved ships are drawn up on either hand of the mole,
for all the folk have stations for their vessels, each man one
for himself. And there is the place of assembly about the
goodly temple of Poseidon, furnished with heavy stones,
deep bedded in the earth. There men look to the gear of
the black ships, hawsers and sails, and there they fine down
the oars. For the Phaeacians care not for bow nor quiver,
but for masts, and oars of ships, and gallant barques, wherein
rejoicing they cross the grey sea. Their ungracious speech it
is that I would avoid, lest some man afterward rebuke me,
and there are but too many insolent folk among the people.
And some one of the baser sort might meet me and say:
'Who is this that goes with Nausicaa, this tall and goodly
stranger? Where found she him? Her husband he will be, her
very own. Either she has taken in some shipwrecked wanderer of strange men,—for no men dwell near us; or some
god has come in answer to her instant prayer; from heaven
has he descended, and will have her to wife for evermore.
Better so, if herself she has ranged abroad and found a lord
from a strange land, for verily she holds in no regard the
Phaeacians here in this country, the many men and noble
who are her wooers.' So will they speak, and this would turn
to my reproach. Yea, and I myself would think it blame of
another maiden who did such things in despite of her
friends, her father and mother being still alive, and was conversant with men before the day of open wedlock. But,
stranger, heed well what I say, that as soon as may be thou
mayest gain at my father's hands an escort and a safe return. Thou shalt find a fair grove of Athene, a poplar grove
near the road, and a spring wells forth therein, and a
meadow lies all around. There is my father's demesne, and
his fruitful close, within the sound of a man's shout from the
city. Sit thee down there and wait until such time as we
may have come into the city, and reached the house of my
father. But when thou deemest that we are got to the palace,

then go up to the city of the Phaeacians, and ask for the house of my father Alcinous, high of heart. It is easily known, and a young child could be thy guide, for nowise like it are builded the houses of the Phaeacians, so goodly is the palace of the hero Alcinous. But when thou art within the shadow of the halls and the court, pass quickly through the great chamber, till thou comest to my mother, who sits at the hearth in the light of the fire, weaving yarn of sea-purple stain, a wonder to behold. Her chair is leaned against a pillar, and her maidens sit behind her. And there my father's throne leans close to hers, wherein he sits and drinks his wine, like an immortal. Pass thou by him, and cast thy hands about my mother's knees, that thou mayest see quickly and with joy the day of thy returning, even if thou art from a very far country. If but her heart be kindly disposed toward thee, then is there hope that thou shalt see thy friends, and come to thy well-builded house, and to thine own country."

She spake, and smote the mules with the shining whip, and quickly they left behind them the streams of the river. And well they trotted and well they paced, and she took heed to drive in such wise that the maidens and Odysseus might follow on foot, and cunningly she plied the lash. Then the sun set, and they came to the famous grove, the sacred place of Athene; so there the goodly Odysseus sat him down. Then straightway he prayed to the daughter of mighty Zeus: "Listen to me, child of Zeus, lord of the aegis, unwearied maiden; hear me even now, since before thou heardest not when I was smitten on the sea, when the renowned Earth-shaker smote me. Grant me to come to the Phaeacians as one dear, and worthy of pity."

So he spake in prayer, and Pallas Athene heard him; but she did not yet appear to him face to face, for she had regard unto her father's brother, who furiously raged against the godlike Odysseus, till he should come to his own country.

VII

Listening to the Tales of Odysseus.
PAINTING FROM AN AMPHORA.
(VATICAN MUSEUM)

The Palace of Alcinous

⟪ Odysseus, with the help of Athene, reaches the hall of
Alcinous safely. He is astonished by the beauty of the brazen
walls, the golden doors and silver door-posts. Within is marvellous handwork from the looms of the Phaeacian women. In the
courtyards are trees that never fail of their fruit.

Going into the hall, Odysseus clasps the knees of Queen
Arete and begs her aid. He is welcomed, promised convoy to his
own land by Alcinous, and feasted. He does not at this time
reveal his name.

The others having left the hall, Odysseus tells Alcinous and
Arete part of his story, beginning with his sojourn on Calypso's
island and ending with his meeting with Nausicaa. Alcinous re-
peats his promise of aid, after which they sleep.

VIII

Games in Phaeacia

❡ The next morning, Alcinous tells the Phaeacians his plans for helping the stranger to return to his home. But first there is entertainment: feasting and the song of the minstrel, Demodocus. Seeing Odysseus weep during a song which tells of his own deeds, Alcinous suggests divers games. There follow various athletic contests: the foot race, wrestling, leaping, weight-throwing, and boxing.

Odysseus is challenged by Laodamas, son of Alcinous: "Come try thy skill in sports . . . for there is no greater glory for a man while yet he lives, than that which he achieves by hand and foot." Still overcome by his sorrow, Odysseus refuses until he is stirred by the taunts of Euryalus, whereupon he shows his strength by throwing a weight far beyond the marks of all the others.

There is a marvelous dance by boys in their first bloom as Demodocus plays.

Now as the minstrel touched the lyre, he lifted up his voice in sweet song, and he sang of the love of Ares and Aphrodite, of the fair crown, how at the first they lay together in the house of Hephaestus privily; and Ares gave her many gifts, and dishonoured the marriage bed of the lord Hephaestus. And anon there came to him one to report the thing, even Helios, that had seen them at their pastime. Now when Hephaestus heard the bitter tidings, he went his way to the forge, devising evil in the deep of his heart, and set the great anvil on the stithy, and wrought fetters that none might snap or loosen, that the lovers might there un-moveably remain. Now when he had forged the crafty net in his anger against Ares, he went on his way to the chamber where his marriage bed was set out, and strewed his snares all about the posts of the bed, and many too were hung aloft from the main beam, subtle as spiders' webs, so that none might see them, even of the blessed gods so cunningly were they forged. Now after he had done winding the snare about

Games Organized by Alcinous on the Agora.

PAINTING FROM A KYLIX BY EUPHRONIUS.
(BOURGUIGNON COLL., NAPLES)

the bed, he made as though he would go to Lemnos, that stablished castle, and this was far the dearest of all lands in his sight. But Ares of the golden rein kept no blind watch, what time he saw Hephaestus, the famed craftsman, depart afar. So he went on his way to the house of renowned Hephaestus, eager for the love of crowned Aphrodite. Now she was but newly come from her sire, the mighty Zeus, and as it chanced had sat her down; and Ares entered the house, and clasped her hand, and spake, and hailed her:

"Come, my beloved, let us to bed, and take our pleasure of love, for Hephaestus is no longer among his own people;

methinks he is already gone to Lemnos, to the Sintians, men of savage speech."

So spake he, and a glad thing it seemed to her to lie with him. So they twain went to the couch, and laid them to sleep, and around them clung the cunning bonds of skilled Hephaestus, so that they could not move nor raise a limb. Then at the last they knew it, when there was no way to flee. Now the famous god of the strong arms drew near to them, having turned him back ere he reached the land of Lemnos. For Helios had kept watch, and told him all. So heavy at heart he went his way to his house, and stood at the entering in of the gate, and wild rage gat hold of him, and he cried terribly, and shouted to all the gods:

"Father Zeus, and ye other blessed gods, that live for ever, come hither, that ye may see a mirthful thing and a cruel, for that Aphrodite, daughter of Zeus, ever dishonours me by reason of my lameness, and sets her heart on Ares the destroyer, because he is fair and straight of limb, but as for me, feeble was I born. Howbeit, there is none to blame but my father and mother,—would they had never begotten me! But now shall ye see where these have gone up into my bed, and sleep together in love; and I am troubled at the sight. Yet, methinks, they will not care to lie thus even for a little while longer, despite their great love. Soon will they have no desire to sleep together, but the snare and the bond shall hold them, till her sire give back to me the gifts of wooing, one and all, those that I bestowed upon him for the hand of his shameless girl; for that his daughter is fair, but without discretion."

So spake he; and lo, the gods gathered together to the house of the brazen floor. Poseidon came, the girdler of the earth, and Hermes came, the bringer of luck, and prince Apollo came, the archer. But the lady goddesses abode each within her house for shame. So the gods, the givers of good things, stood in the porch: and laughter unquenchable arose among the blessed gods, as they beheld the sleight of cunning Hephaestus. And thus would one speak, looking to his neighbour.

"Ill deed, ill speed! The slow catcheth the swift! Lo, how Hephaestus, slow as he is, hath overtaken Ares, albeit he is the swiftest of the gods that hold Olympus, by his craft hath he taken him despite his lameness; wherefore surely Ares oweth the fine of the adulterer." Thus they spake one to the other. But the lord Apollo, son of Zeus, spake to Hermes:

"Hermes, son of Zeus, messenger and giver of good things, wouldst thou be fain, aye, pressed by strong bonds though it might be, to lie on the couch by golden Aphrodite?"

Then the messenger, the slayer of Argos, answered him: "I would that this might be, Apollo, my prince of archery! So might thrice as many bonds innumerable encompass me about, and all ye gods be looking on and all the goddesses, yet would I lie by golden Aphrodite."

So spake he, and laughter rose among the deathless gods. Howbeit Poseidon laughed not, but was instant with Hephaestus, the renowned artificer, to loose the bonds of Ares: and he uttered his voice, and spake to him winged words:

"Loose him, I pray thee, and I promise even as thou biddest me, that he shall himself pay all fair forfeit in the presence of the deathless gods."

Then the famous god of the strong arms answered him: "Require not this of me, Poseidon, girdler of the earth. Evil are evil folk's pledges to hold. How could I keep thee bound among the deathless gods, if Ares were to depart, avoiding the debt and the bond?"

Then Poseidon answered him, shaker of the earth: "Hephaestus, even if Ares avoid the debt and flee away, I myself will pay thee all."

Then the famous god of the strong arms answered him: "It may not be that I should say thee nay, neither is it meet."

Therewith the mighty Hephaestus loosed the bonds, and the twain, when they were freed from that strong bond, sprang up straightway, and departed, he to Thrace, but laughter-loving Aphrodite went to Paphos of Cyprus, where is her precinct and fragrant altar. There the Graces bathed and anointed her with oil imperishable, such as is laid upon the everlasting gods. And they clad her in lovely raiment, a wonder to see.

This was the song the famous minstrel sang; and Odysseus listened and was glad at heart, and likewise did the Phaeacians, of the long oars, those mariners renowned.

Then Alcinous bade Halius and Laodamas dance alone, for none ever contended with them. So when they had taken in their hands the goodly ball of purple hue, that cunning Polybus had wrought for them, the one would bend backwards, and throw it towards the shadowy clouds; and the other would leap upward from the earth, and catch it lightly in his turn, before his feet touched the ground. Now after they had made trial of throwing the ball straight up, the twain set to dance upon the bounteous earth, tossing the ball from hand to hand, and the other youths stood by the lists and beat time, and a great din uprose.

Then it was that goodly Odysseus spake unto Alcinous: "My lord Alcinous, most notable among all the people, thou didst boast thy dancers to be the best in the world, and lo, thy words are fulfilled; I wonder as I look on them."

So spake he, and the mighty king Alcinous rejoiced and spake at once among the Phaeacians, masters of the oar:

"Hearken ye, captains and counsellors of the Phaeacians, this stranger seems to me a wise man enough. Come then, let us give him a stranger's gift, as is meet. Behold, there are twelve glorious princes who rule among this people and bear sway, and I myself am the thirteenth. Now each man among you bring a fresh robe and a doublet, and a talent of fine gold, and let us speedily carry all these gifts together, that the stranger may take them in his hands, and go to supper with a glad heart. As for Euryalus let him yield amends to the man himself with soft speech and with a gift, for his was no gentle saying."

So spake he, and they all assented thereto, and would have it so. And each one sent forth his henchman to fetch his gift, and Euryalus answered the king and spake, saying:

"My lord Alcinous, most notable among all the people,

I will make atonement to thy guest according to thy word. I will give him a hanger all of bronze, with a silver hilt thereto, and a sheath of fresh-sawn ivory covers it about, and it shall be to him a thing of price."

Therewith he puts into his hands the hanger dight with silver, and uttering his voice spake to him winged words: "Hail, stranger and father; and if aught grievous hath been spoken, may the storm-winds soon snatch and bear it away. But may the gods grant thee to see thy wife and to come to thine own country, for all too long hast thou endured affliction away from thy friends."

And Odysseus of many counsels answered him saying: "Thou too, my friend, all hail; and may the gods vouchsafe thee happiness, and mayst thou never miss this sword which thou hast given me, thou that with soft speech hast yielded me amends."

He spake and hung about his shoulders the silver-studded sword. And the sun sank, and the noble gifts were brought him. Then the proud henchmen bare them to the palace of Alcinous, and the sons of noble Alcinous took the fair gifts, and set them by their reverend mother. And the mighty king Alcinous led the way, and they came in and sat them down on the high seats. And the mighty Alcinous spake unto Arete:

"Bring me hither, my lady, a choice coffer, the best thou hast, and thyself place therein a fresh robe and a doublet, and heat for our guest a caldron on the fire, and warm water, that after the bath the stranger may see all the gifts duly arrayed which the noble Phaeacians bare hither, and that he may have joy in the feast, and in hearing the song of the minstrelsy. Also I will give him a beautiful golden chalice of mine own, that he may be mindful of me all the days of his life when he poureth the drink-offering to Zeus and to the other gods."

So spake he, and Arete bade her handmaids to set a great caldron on the fire with what speed they might. And they set the caldron for the filling of the bath on the blazing fire, and poured water therein, and took faggots and kindled

The maid brought the cauldron for Odysseus' bath.
PAINTING FROM A KYLIX BY HERMAIOS.
(VAN BRANTEGHEM COLL.)

them beneath. So the fire began to circle round the belly of the caldron, and the water waxed hot. Meanwhile Arete brought forth for her guest the beautiful coffer from the treasure chamber, and bestowed fair gifts therein, raiment and gold, which the Phaeacians gave him. And with her own hands she placed therein a robe and goodly doublet, and uttering her voice spake to him winged words:

"Do thou now look to the lid, and quickly tie the knot, lest any man spoil thy goods by the way, when presently thou fallest on sweet sleep travelling in thy black ship."

Now when the steadfast goodly Odysseus heard this saying, forthwith he fixed on the lid, and quickly tied the curious knot, which the lady Circe on a time had taught him. Then straightway the housewife bade him go to the bath and bathe him; and he saw the warm water and was glad, for he was not wont to be so cared for, from the day that he left the house of fair-tressed Calypso, but all that while he had comfort continually as a god.

Now after the maids had bathed him and anointed him with olive oil, and had cast a fair mantle and a doublet upon him, he stept forth from the bath, and went to be with the chiefs at their wine. And Nausicaa, dowered with beauty by the gods, stood by the pillar of the well-builded roof, and marvelled at Odysseus, beholding him before her eyes, and she uttered her voice and spake to him winged words:

"Farewell, stranger, and even in thine own country bethink thee of me upon a time, for that to me first thou owest the ransom of life."

And Odysseus of many counsels answered her saying: "Nausicaa, daughter of great-hearted Alcinous, yea, may Zeus, the thunderer, the lord of Here, grant me to reach my home and see the day of my returning; so would I, even there, do thee worship as to a god, all my days for evermore, for thou, lady, hast given me my life."

He spake and sat him in the high seat by king Alcinous. And now they were serving out the portions and mixing the wine. Then the henchman drew nigh leading the sweet minstrel, Demodocus, that was had in honour of the people. So he set him in the midst of the feasters, and made him lean against a tall column. Then to the henchman spake Odysseus of many counsels, for he had cut off a portion of the chine of a white-toothed boar, whereon yet more was left, with rich fat on either side:

"Lo, henchman, take this helping, and hand it to Demodocus, that he may eat, and I will bid him hail, despite my sorrow. For minstrels from all men on earth get their meed of honour and worship; inasmuch as the Muse teacheth them the paths of song, and loveth the tribe of minstrels."

the Trojan horse yarn

Thus he spake, and the henchman bare the mess, and set it upon the knees of the lord Demodocus, and he took it, and was glad at heart. Then they stretched forth their hands upon the good cheer set before them. Now after they had put from them the desire of meat and drink, then Odysseus of many counsels spake to Demodocus, saying:

"Demodocus, I praise thee far above all mortal men, whether it be the Muse, the daughter of Zeus, that taught thee, or even Apollo, for right duly dost thou chant the faring of the Achaeans, even all that they wrought and suffered, and all their travail, as if, methinks, thou hadst been present, or heard the tale from another. Come now, change thy strain, and sing of the fashioning of the horse of wood, which Epeius made by the aid of Athene, even the guileful thing, that goodly Odysseus led up into the citadel, when he had laden it with the men who wasted Ilium. If thou wilt indeed rehearse me this aright, so will I be thy witness among all men, how the god of his grace hath given thee the gift of wondrous song."

So spake he, and the minstrel, being stirred by the god, began and showed forth his minstrelsy. He took up the tale where it tells how the Argives of the one part set fire to their huts, and went aboard their decked ships and sailed away, while those others, the fellowship of renowned Odysseus, were now seated in the assembly-place of the Trojans, all hidden in the horse, for the Trojans themselves had dragged him to the citadel. So the horse stood there, while seated all around him the people spake many things confusedly and three ways their counsel looked; either to cleave the hollow timber with the pitiless spear, or to drag it to the brow of the hill, and hurl it from the rocks, or to leave it as a mighty offering to appease the gods. And on this wise it was to be at the last. For the doom was on them to perish when their city should have closed upon the great horse of wood, wherein sat all the bravest of the Argives, bearing to the Trojans death and destiny. And he sang how the sons of the Achaeans poured forth from the horse, and left the hollow lair, and sacked the city. And he sang how and where each man wasted the town, and of Odysseus, how he went like Ares to the house of Deiphobus [1] with godlike Menelaus. It was there, he said, that Odysseus adventured the most grievous battle, and in the end prevailed, by grace of great-hearted Athene.

This was the song that the famous minstrel sang. But the heart of Odysseus melted, and the tear wet his cheeks beneath the eyelids. And as a woman throws herself wailing about her dear lord, who hath fallen before his city and the host, warding from his town and his children the pitiless day; and she beholds him dying and drawing difficult breath, and embracing his body wails aloud, while the foemen behind smite her with spears on back and shoulders and lead her up into bondage, to bear labour and trouble, and with the most pitiful grief her cheeks are wasted; even so pitifully fell the tears beneath the brows of Odysseus. Now none of all the company marked him weeping; but Alcinous alone noted it, and was aware thereof, as he sat nigh him and heard him groaning heavily. And presently he spake among the Phaeacians, masters of the oar:

"Hearken, ye captains and counsellors of the Phaeacians, and now let Demodocus hold his hand from the loud lyre, for this song of his is nowise pleasing alike to all. From the time that we began to sup, and that the divine minstrel was moved to sing, ever since hath yonder stranger never ceased from woeful lamentation; sore grief, methinks, hath encompassed his heart. Nay, but let the minstrel cease, that we may all alike make merry, hosts and guest, since it is far meeter so. For all these things are ready for the sake of the honourable stranger, even the convoy and the loving gifts which we give him out of our love. In a brother's place stand the stranger and the suppliant, to him whose wits have even a little range. Wherefore do thou too hide not now with crafty purpose aught whereof I ask thee; it were more meet for thee to tell it out. Say, what is the name whereby they called thee at home, even thy father and thy mother, and

---

[1] Son of Priam; husband of Helen after the death of Paris.

others thy townsmen and the dwellers round about? For there is none of all mankind nameless, neither the mean man nor yet the noble, from first hour of his birth, but parents bestow a name on every man so soon as he is born. Tell me too of thy land, thy township, and thy city, that our ships may conceive of their course to bring thee thither. For the Phaeacians have no pilots nor any rudders after the manner of other ships, but their barques themselves understand the thoughts and intents of men; they know the cities and fat fields of every people, and most swiftly they traverse the gulf of the salt sea, shrouded in mist and cloud, and never do they go in fear of wreck or ruin. Howbeit I heard upon a time this word thus spoken by my father Nausithous, who was wont to say that Poseidon was jealous of us for that we give safe escort to all men. He said that Poseidon would some day smite a well-wrought ship of the Phaeacians as she came home from a convoy over the misty deep, and would over-shadow our city with a great mountain. Thus that ancient one would speak, and thus the god may bring it about, or leave it undone, according to the good pleasure of his will. But come now, declare me this and plainly tell it all; whither wast thou borne wandering, and to what shores of men thou camest; tell me of the people and of their fair-lying cities, of those whoso are hard and wild and unjust, and of those likewise who are hospitable and of a god-fearing mind. Declare, too, wherefore thou dost weep and mourn in spirit at the tale of the faring of the Argive Danaans and the lay of Ilium. All this the gods have fashioned, and have woven the skein of death for men, that there might be a song in the ears even of the folk of aftertime. Hadst thou even a kinsman by marriage that fell before Ilium, a true man, a daughter's husband or wife's father, such as are nearest us after those of our own stock and blood? Or else, may be, some loving friend, a good man and true; for a friend with an understanding heart is no whit worse than a brother."

IX

Polyphemus

AND Odysseus of many counsels answered him saying:
"King Alcinous, most notable of all the people, verily it
is a good thing to list to a minstrel such as this one, like to
the gods in voice. Nay, as for me, I say that there is no more
gracious or perfect delight than when a whole people makes
merry, and the men sit orderly at feast in the halls and listen
to the singer, and the tables by them are laden with bread
and flesh, and a wine-bearer drawing the wine serves it round
and pours it into the cups. This seems to me well-nigh the
fairest thing in the world. But now thy heart was inclined
to ask of my grievous troubles, that I may mourn for more
exceeding sorrow. What then shall I tell of first, what last,
for the gods of heaven have given me woes in plenty? Now,
first, will I tell my name, that ye too may know it, and that
I, when I have escaped the pitiless day, may yet be your
host, though my home is in a far country. I am ODYSSEUS,
SON OF LAERTES, who am in men's minds for all manner of
wiles, and my fame reaches unto heaven. And I dwell in
clear-seen Ithaca, wherein is a mountain Neriton, with trembling forest leaves, standing manifest to view, and many islands lie around, very near one to the other, Dulichium and
Same, and wooded Zacynthus. Now Ithaca lies low, furthest
up the sea-line toward the darkness, but those others face
the dawning and the sun; a rugged isle, but a good nurse of
noble youths; and for myself I can see nought beside sweeter
than a man's own country. Verily Calypso, the fair goddess,

would fain have kept me with her in her hollow caves, longing to have me for her lord; and likewise too, guileful Circe of Aia, would have stayed me in her halls, longing to have me for her lord. But never did they prevail upon my heart within my breast. So surely is there nought sweeter than a man's own country and his parents, even though he dwell far off in a rich home in a strange land, away from them that begat him. But come, let me tell thee too of the troubles of my journeying, which Zeus laid on me as I came from Troy.

"The wind that bare me from Ilium brought me nigh to the Cicones, even to Ismarus, whereupon I sacked their city

Fight between Odysseus' Companions and the Cicones.

PAINTING FROM AN AMPHORA.
(MUNICH PINAKOTHEK)

and slew the people. And from out the city we took their wives and much substance, and divided them amongst us, that none through me might go lacking his proper share. Howbeit, thereafter I commanded that we should flee with a swift foot, but my men in their great folly hearkened not. There was much wine still a-drinking, and still they slew many flocks of sheep by the seashore and kine with trailing feet and shambling gait. Meanwhile the Cicones went and raised a cry to other Cicones their neighbours, dwelling inland, who were more in number than they and braver withal: skilled they were to fight with men from chariots, and when need was on foot. So they gathered in the early morning as thick as leaves and flowers that spring in their season—yea and in that hour an evil doom of Zeus stood by us, ill-fated men, that so we might be sore afflicted. They

battle fever is still in them

they are tempted by greed for booty

set their battle in array by the swift ships, and the hosts cast at one another with their bronze-shod spears. So long as it was morn and the sacred day waxed stronger, so long we abode their assault and beat them off, albeit they outnumbered us. But when the sun was wending to the time of the loosing of cattle, then at last the Cicones drave in the Achaeans and overcame them, and six of my goodly-greaved company perished from each ship: but the remnant of us escaped death and destiny.

"Thence we sailed onward stricken at heart, yet glad as men saved from death, albeit we had lost our dear companions. Nor did my curved ships move onward ere we had called thrice on each of those our hapless fellows, who died at the hands of the Cicones on the plain. Now Zeus, gatherer of the clouds, aroused the North Wind against our ships with a terrible tempest, and covered land and sea alike with clouds, and down sped night from heaven. Thus the ships were driven headlong, and their sails were torn to shreds by the might of the wind. So we lowered the sails into the hold, in fear of death, but rowed the ships landward apace. There for two nights and two days we lay continually, consuming our hearts with weariness and sorrow. But when the fair-tressed Dawn had at last brought the full light of the third day, we set up the masts and hoisted the white sails and sat us down, while the wind and the helmsman guided the ships. And now I should have come to mine our country all unhurt, but the wave and the stream of the sea and the North Wind swept me from my course as I was doubling Malea, and drave me wandering past Cythera.

"Thence for nine whole days was I borne by ruinous winds over the teeming deep; but on the tenth day we set foot on the land of the lotus-eaters, who eat a flowery food. So we stepped ashore and drew water, and straightway my company took their midday meal by the swift ships. Now when we had tasted meat and drink I sent forth certain of my company to go and make search what manner of men they were who here live upon the earth by bread, and I chose out two of my fellows, and sent a third with them as herald.

Then straightway they went and mixed with the men of the lotus-eaters, and so it was that the lotus-eaters devised not death for our fellows, but gave them of the lotus to taste. Now whosoever of them did eat the honey-sweet fruit of the lotus, had no more wish to bring tidings nor to come back, but there he chose to abide with the lotus-eating men, ever feeding on the lotus, and forgetful of his homeward way. Therefore I led them back to the ships weeping, and sore against their will, and dragged them beneath the benches, and bound them in the hollow barques. But I commanded the rest of my well-loved company to make speed and go on board the swift ships, lest haply any should eat of the lotus and be forgetful of returning. Right soon they embarked and sat upon the benches, and sitting orderly they smote the grey sea water with their oars.

"Thence we sailed onward stricken at heart. And we came to the land of the Cyclopes, a froward and a lawless folk, who trusting to the deathless gods plant not aught with their hands, neither plough: but, behold, all these things spring for them in plenty, unsown and untilled, wheat, and barley, and vines, which bear great clusters of the juice of the grape, and the rain of Zeus gives them increase. These have neither gatherings for council nor oracles of law, but they dwell in hollow caves on the crests of the high hills, and each one utters the law to his children and his wives, and they reck not one of another.

"Now there is a waste isle stretching without the harbour of the land of the Cyclopes, neither nigh at hand nor yet afar off, a woodland isle, wherein are wild goats unnumbered, for no path of men scares them, nor do hunters resort thither who suffer hardships in the wood, as they range the mountain crests. Moreover it is possessed neither by flocks nor by ploughed lands, but the soil lies unsown evermore and untilled, desolate of men, and feeds the bleating goats. For the Cyclopes have by them no ships with vermilion cheek, not yet are there shipwrights in the island, who might fashion decked barques, which should accomplish all their desire, voyaging to the towns of men (as ofttimes men cross the sea to one another in ships), who might likewise have made of their isle a goodly settlement. Yea, it is in no wise a sorry land, but would bear all things in their season; for therein are soft water-meadows by the shores of the grey salt sea, and there the vines know no decay, and the land is level to plough; thence might they reap a crop exceeding deep in due season, for verily there is fatness beneath the soil. Also there is a fair haven, where is no need of moorings, either to cast anchor or to fasten hawsers, but men may run the ship on the beach, and tarry until such time as the sailors are minded to be gone, and favourable breezes blow. Now at the head of the harbour is a well of bright water issuing from a cave, and round it are poplars growing. Thither we sailed, and some god guided us through the night, for it was dark and there was no light to see, a mist lying deep about the ships, nor did the moon show her light from heaven, but was shut in with clouds. No man then beheld that island, neither saw we the long waves rolling to the beach, till we had run our decked ships ashore. And when our ships were beached, we took down all their sails, and ourselves too stept forth upon the strand of the sea, and there we fell into sound sleep and waited for the bright Dawn.

"So soon as early Dawn shone forth, the rosy-fingered, in wonder at the island we roamed over the length thereof: and the Nymphs, the daughters of Zeus, lord of the aegis, started the wild goats of the hills, that my company might have wherewith to sup. Anon we took to us our curved bows from out the ships and long spears, and arrayed in three bands we began shooting at the goats; and the god soon gave us game in plenty. Now twelve ships bare me company, and to each ship fell nine goats for a portion, but for me alone they set ten apart.

"Thus we sat there the livelong day until the going down of the sun, feasting on abundant flesh and on sweet wine. For the red wine was not yet spent from out the ships, but somewhat was yet therein, for we had each one drawn off large store thereof in jars, when we took the sacred citadel of the Cicones. And we looked across to the land of the

[handwritten note: O. goes alone with his men]

Cyclopes who dwell nigh, and to the smoke, and to the voice of the men, and of the sheep and of the goats. And when the sun had sunk and darkness had come on, then we laid us to rest upon the sea-beach. So soon as early Dawn shone forth, the rosy-fingered, then I called a gathering of my men, and spake among them all:

" 'Abide here all the rest of you, my dear companions; but I will go with mine own ship and my ship's company, and make proof of these men, what manner of folk they are, whether froward, and wild, and unjust, or hospitable and of god-fearing mind.'

"So I spake, and I climbed the ship's side, and bade my company themselves to mount, and to loose the hawsers. So they soon embarked and sat upon the benches, and sitting orderly smote the grey sea water with their oars. Now when we had come to the land that lies hard by, we saw a cave on the border near to the sea, lofty and roofed over with laurels, and there many flocks of sheep and goats were used to rest. And about it a high outer court was built with stones, deep bedded, and with tall pines and oaks with their high crown of leaves. And a man was wont to sleep therein, of monstrous size, who shepherded his flocks alone and afar, and was not conversant with others, but dwelt apart in lawlessness of mind. Yea, for he was a monstrous thing and fashioned marvellously, nor was he like to any man that lives by bread, but like a wooded peak of the towering hills, which stands out apart and alone from others.

"Then I commanded the rest of my well-loved company to tarry there by the ship, and to guard the ship, but I chose out twelve men, the best of my company, and sallied forth. Now I had with me a goat-skin of the dark wine and sweet, which Maron, son of Euanthes, had given me, the priest of Apollo, the god that watched over Ismarus. And he gave it, for that we had protected him with his wife and child reverently; for he dwelt in a thick grove of Phoebus Apollo. And he made me splendid gifts; he gave me seven talents of gold well wrought, and he gave me a mixing bowl of pure silver, and furthermore wine which he drew off in twelve jars in all,

sweet wine unmingled, a draught divine; nor did any of his
servants or of his handmaids in the house know thereof, but
himself and his dear wife and one house-dame only. And as
often as they drank that red wine honey sweet, he would fill
one cup and pour it into twenty measures of water, and a
marvellous sweet smell went up from the mixing bowl; then
truly it was no pleasure to refrain.

"With this wine I filled a great skin, and bare it with me,
and corn too I put in a wallet, for my lordly spirit straightway
had a boding that a man would come to me, a strange man,
clothed in mighty strength, one that knew not judgment and
justice.

"Soon we came to the cave, but we found him not within;
he was shepherding his fat flocks in the pastures. So we went
into the cave, and gazed on all that was therein. The baskets
were well laden with cheeses, and the folds were thronged
with lambs and kids; each kind was penned by itself, the
firstlings apart, and the summer lambs apart, apart too the
younglings of the flock. Now all the vessels swam with whey,
the milk-pails and the bowls, the well-wrought vessels where-
into he milked. My company then spake and besought me
first of all to take of the cheeses and to return, and afterwards
to make haste and drive off the kids and lambs to the swift
ships from out the pens, and to sail over the salt sea water.
Howbeit I hearkened not (and far better would it have
been), but waited to see the giant himself, and whether he
would give me gifts as a stranger's due. Yet was not his coming to be with joy to my company.

"Then we kindled a fire, and made burnt-offering, and
ourselves likewise took of the cheeses, and did eat, and sat
waiting for him within till he came back, shepherding his
flocks. And he bore a grievous weight of dry wood, against
supper time. This log he cast down with a din inside the
cave, and in fear we fled to the secret place of the rock. As
for him, he drave his fat flocks into the wide cavern, even
all that he was wont to milk; but the males both of the sheep
and of the goats he left without in the deep yard. Thereafter
he lifted a huge doorstone and weighty, and set it in the

mouth of the cave, such an one as two and twenty good four-wheeled wains could not raise from the ground, so mighty a sheer rock did he set against the doorway. Then he sat down and milked the ewes and bleating goats all orderly, and beneath each ewe he placed her young. And anon he curdled one half of the white milk, and massed it together, and stored it in wicker-baskets, and the other half he let stand in pails, that he might have it to take and drink against supper time. Now when he had done all his work busily then he kindled the fire anew, and espied us, and made question:

" 'Strangers, who are ye? Whence sail ye over the wet ways? On some trading enterprise or at adventure do ye rove, even as sea-robbers over the brine, for at hazard of their own lives they wander, bringing bale to alien men.'

"So spake he, but as for us our heart within us was broken for terror of the deep voice and his own monstrous shape; yet despite all I answered and spake unto him, saying:

" 'Lo, we are Achaeans, driven wandering from Troy, by all manner of winds over the great gulf of the sea; seeking our homes we fare, but another path have we come, by other ways: even such, methinks, was the will and the counsel of Zeus. And we avow us to be the men of Agamemnon, son of Atreus, whose fame is even now the mightiest under heaven, so great a city did he sack, and destroyed many people; but as for us we have lighted here, and come to these thy knees, if perchance thou wilt give us a stranger's gift, or make any present, as is the due of strangers. Nay, lord, have regard to the gods, for we are thy suppliants; and Zeus is the avenger of suppliants and sojourners, Zeus, the god of the stranger, who fareth in the company of reverend strangers.'

"So I spake, and anon he answered out of his pitiless heart: 'Thou art witless, my stranger, or thou hast come from afar, who biddest me either to fear or shun the gods. For the Cyclopes pay no heed to Zeus, lord of the aegis, nor to the blessed gods, for verily we are better men than they. Nor would I, to shun the enmity of Zeus, spare either thee or thy company, unless my spirit bade me. But tell me where thou didst stay thy well-wrought ship on thy coming? Was it per-

this religious appeal is spurned

This monstrous behaviour is
believable in a giant. But
later there will be real cannibalism

282   THE ODYSSEY

chance at the far end of the island, or hard by, that I may know?'

"So he spake tempting me, but he cheated me not, who knew full much, and I answered him again with words of guile:

" 'As for my ship, Poseidon, the shaker of the earth, brake it to pieces, for he cast it upon the rocks at the border of your country, and brought it nigh the headland, and a wind bare it thither from the sea. But I with these my men escaped from utter doom.'

"So I spake, and out of his pitiless heart he answered me not a word, but sprang up, and laid his hands upon my fellows, and clutching two together dashed them, as they had been whelps, to the earth, and the brains flowed forth upon the ground and the earth was wet. Then cut he them up piecemeal, and made ready his supper. So he ate even as a mountain-bred lion, and ceased not, devouring entrails and flesh and bones with their marrow. And we wept and raised our hands to Zeus, beholding the cruel deeds; and we were at our wits' end. And after the Cyclops had filled his huge maw with human flesh and the milk he drank thereafter, he lay within the cave, stretched out among his sheep.

"So I took counsel in my great heart, whether I should draw near, and pluck my sharp sword from my thigh, and stab him in the breast, where the midriff holds the liver, feeling for the place with my hand. But my second thought withheld me, for so should we too have perished even there with utter doom. For we should not have prevailed to roll away with our hands from the lofty door the heavy stone which he set there. So for that time we made moan, awaiting the bright Dawn.

"Now when early Dawn shone forth, the rosy-fingered, again he kindled the fire and milked his goodly flocks all orderly, and beneath each ewe set her lamb. Anon when he had done all his work busily, again he seized yet other two men and made ready his mid-day meal. And after the meal, lightly he moved away the great door-stone, and drave his fat flocks forth from the cave, and afterwards he set it in his *the weapon to blind Polyph.*

place again, as one might set the lid on a quiver. Then with a loud whoop, the Cyclops turned his fat flocks towards the hills; but I was left devising evil in the deep of my heart, if in any wise I might avenge me, and Athene grant me renown.

"And this was the counsel that showed best in my sight. There lay by a sheep-fold a great club of the Cyclops, a club of olive wood, yet green, which he had cut to carry with him when it should be seasoned. Now when we saw it we likened it in size to the mast of a black ship of twenty oars, a wide merchant vessel that traverses the great sea gulf, so huge it was to view in bulk and length. I stood thereby and cut off from it a portion as it were a fathom's length, and set it by my fellows, and bade them fine it down, and they made it even, while I stood by and sharpened it to a point, and straightway I took it and hardened it in the bright fire. Then I laid it well away, and hid it beneath the dung, which was scattered in great heaps in the depths of the cave. And I bade my company cast lots among them, which of them should risk the adventure with me, and lift the bar and turn it about in his eye, when sweet sleep came upon him. And the lot fell upon those four whom I myself would have been fain to choose, and I appointed myself to be the fifth among them. In the evening he came shepherding his flocks of goodly fleece, and presently he drave his fat flocks into the cave each and all, nor left he any without in the deep court-yard, whether through some foreboding, or perchance that the god so bade him do. Thereafter he lifted the huge door-stone and set it in the mouth of the cave, and sitting down he milked the ewes and bleating goats, all orderly, and beneath each ewe he placed her young. Now when he had done all his work busily, again he seized yet other two and made ready his supper. Then I stood by the Cyclops and spake to him, holding in my hands an ivy bowl of the dark wine:

" 'Cyclops, take and drink wine after thy feast of man's meat, that thou mayest know what manner of drink this was that our ship held. And lo, I was bringing it thee as a drink offering, if haply thou mayest take pity and send me on my way home, but thy mad rage is past all sufferance. O hard of heart, how may another of the many men there be come ever to thee again, seeing that thy deeds have been lawless?'

"So I spake, and he took the cup and drank it off, and found great delight in drinking the sweet draught, and asked me for it yet a second time:

" 'Give it me again of thy grace, and tell me thy name straightway, that I may give thee a stranger's gift, wherein thou mayest be glad. Yea for the earth, the grain-giver, bears for the Cyclopes the mighty clusters of the juice of the grape, and the rain of Zeus gives them increase, but this is a rill of very nectar and ambrosia.'

"So he spake, and again I handed him the dark wine. Thrice I bare and gave it him, and thrice in his folly he drank it to the lees. Now when the wine had got about the wits of the Cyclops, then did I speak to him with soft words:

" 'Cyclops, thou askest me my renowned name, and I will declare it unto thee, and do thou grant me a stranger's gift, as thou didst promise. Noman is my name, and Noman they call me, my father and my mother and all my fellows.'

"So I spake, and straightway he answered me out of his pitiless heart:

" 'Noman will I eat last in the number of his fellows, and the others before him: that shall be thy gift.'

"Therewith he sank backwards and fell with face upturned, and there he lay with his great neck bent round, and sleep, that conquers all men, overcame him. And the wine and the fragments of men's flesh issued forth from his mouth, and he vomited, being heavy with wine. Then I thrust in that stake under the deep ashes, until it should grow hot, and I spake to my companions comfortable words, lest any should hang back from me in fear. But when that bar of olive wood was just about to catch fire in the flame, green though it was, and began to glow terribly, even then I came nigh, and drew it from the coals, and my fellows gathered about me, and some god breathed great courage into us. For their part they seized the bar of olive wood, that was sharpened at the point, and thrust it into his eye, while I

They blind Polyph...
fearsome his typical of the
epic (of Beowulf)

IX · Polyphemus 285

from my place aloft turned it about, as when a man bores
a ship's beam with a drill while his fellows below spin it with
a strap, which they hold at either end, and the auger runs
round continually. Even so did we seize the fiery-pointed
brand and whirled it round in his eye, and the blood flowed
about the heated bar. And the breath of the flame singed his
eyelids and brows all about, as the ball of the eye burnt
away, and the roots thereof crackled in the flame. And as
when a smith dips an axe or adze in chill water with a great
hissing, when he would temper it—for hereby anon comes
the strength of iron—even so did his eye hiss round the stake
of olive. And he raised a great and terrible cry, that the rock
rang around, and we fled away in fear, while he plucked
forth from his eye the brand bedabbled in much blood.
Then maddened with pain he cast it from him with his
hands, and called with a loud voice on the Cyclopes, who
dwelt about him in the caves along the windy heights. And
they heard the cry and flocked together from every side, and
gathering round the cave asked him what ailed him:

" 'What hath so distressed thee, Polyphemus, that thou
criest thus aloud through the immortal night, and makest us
sleepless? Surely no mortal driveth off thy flocks against thy
will: surely none slayeth thyself by force or craft?'

"And the strong Polyphemus spake to them again from
out the cave: 'My friends, Noman is slaying me by guile, nor
at all by force.'

"And they answered and spake winged words: 'If then no
man is violently handling thee in thy solitude, it can in no
wise be that thou shouldest escape the sickness sent by
mighty Zeus. Nay, pray thou to thy father, the lord Poseidon.'

"On this wise they spake and departed; and my heart
within me laughed to see how my name and cunning counsel had beguiled them. But the Cyclops, groaning and travail-
ing in pain, groped with his hands, and lifted away the stone
from the door of the cave, and himself sat in the entry, with
arms outstretched to catch, if he might, any one that was
going forth with his sheep, so witless, methinks, did he hope

to find me. But I advised me how all might be for the very
best, if perchance I might find a way of escape from death
for my companions and myself, and I wove all manner of
craft and counsel, as a man will for his life, seeing that great
mischief was nigh. And this was the counsel that showed
best in my sight. The rams of the flock were well nurtured
and thick of fleece, great and goodly, with wool dark as the
violet. Quietly I lashed them together with twisted withies,
whereon the Cyclops slept, that lawless monster. Three together I took: now the middle one of the three would bear
each a man, but the other twain went on either side, saving
my fellows. Thus every three sheep bare their man. But as
for me I laid hold of the back of a young ram who was far
the best and the goodliest of all the flock, and curled beneath his shaggy belly there I lay, and so clung face upward,
grasping the wondrous fleece with a steadfast heart. So for
that time making moan we awaited the bright Dawn.

"So soon as early Dawn shone forth, the rosy-fingered,
then did the rams of the flock hasten forth to pasture, but
the ewes bleated unmilked about the pens, for their udders
were swollen to bursting. Then their lord, sore stricken with
pain, felt along the backs of all the sheep as they stood up
before him, and guessed not in his folly how that my men
were bound beneath the breasts of his thick-fleeced flocks.
Last of all the sheep came forth the ram, cumbered with his
wool, and the weight of me and my cunning. And the strong
Polyphemus laid his hands on him and spake to him, saying:

"'Dear ram, wherefore, I pray thee, art thou the last of all
the flocks to go forth from the cave, who of old wast not
wont to lag behind the sheep, but wert ever the foremost to
pluck the tender blossom of the pasture, faring with long
strides, and wert still the first to come to the streams of the
rivers, and first didst long to return to the homestead in the
evening. But now art thou the very last. Surely thou art
sorrowing for the eye of thy lord, which an evil man blinded,
with his accursed fellows, when he had subdued my wits with
wine, even Noman, whom I say hath not yet escaped destruction. Ah, if thou couldst feel as I, and be endued with

speech, to tell me where he shifts about to shun my wrath; then should he be smitten, and his brains be dashed against the floor here and there about the cave, and my heart be lightened of the sorrows which Noman, nothing worth, hath brought me!'

"Therewith he sent the ram forth from him, and when we had gone but a little way from the cave and from the yard, first I loosed myself from under the ram and then I set my fellows free. And swiftly we drave on those stiff-shanked sheep, so rich in fat, and often turned to look about, till we came to the ship. And a glad sight to our fellows were we that had fled from death, but the others they would have bemoaned with tears; howbeit I suffered it not, but with frowning brows forbade each man to weep. Rather I bade them to cast on board the many sheep with goodly fleece, and to sail over the salt sea water. So they embarked forthwith, and sate upon the benches, and sitting orderly smote the grey sea water with their oars. But when I had not gone so far, but that a man's shout might be heard, then I spoke unto the Cyclops taunting him:

" 'Cyclops, so thou wert not to eat the company of a weakling by main might in thy hollow cave! Thine evil deeds were very sure to find thee out, thou cruel man, who hadst no shame to eat thy guests within thy gates, wherefore Zeus hath requited thee, and the other gods.'

"So I spake, and he was mightily angered at heart, and he brake off the peak of a great hill and threw it at us, and it fell in front of the dark-prowed ship. And the sea heaved beneath the fall of the rock, and the backward flow of the wave bare the ship quickly to the dry land, with the wash from the deep sea, and drave it to the shore. Then I caught up a long pole in my hands, and thrust the ship from off the land, and roused my company, and with a motion of the head bade them dash in with their oars, that so we might escape our evil plight. So they bent to their oars and rowed on. But when we had now made twice the distance over the brine, I would fain have spoken to the Cyclops, but my company stayed me on every side with soft words, saying:

" 'Foolhardy that thou art, why wouldst thou rouse a wild man to wrath, who even now hath cast so mighty a throw towards the deep and brought our ship back to land, yea and we thought that we had perished even there? If he had heard any of us utter sound or speech he would have crushed our heads and our ship timbers with a cast of a rugged stone, so mightily he hurls.'

"So spake they, but they prevailed not on my lordly spirit, and I answered him again from out an angry heart:

" 'Cyclops, if any one of mortal men shall ask thee of the unsightly blinding of thine eye, say that it was Odysseus that blinded it, the waster of cities, son of Laertes, whose dwelling is in Ithaca.'

"So I spake, and with a moan he answered me, saying:

" 'Lo now, in very truth the ancient oracles have come upon me. There lived here a soothsayer, a noble man and a mighty, Telemus, son of Eurymus, who surpassed all men in soothsaying, and waxed old as a seer among the Cyclopes. He told me that all these things should come to pass in the aftertime, even that I should lose my eyesight at the hand of Odysseus. But I ever looked for some tall and goodly man to come hither, clad in great might, but behold now one that is a dwarf, a man of no worth and a weakling, hath blinded me of my eye after subduing me with wine. Nay come hither, Odysseus, that I may set by thee a stranger's cheer, and speed thy parting hence, that so the Earth-shaker may vouchsafe it thee, for his son am I, and he avows himself my father. And he himself will heal me, if it be his will; and none other of the blessed gods or of mortal men.'

"Even so he spake, but I answered him, and said: 'Would god that I were as sure to rob thee of soul and life, and send thee within the house of Hades, as I am that not even the Earth-shaker will heal thine eye!'

"So I spake, and then he prayed to the lord Poseidon stretching forth his hands to the starry heaven: 'Hear me, Poseidon, girdler of the earth, god of the dark hair, if indeed I be thine, and thou avowest thee my sire,—grant that he may never come to his home, even Odysseus, waster of cities, the son of Laertes, whose dwelling is in Ithaca; yet if he is ordained to see his friends and come unto his well-builded house, and his own country, late may he come in evil case, with the loss of all his company, in the ship of strangers, and find sorrows in his house.'

"So he spake in prayer, and the god of the dark locks heard him. And once again he lifted a stone, far greater than the first, and with one swing he hurled it, and he put forth a measureless strength, and cast it but a little space behind the dark-prowed ship, and all but struck the end of the rudder. And the sea heaved beneath the fall of the rock, but the wave bare on the ship and drave it to the further shore.

"But when we had now reached that island, where all our other decked ships abode together, and our company were gathered sorrowing, expecting us nevermore, on our coming thither we ran our ship ashore upon the sand, and ourselves too stept forth upon the sea-beach. Next we took forth the sheep of the Cyclops from out the hollow ship, and divided them, that none through me might go lacking his proper share. But the ram for me alone my goodly-greaved company chose out, in the dividing of the sheep, and on the shore I offered him up to Zeus, even to the son of Cronos, who dwells in the dark clouds, and is lord of all, and I burnt the slices of the thighs. But he heeded not the sacrifice, but was devising how my decked ships and my dear company might perish utterly. Thus for that time we sat the livelong day, until the going down of the sun, feasting on abundant flesh and sweet wine. And when the sun had sunk and darkness had come on, then we laid us to rest upon the sea-beach. So soon as early Dawn shone forth, the rosy-fingered, I called to my company, and commanded them that they should themselves climb the ship and loose the hawsers. So they soon embarked and sat upon the benches, and sitting orderly smote the grey sea water with their oars.

"Thence we sailed onward stricken at heart, yet glad as men saved from death, albeit we had lost our dear companions."

X

Circe

THEN we came to the isle Aeolian, where dwelt Aeolus, son of Hippotas, dear to the deathless gods, in a floating island, and all about it is a wall of bronze unbroken, and the cliff runs up sheer from the sea. His twelve children too abide there in his halls, six daughters and six lusty sons; and, behold, he gave his daughters to his sons to wife. And they feast evermore by their dear father and their kind mother, and dainties innumerable lie ready to their hands. And the house is full of the savour of feasting, and the noise thereof rings round, yea in the courtyard, by day, and in the night they sleep each one by his chaste wife in coverlets and on jointed bedsteads. So then we came to their city and their goodly dwelling, and the king treated me kindly for a whole month, and inquired about each thing, Ilium and the ships of the Argives, and the return of the Achaeans. So I told him all the tale in order duly. But when I in turn took the word and asked of my journey, and bade him send me on my way, he too denied me not, but furnished an escort. He gave me a wallet, made of the hide of an ox of nine seasons old, which he had flayed, and therein he bound the ways of all the noisy winds; for him the son of Cronos made keeper of the winds, either to lull or to rouse what blasts he will. And he made it fast in the hold of the ship with a shining silver thong, that not the faintest breath might escape. Then he sent forth the blast of the West Wind to blow for me, to bear our ships and ourselves upon our way; but this he was never to bring to pass, for we were undone through our own heedlessness.

"For nine whole days we sailed by night and day continually, and now on the tenth day my native land came in sight, and already we were so near that we beheld the folk tending the beacon fires. Then over me there came sweet slumber in my weariness, for all the time I was holding the sheet of my ship, nor gave it to any of my company, that so we might come quicker to our own country. Meanwhile my company held converse together, and said that I was bringing home for myself gold and silver, gifts from Aeolus the high-hearted son of Hippotas. And thus would they speak looking each man to his neighbour:

" 'Lo now, how beloved he is and highly esteemed among all men, to the city and land of whomsoever he may come. Many are the goodly treasures he taketh with him out of the spoil from Troy, while we who have fulfilled like journeying with him return homeward bringing with us but empty hands. And now Aeolus hath given unto him these things freely in his love. Nay come, let us quickly see what they are, even what wealth of gold and silver is in the wallet.'

"So they spake, and the evil counsel of my company prevailed. They loosed the wallet, and all the winds brake forth. And the violent blast seized my men, and bare them towards the high seas weeping, away from their own country; but as for me, I awoke and communed with my great heart, whether I should cast myself from the ship and perish in the deep, or endure in silence and abide yet among the living. Howbeit I hardened my heart to endure, and muffling my head I lay still in the ship. But the vessels were driven by the evil stormwind back to the isle Aeolian, and my company made moan.

"There we stepped ashore and drew water, and my company presently took their midday meal by the swift ships. Now when we had tasted bread and wine, I took with me a herald and one of my company, and went to the famous dwelling of Aeolus: and I found him feasting with his wife and children. So we went in and sat by the pillars of the door on the threshold, and they all marvelled and asked us:

" 'How hast thou come hither, Odysseus? What evil god assailed thee? Surely we sent thee on thy way with all diligence, that thou mightest get thee to thine own country and thy home, and whithersoever thou wouldest.'

"Even so they said, but I spake among them heavy at heart: 'My evil company hath been my bane, and sleep thereto remorseless. Come, my friends, do ye heal the harm, for yours is the power.'

"So I spake, beseeching them in soft words, but they held their peace. And the father answered, saying: 'Get thee forth from the island straightway, thou that art the most reprobate of living men. Far be it from me to help or to further that man whom the blessed gods abhor! Get thee forth, for lo, thy coming marks thee hated by the deathless gods.'

"Therewith he sent me forth from the house making heavy moan. Thence we sailed onwards stricken at heart. And the spirit of the men was spent beneath the grievous rowing by reason of our vain endeavour, for there was no more any sign of a wafting wind. So for the space of six days we sailed by night and day continually, and on the seventh we came to the steep stronghold of Lamos, Telepylos of the Laestrygons, where herdsman hails herdsman as he drives in his flock, and the other who drives forth answers the call. There might a sleepless man have earned a double wage, the one as neatherd, the other shepherding white flocks: so near are the outgoings of the night and of the day. Thither when we had come to the fair haven, whereabout on both sides goes one steep cliff unbroken, and jutting headlands over against each other stretch forth at the mouth of the harbour, and strait is the entrance; thereinto all the others steered their curved ships. Now the vessels were bound within the hollow harbour each hard by other, for no wave ever swelled within it, great or small, but there was a bright calm all around. But I alone moored my dark ship without the harbour, at the uttermost point thereof, and made fast the hawser to a rock. And I went up a craggy hill, a place of outlook, and stood thereon: thence there was no sign of the labour of men or oxen, only we saw the smoke

Cannibalistic giants again —
another version of the
Cyclops?

curling upward from the land. Then I sent forth certain of
my company to go and search out what manner of men they
were who here live upon the earth by bread, choosing out
two of my company and sending a third with them as herald.
Now when they had gone ashore, they went along a level
road whereby wains were wont to draw down wood from
the high hills to the town. And without the town they fell
in with a damsel drawing water, the noble daughter of
Laestrygonian Antiphates. She had come down to the clear-
flowing spring Artacia, for thence it was custom to draw water to the town. So they stood by her and spake unto her, and
asked who was king of that land, and who they were he ruled
over. Then at once she showed them the high-roofed hall of
her father. Now when they had entered the renowned house,
they found his wife therein: she was huge of bulk as a mountain peak and was loathly in their sight. Straightway she
called the renowned Antiphates, her lord, from the assembly-
place, and he contrived a pitiful destruction for my men.
Forthwith he clutched up one of my company and made
ready his midday meal, but the other twain sprang up and
came in flight to the ships. Then he raised the war-cry
through the town, and the valiant Laestrygonians at the
sound thereof, flocked together from every side, a host past
number, not like men but like the Giants. They cast at us
from the cliffs with great rocks, each of them a man's burden,
and anon there arose from the fleet an evil din of men dying
and ships shattered withal. And like folk spearing fishes they
bare home their hideous meal. While as yet they were slaying
my friends within the deep harbour, I drew my sharp sword
from my thigh, and with it cut the hawsers of my dark-
prowed ship. Quickly then I called to my company, and bade
them dash in with the oars, that we might clean escape this
evil plight. And all with one accord they tossed the sea water with the oar-blade, in dread of death, and to my delight
my barque flew forth to the high seas away from the beetling
rocks, but those other ships were lost there, one and all.

"Thence we sailed onward stricken at heart, yet glad as
men saved from death, albeit we had lost our dear com-

Odyssey + his crew
are now alone !

panions. And we came to the isle Aeaean, where dwelt Circe
of the braided tresses, an awful goddess of mortal speech,
own sister to the wizard Aeetes. Both were begotten of Helios, who gives light to all men, and their mother was Perse,
daughter of Oceanus. There on the shore we put in with our
ship into the sheltering haven silently, and some god was
our guide. Then we stept ashore, and for two days and two
nights lay there, consuming our own hearts for weariness
and pain. But when now the fair-tressed Dawn had brought
the full light of the third day, then did I seize my spear and
my sharp sword, and quickly departing from the ship I went
up unto a place of wide prospect, if haply I might see any
sign of the labour of men and hear the sound of their speech.
So I went up a craggy hill, a place of out-look, and I saw
the smoke rising from the broad-wayed earth in the halls of
Circe, through the thick coppice and the woodland. Then
I mused in my mind and heart whether I should go and
make discovery, for that I had seen the smoke and flame.
And as I thought thereon this seemed to me the better counsel, to go first to the swift ship and to the sea-banks, and
give my company their midday meal, and then send them
to make search. But as I came and drew nigh to the curved
ship, some god even then took pity on me in my loneliness,
and sent a tall antlered stag across my very path. He was
coming down from his pasture in the woodland to the river
to drink, for verily the might of the sun was sore upon him.
And as he came up from out of the stream, I smote him on
the spine in the middle of the back, and the brazen shaft
went clean through him, and with a moan he fell in the dust,
and his life passed from him. Then I set my foot on him
and drew forth the brazen shaft from the wound, and laid
it hard by upon the ground and let it lie. Next I broke
withies and willow twigs, and wove me a rope a fathom in
length, well twisted from end to end, and bound together
the feet of the huge beast, and went to the black ship bearing him across my neck, and leaning on a spear, for it was in
no wise possible to carry him on my shoulder with the one
hand, for he was a mighty quarry. And I threw him down

before the ship and roused my company with soft words, standing by each man in turn:

" 'Friends, for all our sorrows we shall not yet a while go down to the house of Hades, ere the coming of the day of destiny; go to then, while as yet there is meat and drink in the swift ship, let us take thought thereof, that we be not famished for hunger.'

"Even so I spake, and they speedily hearkened to my words. They unmuffled their heads, and there on the shore of the unharvested sea gazed at the stag, for he was a mighty quarry. But after they had delighted their eyes with the sight of him, they washed their hands and got ready the glorious feast. So for that time we sat the live-long day till the going down of the sun, feasting on abundant flesh and sweet wine. But when the sun sank and darkness had come on, then we laid us to rest upon the sea beach. So soon as early Dawn shone forth, the rosy-fingered, I called a gathering of my men and spake in the ears of them all:

" 'Hear my words, my fellows, despite your evil case. My friends, lo, now we know not where is the place of darkness or of dawning, nor where the Sun, that gives light to men, goes beneath the earth, nor where he rises; therefore let us advise us speedily if any counsel yet may be: as for me, I deem there is none. For I went up a craggy hill, a place of out-look, and saw the island crowned about with the circle of the endless sea, the isle itself lying low; and in the midst thereof mine eyes beheld the smoke through the thick coppice and the woodland.'

"Even so I spake, but their spirit within them was broken, as they remembered the deeds of Antiphates the Laestrygonian, and all the evil violence of the haughty Cyclops, the man-eater. So they wept aloud shedding big tears. Howbeit no avail came of their weeping.

"Then I numbered my goodly-greaved company in two bands, and appointed a leader for each, and I myself took the command of the one part, and godlike Eurylochus of the other. And anon we shook the lots in a brazen-fitted helmet, and out leapt the lot of proud Eurylochus. So he went on his way, and with him two and twenty of my fellowship all weeping; and we were left behind making lament. In the forest glades they found the halls of Circe builded, of polished stone, in a place with wide prospect. And all around the palace mountain-bred wolves and lions were roaming, whom she herself had bewitched with evil drugs that she gave them. Yet the beasts did not set on my men, but lo, they ramped about them and fawned on them, wagging their long tails. And as when dogs fawn about their lord when he comes from the feast, for he always brings them the fragments that soothe their mood, even so the strong-clawed wolves and the lions fawned around them; but they were affrighted when they saw the strange and terrible creatures. So they stood at the outer gate of the fair-tressed goddess, and within they heard Circe singing in a sweet voice, as she fared to and fro before the great web imperishable, such as is the handiwork of goddesses, fine of woof and full of grace and splendour. Then Polites, a leader of men, the dearest to me and the trustiest of all my company, first spake to them:

" 'Friends, forasmuch as there is one within that fares to and fro before a mighty web singing a sweet song, so that all the floor of the hall makes echo, a goddess she is or a woman; come quickly and cry aloud to her.'

"He spake the word and they cried aloud and called to her. And straightway she came forth and opened the shining doors and bade them in, and all went with her in their heedlessness. But Eurylochus tarried behind, for he guessed that there was some treason. So she led them in and set them upon the chairs and high seats, and made them a mess of cheese and barley-meal and yellow honey with Pramnian wine, and mixed harmful drugs with the food to make them utterly forget their own country. Now when she had given them the cup and they had drunk it off, presently she smote them with a wand, and in the styes of the swine she penned them. So they had the head and voice, the bristles and the shape of swine, but their mind abode even as of old. Thus were they penned there weeping, and Circe flung them acorns and mast and fruit of the cornel tree to eat, whereon wallowing swine do always batten.

"Now Eurylochus came back to the swift black ship to bring tidings of his fellows, and of their unseemly doom. Not a word could he utter, for all his desire, so deeply smitten was he to the heart with grief, and his eyes were filled with tears and his soul was fain of lamentation. But when we all had pressed him with our questions in amazement, even then he told the fate of the remnant of our company.

" 'We went, as thou didst command, through the coppice, noble Odysseus: we found within the forest glades the fair halls, builded of polished stone, in a place with wide prospect. And there was one that fared before a mighty web and sang a clear song, a goddess she was or a woman, and they cried aloud and called to her. And straightway she came forth, and opened the shining doors and bade them in, and they all went with her in their heedlessness. But I tarried behind, for I guessed that there was some treason. Then they vanished away one and all, nor did any of them appear again, though I sat long time watching.'

"So spake he, whereon I cast about my shoulder my silver-studded sword, a great blade of bronze, and slung my bow about me and bade him lead me again by the way that he came. But he caught me with both hands, and by my knees he besought me, and bewailing him spake to me winged words:

" 'Lead me not thither against my will, oh fosterling of Zeus, but leave me here! For well I know thou shalt thyself return no more, nor bring any one of all thy fellowship; nay, let us flee the swifter with those that be here, for even yet may we escape the evil day.'

"On this wise he spake, but I answered him, saying: 'Eurylochus, abide for thy part here in this place, eating and drinking by the black hollow ship: but I will go forth, for a strong constraint is laid on me.'

"With that I went up from the ship and the sea-shore. But lo, when in my faring through the sacred glades I was now drawing near to the great hall of the enchantress

Circe, then did Hermes, of the golden wand, meet me as I approached the house, in the likeness of a young man with the first down on his lip, the time when youth is most gracious. So he clasped my hand and spake and hailed me:

" 'Ah, hapless man, whither away again, all alone through the wolds, thou that knowest not this country? And thy company yonder in the hall of Circe are penned in the guise of swine, in their deep lairs abiding. Is it in hope to free them that thou art come hither? Nay, methinks, thou thyself shalt never return but remain there with the others. Come then, I will redeem thee from thy distress, and bring deliverance. Lo, take this herb of virtue, and go to the dwelling of Circe, that it may keep from thy head the evil day. And I will tell thee all the magic sleight of Circe. She will mix thee a potion and cast drugs into it; but not even so shall she be able to enchant thee; so helpful is this charmed herb that I shall give thee, and I will tell thee all. When it shall be that Circe smites thee with her long wand, even then draw thou thy sharp sword from thy thigh, and spring on her, as one eager to slay her. And she will shrink away and be instant with thee to lie with her. Thenceforth disdain not thou the bed of the goddess, that she may deliver thy company and kindly entertain thee. But command her to swear a mighty oath by the blessed gods, that she will plan nought else of mischief to thine own hurt, lest she make thee a dastard and unmanned, when she hath thee naked.'

"Therewith the slayer of Argus gave me the plant that he had plucked from the ground, and he showed me the growth thereof. It was black at the root, but the flower was like to milk. Moly the gods call it, but it is hard for mortal men to dig; howbeit with the gods all things are possible.

"Then Hermes departed toward high Olympus, up through the woodland isle, but as for me I held on my way to the house of Circe, and my heart was darkly troubled as I went. So I halted in the portals of the fair-tressed goddess; there I stood and called aloud and the goddess heard my voice, who presently came forth and opened the shining doors and bade me in, and I went with her heavy at heart.

So she led me in and set me on a chair with studs of silver, a goodly carven chair, and beneath was a footstool for the feet. And she made me a potion in a golden cup, that I might drink, and she also put a charm therein, in the evil counsel of her heart. Now when she had given it and I had drunk it off and was not bewitched, she smote me with her wand and spake and hailed me:

" 'Go thy way now to the stye, couch thee there with the rest of thy company.'

"So spake she, but I drew my sharp sword from my thigh and sprang upon Circe, as one eager to slay her. But with a great cry she slipped under, and clasped my knees, and bewailing herself spake to me winged words:

" 'Who art thou of the sons of men, and whence? Where is thy city? Where are they that begat thee? I marvel to see how thou hast drunk of this charm, and wast nowise subdued. Nay, for there lives no man else that is proof against this charm, whoso hath drunk thereof, and once it hath passed his lips. But thou hast, methinks, a mind within thee that may not be enchanted. Verily thou art Odysseus, ready at need, whom he of the golden wand, the slayer of Argus, full often told me was to come hither, on his way from Troy with his swift black ship. Nay come, put thy sword into the sheath, and thereafter let us go up into my bed, that meeting in love and sleep we may trust each the other.'

"So spake she, but I answered her, saying: 'Nay, Circe, how canst thou bid me be gentle to thee, who hast turned my company into swine within thy halls, and holding me here with a guileful heart requirest me to pass within thy chamber and go up into thy bed, that so thou mayest make me a dastard and unmanned when thou hast me naked? Nay, never will I consent to go up into thy bed, except thou wilt deign, goddess, to swear a mighty oath, that thou wilt plan nought else of mischief to mine own hurt.'

"So I spake, and she straightway swore the oath not to harm me, as I bade her. But when she had sworn and had done that oath, then at last I went up into the beautiful bed of Circe.

Circe to Odysseus: "Come on to my bed . . ."

PAINTING FROM A CRATER OF THE BASILICATE.
(BRITISH MUSEUM)

"Now all this while her handmaids busied them in the halls, four maidens that are her serving women in the house. They are born of the wells and of the woods and of the holy rivers, that flow forward into the salt sea. Of these one cast upon the chairs goodly coverlets of purple above, and spread a linen cloth thereunder. And lo, another drew up silver tables to the chairs, and thereon set for them golden baskets. And a third mixed sweet honey-hearted wine in a silver bowl, and set out cups of gold. And a fourth bare water, and kindled a great fire beneath the mighty caldron. So the water waxed warm; but when it boiled in the bright brazen vessel, she set me in a bath and bathed me with water from out a great caldron, pouring it over head and shoulders, when she had mixed it to a pleasant warmth, till from my limbs she took away the consuming weariness. Now after she had bathed me and anointed me well with olive oil, and cast about me a fair mantle and a doublet, she led me into the halls and set me on a chair with studs of silver, a goodly carven chair, and beneath was a footstool for the feet. And a handmaid bare water for the hands in a goodly golden ewer, and poured it forth over a silver basin to wash withal; and to my side she drew a polished table, and a grave dame bare wheaten bread and set it by me, and laid on the board many dainties, giving freely of such things as she had by her. And she bade me eat, but my soul found no pleasure therein. I sat with other thoughts, and my heart had a boding of ill.

"Now when Circe saw that I sat thus, and that I put not forth my hands to the meat, and that I was mightily afflicted, she drew near to me and spake to me winged words:

" 'Wherefore thus, Odysseus, dost thou sit there like a speechless man, consuming thine own soul, and dost not touch meat nor drink? Dost thou indeed deem there is some further guile? Nay, thou hast no cause to fear, for already I have sworn thee a strong oath not to harm thee.'

"So spake she, but I answered her, saying: 'Oh, Circe, what righteous man would have the heart to taste meat and drink ere he had redeemed his company, and beheld them

Thinks of his men -
a good captain

face to face? But if in good faith thou biddest me eat and drink, then let them go free, that mine eyes may behold my dear companions.'

"So I spake, and Circe passed out through the hall with the wand in her hand, and opened the doors of the stye, and drave them forth in the shape of swine of nine seasons old. There they stood before her, and she went through their midst, and anointed each one of them with another charm. And lo, from their limbs the bristles dropped away, wherewith the venom had erewhile clothed them, that lady Circe gave them. And they became men again, younger than before they were, and goodlier far, and taller to behold. And they all knew me again and each one took my hands, and wistful was the lament that sank into their souls, and the roof around rang wondrously. And even the goddess herself was moved with compassion.

"Then standing nigh me the fair goddess spake unto me: 'Son of Laertes, of the seed of Zeus, Odysseus of many devices, depart now to thy swift ship and the sea-banks. And first of all, draw ye up the ship ashore, and bestow the goods in the caves and all the gear. And thyself return again, and bring with thee thy dear companions.'

"So spake she, and my lordly spirit consented thereto. So I went on my way to the swift ship and the sea-banks, and there I found my dear company on the swift ship lamenting piteously, shedding big tears. And as when calves of the homestead gather round the droves of kine that have returned to the yard, when they have had their fill of pasture, and all with one accord frisk before them, and the folds may no more contain them, but with a ceaseless lowing they skip about their dams, so flocked they all about me weeping, when their eyes beheld me. Yea, and to their spirit it was as though they had got to their dear country, and the very city of rugged Ithaca, where they were born and reared.

"Then making lament they spake to me winged words: 'O fosterling of Zeus, we were none otherwise glad at thy returning, than if we had come to Ithaca, our own country. Nay come, of our other companions tell us the tale of their ruin.'

"So spake they, but I answered them with soft words: 'Behold, let us first of all draw up the ship ashore, and bestow our goods in the caves and all our gear. And do ye bestir you, one and all, to go with me, that ye may see your fellows in the sacred dwelling of Circe, eating and drinking, for they have continual store.'

"So spake I, and at once they hearkened to my words, but Eurylochus alone would have holden all my companions, and uttering his voice he spake to them winged words:

" 'Wretched men that we are! whither are we going? Why are your hearts so set on sorrow that ye should go down to the hall of Circe, who will surely change us all to swine, or wolves, or lions, to guard her great house perforce, just the same sort of thing that the Cyclops wrought, when certain of our company went to his inmost fold, and with them went Odysseus, ever hardy, for through the blindness of his heart did they too perish?'

"So spake he, but I mused in my heart whether to draw my long hanger from my stout thigh, and therewith smite off his head and bring it to the dust, albeit he was very near of kin to me; but the men of my company stayed me on every side with soothing words:

" 'Prince of the seed of Zeus, as for this man, we will suffer him, if thou wilt have it so, to abide here by the ship and guard the ship; but as for us, be our guide to the sacred house of Circe.'

"So they spake and went up from the ship and the sea. Nay, nor yet was Eurylochus left by the hollow ship, but he went with us, for he feared my terrible rebuke.

"Meanwhile Circe bathed the rest of my company in her halls with all care, and anointed them well with olive oil; and cast thick mantles and doublets about them. And we found them all feasting nobly in the halls. And when they saw and knew each other face to face, they wept and mourned, and the house rang around. Then she stood near me, that fair goddess, and spake saying:

" 'Son of Laertes, of the seed of Zeus, Odysseus of many devices, no more now wake this plenteous weeping: myself I know of all the pains ye endured upon the teeming deep, and the great despite done you by unkindly men upon the land. Nay come, eat ye meat and drink wine, till your spirit shall return to you again, as it was when first ye left your own country of rugged Ithaca; but now are ye wasted and wanting heart, mindful evermore of your sore wandering, nor has your heart ever been merry, for very grievous hath been your trial.'

"So spake she, and our lordly spirit consented thereto. So there we sat day by day for the full circle of a year, feasting on abundant flesh and sweet wine. But when now a year had gone, and the seasons returned as the months waned, and the long days came in their course, then did my dear company call me forth, and say:

" 'Good sir, now is it high time to mind thee of thy native land, if it is ordained that thou shalt be saved, and come to thy lofty house and thine own country.'

"So spake they and my lordly spirit consented thereto. So for that time we sat the livelong day till the going down of the sun, feasting on abundant flesh and sweet wine. But when the sun sank and darkness came on, they laid them to rest throughout the shadowy halls.

"But when I had gone up into the fair bed of Circe, I besought her by her knees, and the goddess heard my speech, and uttering my voice I spake to her winged words: 'Circe, fulfil for me the promise which thou madest me to send me on my homeward way. Now is my spirit eager to be gone, and the spirit of my company, that wear away my heart as they mourn around me, when haply thou art not with us.'

"So spake I, and the fair goddess answered me anon: 'Son of Laertes, of the seed of Zeus, Odysseus of many devices, tarry ye now no longer in my house against your will; but first must ye perform another journey, and reach the dwelling of Hades and of dread Persephone to seek the spirit of Theban Teiresias, the blind soothsayer, whose wits abide steadfast. To him Persephone hath given judgment, even in death, that he alone should have understanding; but the other souls sweep shadow-like around.'

"Thus spake she, but as for me, my heart was broken,

and I wept as I sat upon the bed, and my soul had no more care to live and to see the sunlight. But when I had my' fill of weeping and grovelling, then at the last I answered and spake unto her saying: 'And who, Circe, will guide us on this way? for no man ever yet sailed to hell in a black ship.'

"So spake I, and the fair goddess answered me anon: 'Son of Laertes, of the seed of Zeus, Odysseus of many devices, nay, trouble not thyself for want of a guide, by thy ship abiding, but set up the mast and spread abroad the white sails and sit thee down; and the breeze of the North Wind will bear thy vessel on her way. But when thou hast now sailed in thy ship across the stream Oceanus, where is a waste shore and the groves of Persephone, even tall poplar trees and willows that shed their fruit before the season, there beach thy ship by deep eddying Oceanus, but go thyself to the dank house of Hades. Thereby into Acheron flows Pyriphlegethon, and Cocytus, a branch of the water of the Styx, and there is a rock, and the meeting of the two roaring waters. So, hero, draw nigh thereto, as I command thee, and dig a trench as it were a cubit in length and breadth, and about it pour a drink-offering to all the dead, first with mead and thereafter with sweet wine, and for the third time with water, and sprinkle white meal thereon; and entreat with many prayers the strengthless heads of the dead, and promise that on thy return to Ithaca thou wilt offer in thy halls a barren heifer, the best thou hast, and wilt fill the pyre with treasure, and wilt sacrifice apart, to Teiresias alone, a black ram without spot, the fairest of your flock. But when thou hast with prayers made supplication to the lordly races of the dead, then offer up a ram and a black ewe, bending their heads down towards Hades and thyself turn thy back, with thy face set toward the shore of the river. Then will many spirits come to thee of the dead that be departed. Thereafter thou shalt call to thy company and command them to flay the sheep which even now lie slain by the pitiless sword, and to consume them with fire, and to make prayer to the gods, to mighty Hades and to dread Persephone. And thyself draw the sharp sword from thy

thigh and sit there, suffering not the strengthless heads of
the dead to draw nigh to the blood, ere thou hast word of
Teiresias. Then the seer will come to thee quickly, leader
of the people; he will surely declare to thee the way and
the measure of thy path, and as touching thy returning, how
thou mayst go over the teeming deep.'

"So spake she, and anon came the golden throned Dawn.
Then she put on me a mantle and a doublet for raiment,
and the nymph clad herself in a great shining robe, light
of woof and gracious, and about her waist she cast a fair
golden girdle, and put a veil upon her head. But I passed
through the halls and roused my men with smooth words,
standing by each one in turn:

" 'Sleep ye now no more nor breathe the sweet slumber;
but let us go on our way, for surely she hath shown me all,
the lady Circe.'

"So spake I, and their lordly soul consented thereto. Yet
even thence I led not my company safe away. There was
one, Elpenor, the youngest of us all, not very valiant in
war neither steadfast in mind. He was lying apart from the
rest of my men on the housetop of Circe's sacred dwelling,
very fain of the cool air, as one heavy with wine. Now when
he heard the noise of the voices and of the feet of my fellows
as they moved to and fro, he leaped up of a sudden and
minded him not to descend again by the way of the tall ladder, but fell right down from the roof, and his neck was
broken from the bones of the spine, and his spirit went
down to the house of Hades.

"Then I spake among my men as they went on their way,
saying: 'Ye deem now, I see, that ye are going to your own
dear country; but Circe hath showed us another way, even
to the dwelling of Hades and of dread Persephone, to seek
to the spirit of Theban Teiresias.'

"Even so I spake, but their heart within them was broken,
and they sat them down even where they were, and made
lament and tore their hair. Howbeit no help came of their
weeping.

"But as we were now wending sorrowful to the swift ship and the sea-banks, shedding big tears, Circe meanwhile had gone her ways and made fast a ram and a black ewe by the dark ship, lightly passing us by: who may behold a god against his will, whether going to or fro?"

XI

The Place of the Dead

Now when we had gone down to the ship and to the sea, first of all we drew the ship unto the fair salt water, and placed the mast and sails in the black ship, and took those sheep and put them therein, and ourselves too climbed on board, sorrowing, and shedding big tears. And in the wake of our dark-prowed ship she sent a favouring wind that filled the sails, a kindly escort,—even Circe of the braided tresses, a dread goddess of human speech. And we set in order all the gear throughout the ship and sat us down; and the wind and the helmsman guided our barque. And all day long her sails were stretched in her seafaring; and the sun sank and all the ways were darkened.

"She came to the limits of the world, to the deep flowing Oceanus. There is the land and the city of the Cimmerians, shrouded in mist and cloud, and never does the shining sun look down on them with his rays, neither when he climbs up the starry heavens, nor when again he turns earthward from the firmament, but deadly night is outspread over miserable mortals. Thither we came and ran the ship ashore and took out the sheep; but for our part we held on our way along the stream of Oceanus, till we came to the place which Circe had declared to us.

"There Perimedes and Eurylochus held the victims, but I drew my sharp sword from my thigh, and dug a pit, as it were a cubit in length and breadth, and about it poured a drink-offering to all the dead, first with mead and thereafter with sweet wine, and for the third time with water. And I sprinkled white meal thereon, and entreated with many prayers the strengthless heads of the dead, and promised that on my return to Ithaca I would offer in my halls a barren heifer, the best I had, and fill the pyre with treasure, and apart unto Teiresias alone sacrifice a black ram without spot, the fairest of my flock. But when I had be-

Hades. — The Infernal Regions.

PAINTING FROM AN AMPHORA FOUND AT CANOSA.
(MUNICH PINAKOTHEK)

sought the tribes of the dead with vows and prayers, I took the sheep and cut their throats over the trench, and the dark blood flowed forth, and lo, the spirits of the dead that be departed gathered them from out of Hades. Brides and youths unwed, and old men of many and evil days, and tender maidens with grief yet fresh at heart; and many there were, wounded with bronze-shod spears, men slain in fight with their bloody mail about them. And these many ghosts flocked together from every side about the trench with a wondrous cry, and pale fear gat hold on me. Then did I speak to my company and command them to flay the sheep that lay slain by the pitiless sword, and to consume them with fire, and to make prayer to the gods, to mighty Hades and to dread Persephone, and myself I drew the sharp sword from my thigh and sat there, suffering not the strengthless heads of the dead to draw nigh to the blood, ere I had word of Teiresias.

"And first came the soul of Elpenor, my companion, that had not yet been buried beneath the wide-wayed earth; for we left the corpse behind us in the hall of Circe, unwept and unburied, seeing that another task was instant on us. At the sight of him I wept and had compassion on him, and uttering my voice spake to him winged words: 'Elpenor, how hast thou come beneath the darkness and the shadow? Thou hast come fleeter on foot than I in my black ship.'

"So spake I, and with a moan he answered me, saying: 'Son of Laertes, of the seed of Zeus, Odysseus of many devices, an evil doom of some god was my bane and wine out of measure. When I laid me down on the house-top of Circe I minded me not to descend again by the way of the tall ladder, but fell right down from the roof, and my neck was broken off from the bones of the spine, and my spirit went down to the house of Hades. And now I pray thee in the name of those whom we left, who are no more with us, thy wife, and thy sire who cherished thee when as yet thou wert a little one, and Telemachus, whom thou didst leave in thy halls alone; forasmuch as I know that on thy way hence from out the dwelling of Hades, thou wilt stay thy well-wrought ship at the isle Aeaean, even then, my lord, I charge thee to think on me. Leave me not unwept and unburied as thou goest hence, nor turn thy back upon me, lest haply I bring on thee the anger of the gods. Nay, burn me there with mine armour, all that is mine, and pile me a barrow on the shore of the grey sea, the grave of a luckless man, that even men unborn may hear my story. Fulfil me this and plant upon the barrow mine oar, wherewith I rowed in the days of my life, while yet I was among my fellows.'

"Even so he spake, and I answered him saying: 'All this, luckless man, will I perform for thee and do.'

"Even so we twain were sitting holding sad discourse, I on the one side, stretching forth my sword over the blood, while on the other side the ghost of my friend told all his tale.

"Anon came up the soul of my mother dead, Anticleia, the daughter of Autolycus the great-hearted, whom I left alive when I departed for sacred Ilium. At the sight of her I wept, and was moved with compassion, yet even so, for all my sore grief, I suffered her not to draw nigh to the blood, ere I had word of Teiresias.

"Anon came the soul of Theban Teiresias, with a golden sceptre in his hand, and he knew me and spake unto me: 'Son of Laertes, of the seed of Zeus, Odysseus of many devices, what seekest thou *now*, wretched man, wherefore hast thou left the sunlight and come hither to behold the dead and a land desolate of joy? Nay, hold off from the ditch and draw back thy sharp sword, that I may drink of the blood and tell thee sooth.'

"So spake he and I put up my silver-studded sword into the sheath, and when he had drunk the dark blood, even then did the noble seer speak unto me, saying: 'Thou art asking of thy sweet returning, great Odysseus, but that will the god make hard for thee; for methinks thou shalt not pass unheeded by the Shaker of the Earth, who hath laid up wrath in his heart against thee, for rage at the blinding of his dear son. Yet even so, through many troubles, ye may come home, if thou wilt restrain thy spirit and the spirit of thy men so soon as thou shalt bring thy well-wrought ship nigh to the isle Thrinacia, fleeing the sea of violet blue, when ye find the herds of Helios grazing and his brave flocks, of Helios who overseeth all and overheareth all things. If thou doest these no hurt, being heedful of thy return, so may ye yet reach Ithaca, albeit in evil case. But if thou hurtest them, I foreshow ruin for thy ship and for thy men, and even though thou shalt thyself escape, late shalt thou return in evil plight, with the loss of all thy company, on board the ship of strangers, and thou shalt find sorrows in thy house, even proud men that devour thy living, while they woo thy godlike wife and offer the gifts of wooing. Yet I tell thee, on thy coming thou shalt avenge their violence. But when thou hast slain the wooers in thy halls, whether by guile, or openly with the edge of the sword, thereafter go thy way, taking with thee a shapen oar, till thou shalt come to such men as know not the sea, neither eat meat savoured with salt; yea, nor have they knowledge of purple ships nor shapen oars which serve for wings to ships. And I will give thee a most manifest token, which cannot escape thee. In the day when another wayfarer shall meet thee and say that thou hast a winnowing fan on thy stout shoulder, even then make fast thy shapen oar in the earth and do goodly sacrifice to the lord Poseidon, even with a ram and a bull and a boar, the mate of swine, and depart for home and offer holy hecatombs to the deathless gods that keep the wide heaven, to each in order due. And from the sea shall thine own death come, the gentlest death that may be, which shall end thee foredone with smooth old age, and the folk shall dwell happily around thee. This that I say is sooth.'

"So spake he, and I answered him, saying: 'Teiresias, all these threads, methinks, the gods themselves have spun. But come, declare me this and plainly tell me all. I see here the spirit of my mother dead; lo, she sits in silence near the blood, nor deigns to look her son in the face nor speak to him! Tell me, prince, how may she know me again that I am he?'

"So spake I, and anon he answered me, and said: 'I will tell thee an easy saying, and will put it in thy heart. Whomsoever of the dead that be departed thou shalt suffer to draw nigh to the blood, he shall tell thee sooth; but if thou shalt grudge any, that one shall go to his own place again.' Therewith the spirit of the prince Teiresias went back within the house of Hades, when he had told all his oracles. But I abode there steadfastly, till my mother drew nigh and drank the dark blood; and at once she knew me, and bewailing herself spake to me winged words:

" 'Dear child, how didst thou come beneath the darkness and the shadow, thou that art a living man? Grievous is the sight of these things to the living, for between us and you are great rivers and dreadful streams; first, Oceanus, which can no wise be crossed on foot, but only if one have a well-wrought ship. Art thou but now come hither with thy ship and thy company in thy long wanderings from Troy? and hast thou not yet reached Ithaca, nor seen thy wife in thy halls?'

"Even so she spake, and I answered her, and said: 'O my mother, necessity was on me to come down to the house of Hades to seek to the spirit of Theban Teiresias. For not yet have I drawn near to the Achaean shore, nor yet have I set foot on mine own country, but have been wandering evermore in affliction, from the day that first I went with goodly Agamemnon to Ilium of the fair steeds, to do battle with the Trojans. But come, declare me this and plainly tell it all. What doom overcame thee of death that lays men at their length? Was it a slow disease, or did Artemis the archer slay thee with the visitation of her gentle shafts? And tell me of my father and my son, that I left behind me; doth my honour yet abide with them, or hath another already taken it, while they say that I shall come home no more? And tell me of my wedded wife, of her counsel and her purpose, doth she abide with her son and keep all secure, or hath she already wedded the best of the Achaeans?'

"Even so I spake, and anon my lady mother answered me: 'Yea verily, she abideth with steadfast spirit in thy halls; and wearily for her the nights wane always and the days in shedding of tears. But the fair honour that is thine no man hath yet taken; but Telemachus sits at peace on his demesne, and feasts at public banquets such as the magistrates are expected to give, for all men bid him to their house. And thy father abides there in the field, and goes not down to the town, nor lies he on bedding or rugs or shining blankets, but all the winter he sleeps, where sleep the thralls in the house, in the ashes by the fire, and is clad in sorry raiment. But when the summer comes and the rich harvest-tide, his beds of fallen leaves are strewn lowly all about the knoll of his vineyard plot. There he lies sorrowing and nurses his mighty grief, for long desire of thy return, and old age withal comes heavy upon him. Yea and even so did I too perish and meet my doom. It was not the archer goddess of the keen sight, who slew me in my halls with the visitation of her gentle shafts, nor did any sickness come upon me, such as chiefly with a sad wasting draws the spirit from the limbs; nay, it was my sore longing for thee, and for thy counsels, great Odysseus, and for thy loving-kindness, that reft me of sweet life.'

"So spake she, and I mused in my heart and would fain have embraced the spirit of my mother dead. Thrice I sprang towards her, and was minded to embrace her; thrice she flitted from my hands as a shadow or even as a dream, and sharp grief arose ever at my heart. And uttering my voice I spake to her winged words:

" 'Mother mine, wherefore dost thou not abide me who am eager to clasp thee, that even in Hades we twain may cast our arms each about the other, and have our fill of chill lament? Is this but a phantom that the high goddess Persephone hath sent me, to the end that I may groan for more exceeding sorrow?'

"So spake I, and my lady mother answered me anon: 'Ah me, my child, of all men most ill-fated, Persephone, the daughter of Zeus, doth in no wise deceive thee, but even on this wise it is with mortals when they die. For the sinews no more bind together the flesh and the bones, but the great force of burning fire abolishes these, so soon as the life hath left the white bones, and the spirit like a dream flies forth and hovers near. But haste with all thine heart toward the sunlight, and mark all this, that even hereafter thou mayest tell it to thy wife.'

"Thus we twain held discourse together; and lo, the women came up, for the high goddess Persephone sent them forth, all they that had been the wives and daughters of mighty men. And they gathered and flocked about the black blood, and I took counsel how I might question them each one. And this was the counsel that showed best in my sight. I drew my long sword from my stalwart thigh, and suffered them not all at one time to drink of the dark blood. So they drew nigh one by one, and each declared her lineage, and I made question of all.

"Then verily did I first see Tyro, sprung of a noble sire, who said that she was the child of noble Salmoneus, and declared herself the wife of Cretheus, son of Aeolus. She loved a river, the divine Enipeus, far the fairest of the floods that run upon the earth, and she would resort to the fair streams of Enipeus. And it came to pass that the girdler of the world, the Earth-shaker, put on the shape of the god, and lay by the lady at the mouths of the whirling stream. Then the dark wave stood around them like a hill-side bowed, and hid the god and the mortal woman. And he undid her maiden girdle, and shed a slumber over her. Now when the god had done the work of love, he clasped her hand and spake and hailed her.

" 'Woman, be glad in our love, and when the year comes round thou shalt give birth to glorious children,—for not weak are the embraces of the gods,—and do thou keep and cherish them. And now go home and hold thy peace, and tell it not: but behold, I am Poseidon, shaker of the earth.'

"Therewith he plunged beneath the heaving deep. And she conceived and bare Pelias and Neleus, who both grew to be mighty men, servants of Zeus. Pelias dwelt in wide Iolcos, and was rich in flocks; and that other abode in sandy Pylos. And the queen of women bare yet other sons to Cretheus, even Aeson and Pheres and Amythaon, whose joy was in chariots.

"And after her I saw Antiope, daughter of Asôpus, and her boast was that she had slept even in the arms of Zeus, and she bare two sons, Amphion and Zethus, who founded first the place of seven-gated Thebes, and they made of it a fenced city, for they might not dwell in spacious Thebes unfenced, for all their valiancy.

"Next to her I saw Alcmene, wife of Amphitryon, who lay in the arms of mighty Zeus, and bare Heracles of the lion-heart, steadfast in the fight. And I saw Megara, daughter of Creon, haughty of heart, whom the strong and tireless son of Amphitryon had to wife.

"And I saw the mother of Oedipus, fair Epicaste, who wrought a dread deed unwittingly, being wedded to her own son, and he that had slain his own father wedded her, and straightway the gods made these things known to men. Yet he abode in pain in pleasant Thebes, ruling the Cadmaeans, by reason of the deadly counsels of the gods. But she went down to the house of Hades, the mighty warder; yea, she tied a noose from the high beam aloft, being fast holden in sorrow; while for him she left pains behind full many, even all that the Avengers of a mother bring to pass.

"And I saw lovely Chloris, whom Neleus wedded on a time for her beauty, and brought gifts of wooing past number. She was the youngest daughter of Amphion, son of Iasus, who once ruled mightily in Minyan Orchomenus. And she was queen of Pylos, and bare glorious children to her lord, Nestor and Chromius, and princely Periclymenus, and stately Pero too, the wonder of all men. All that dwelt around were her wooers; but Neleus would not give her, save to him who should drive off from Phylace the kine of mighty Iphicles, with shambling gait and broad of brow, hard cattle to drive. And none but the noble seer took in hand to drive them; but a grievous fate from the gods fettered him, even hard bonds and the herdsmen of the wild. But when at length the months and days were being fulfilled, as the year returned upon his course, and the seasons came round, then did mighty Iphicles set him free, when he had spoken out all the oracles; and herein was the counsel of Zeus being accomplished.

"And I saw Lede, the famous bed-fellow of Tyndareus, who bare to Tyndareus two sons, hardy of heart, Castor tamer of steeds, and Polydeuces the boxer. These twain yet live, but the quickening earth is over them; and even in the nether world they have honour at the hand of Zeus. And they possess their life in turn, living one day and dying the next, and they have gotten worship even as the gods.

"And after her I beheld Iphimedeia, bed-fellow of Aloeus, who said that she had lain with Poseidon, and she bare children twain, but short of life were they, godlike Otus and far-famed Ephialtes. Now these were the tallest men that earth, the grain-giver, ever reared, and far the goodliest after the renowned Orion. At nine seasons old they were of breadth nine cubits, and nine fathoms in height. They it was who threatened to raise even against the immortals in Olympus the din of stormy war. They strove to pile Ossa on Olympus, and on Ossa Pelion with the trembling forest leaves, that there might be a pathway to the sky. Yea, and they would have accomplished it, had they reached the full measure of manhood. But the son of Zeus, whom Leto of the fair locks bare, destroyed the twain, ere the down had bloomed beneath their temples, and darkened their chins with the blossom of youth.

"And Phaedra and Procris I saw, and fair Ariadne, the daughter of wizard Minos, whom Theseus on a time was bearing from Crete to the hill of sacred Athens, yet had he no joy of her; for Artemis slew her ere that in sea-girt Dia, by reason of the witness of Dionysus.

"And Maera and Clymene I saw, and hateful Eriphyle, who took fine gold for the price of her dear lord's life. But I cannot tell or name all the wives and daughters of the heroes that I saw; ere that, the immortal night would wane. Nay, it is even now time to sleep, whether I go to the swift ship to my company or abide here: and for my convoy you and the gods will care."

So spake he, and dead silence fell on all, and they were spell-bound throughout the shadowy halls. Then Arete of the white arms first spake among them: "Phaeacians, what think you of this man for comeliness and stature, and within for wisdom of heart? Moreover he is my guest, though every one of you hath his share in this honour. Wherefore haste not to send him hence, and stint not these your gifts for one that stands in such sore need of them; for ye have much treasure stored in your halls by the grace of the gods."

Then too spake among them the old man, lord Echeneus,

that was an elder among the Phaeacians: "Friends, behold, the speech of our wise queen is not wide of the mark, nor far from our deeming, so hearken ye thereto. But on Alcinous here both word and work depend."

Then Alcinous made answer, and spake unto him: "Yea, the word that she hath spoken shall hold, if indeed I am yet to live and bear rule among the Phaeacians, masters of the oar. Howbeit let the stranger, for all his craving to return, nevertheless endure to abide until the morrow, till I make up the full measure of the gift; and men shall care for his convoy, all men, but I in chief, for mine is the lordship in the land."

And Odysseus of many counsels answered him, saying: "My lord Alcinous, most notable of all the people, if ye bade me tarry here even for a year, and would speed my convoy and give me splendid gifts, even that I would choose; and better would it be for me to come with a fuller hand to mine own dear country, so should I get more love and worship in the eyes of all men, whoso should see me after I was returned to Ithaca."

And Alcinous answered him, saying: "Odysseus, in no wise do we deem thee, we that look on thee, to be a knave or a cheat, even as the dark earth rears many such broadcast, fashioning lies whence none can even see his way therein. But beauty crowns thy words, and wisdom is within thee; and thy tale, as when a minstrel sings, thou hast told with skill, the weary woes of all the Argives and of thine own self. But come, declare me this and plainly tell it all. Didst thou see any of thy godlike company who went up at the same time with thee to Ilium and there met their doom? Behold, the night is of great length, unspeakable, and the time for sleep in the hall is not yet; tell me therefore of those wondrous deeds. I could abide even till the bright dawn, so long as thou couldst endure to rehearse me these woes of thine in the hall."

And Odysseus of many counsels answered him, saying: "My lord Alcinous, most notable of all the people, there is a time for many words and there is a time for sleep. But if thou art eager still to listen, I would not for my part grudge to tell thee of other things more pitiful still, even the woes of my comrades, those that perished afterward, for they had escaped with their lives from the dread war-cry of the Trojans, but perished in returning by the will of an evil woman.

"Now when holy Persephone had scattered this way and that the spirits of the women folk, thereafter came the soul of Agamemnon, son of Atreus, sorrowing; and round him others were gathered, the ghosts of them who had died with him in the house of Aegisthus and met their doom. And he knew me straightway when he had drunk the dark blood, yea, and he wept aloud, and shed big tears as he stretched forth his hands in his longing to reach me. But it might not be, for he had now no steadfast strength nor power at all in moving, such as was aforetime in his supple limbs.

"At the sight of him I wept and was moved with compassion, and uttering my voice, spake to him winged words: 'Most renowned son of Atreus, Agamemnon, king of men, say what doom overcame thee of death that lays men at their length? Did Poseidon smite thee in thy ships, raising the dolorous blast of contrary winds, or did unfriendly men do thee hurt upon the land, whilst thou wert cutting off their oxen and fair flocks of sheep, or fighting to win a city and the women thereof?'

"So spake I, and straightway he answered, and said unto me: 'Son of Laertes, of the seed of Zeus, Odysseus of many devices, it was not Poseidon that smote me in my ships, and raised the dolorous blast of contrary winds, nor did unfriendly men do me hurt upon the land, but Aegisthus it was that wrought me death and doom and slew me, with the aid of my accursed wife, as one slays an ox at the stall, after he had bidden me to his house, and entertained me at a feast. Even so I died by a death most pitiful, and round me my company likewise were slain without ceasing, like swine with glittering tusks which are slaughtered in the house of a rich and mighty man, whether at a wedding banquet or a joint-feast or a rich clan-drinking. Ere now hast thou been at the slaying of many a man, killed in single fight or in strong battle, yet thou wouldst have sorrowed the most at this sight, how we lay in the hall round the mixing-bowl and the laden boards, and the floor all ran with blood. And most pitiful of all that I heard was the voice of the daughter of Priam, of Cassandra, whom hard by me the crafty Clytemnestra slew. Then I strove to raise my hands as I was dying upon the sword, but to earth they fell. And that shameless one turned her back upon me, and had not the heart to draw down my eyelids with her fingers nor to close my mouth. So surely is there nought more terrible and shameless than a woman who imagines such evil in her heart, even as she too planned a foul deed, fashioning death for her wedded lord. Verily I had thought to come home most welcome to my children and my thralls; but she, out of the depth of her evil knowledge, hath shed shame on herself and on all womankind, which shall be for ever, even on the upright.'

"Even so he spake, but I answered him, saying: 'Lo now, in very sooth, hath Zeus of the far-borne voice wreaked wondrous hatred on the seed of Atreus through the counsels of woman from of old. For Helen's sake so many of us perished, and now Clytemnestra hath practised treason against thee, while yet thou wast afar off.'

"Even so I spake, and anon he answered me, saying: 'Wherefore do thou too, never henceforth be soft even to thy wife, neither show her all the counsel that thou knowest, but a part declare and let part be hid. Yet shalt not thou, Odysseus, find death at the hand of thy wife, for she is very discreet and prudent in all her ways, the wise Penelope, daughter of Icarius. Verily we left her a bride new wed when we went to the war, and a child was at her breast, who now, methinks, sits in the ranks of men, happy in his lot, for his dear father will come home and see him, and he shall embrace his sire as is meet. But as for my wife, she suffered me not so much as to have my fill of gazing on my son; ere that she slew me, even her lord. And yet another thing will I tell thee, and do thou ponder it in thy heart. Put thy ship to land in secret, and not openly, on the shore of thy dear country; for there is no more faith in woman. But come, declare me this and plainly tell it all, if haply ye hear of my son as yet living, either, it may be, in Orchomenus or in sandy Pylos, or perchance with Menelaus in wide Sparta, for goodly Orestes hath not yet perished on the earth.'

"Even so he spake, but I answered him, saying: 'Son of Atreus, wherefore dost thou ask me straitly of these things? Nay I know not at all, whether he be alive or dead; it is ill to speak words light as wind.'

"Thus we twain stood sorrowing, holding sad discourse, while the big tears fell fast: and therewithal came the soul of Achilles, son of Peleus, and of Patroclus and of noble Antilochus and of Aias, who in face and form was goodliest of all the Danaans, after the noble son of Peleus. And the spirit of Achilles, fleet of foot, knew me again, and making lament spake to me winged words:

" 'Son of Laertes, of the seed of Zeus, Odysseus of many devices, man overbold, what new deed and hardier than this wilt thou devise in thy heart? How durst thou come down to the house of Hades, where dwell the senseless dead, the phantoms of men outworn?'

"So he spake, but I answered him: 'Achilles, son of Peleus, mightiest far of the Achaeans, I am come hither to seek to Teiresias, if he may tell me any counsel, how I may come to rugged Ithaca. For not yet have I come nigh the Achaean land, nor set foot on mine own soil, but am still in evil case; while as for thee, Achilles, none other than thou wast heretofore the most blessed of men, nor shall any be hereafter. For of old, in the days of thy life, we Argives gave thee one honour with the gods, and now thou art a great prince here among the dead. Wherefore let not thy death be any grief to thee, Achilles.'

"Even so I spake, and he straightway answered me, and said: 'Nay, speak not comfortably to me of death, oh great Odysseus. Rather would I live on ground as the hireling of another, with a landless man who had no great livelihood, than bear sway among all the dead that be departed. But come, tell me tidings of that lordly son of mine—did he follow to the war to be a leader or not? And tell me of noble

Peleus, if thou hast heard aught,—is he yet held in worship among the Myrmidons, or do they dishonour him from Hellas to Phthia, for that old age binds him hand and foot? For I am no longer his champion under the sun, so mighty a man as once I was, when in wide Troy I slew the best of the host, and succoured the Argives. Ah! could I but come for an hour to my father's house as then I was, so would I make my might and hands invincible, to be hateful to many an one of those who do him despite and keep him from his honour.'

"Even so he spake, but I answered him saying: 'As for noble Peleus, verily I have heard nought of him; but concerning thy dear son Neoptolemus, I will tell thee all the truth, according to thy word. It was I that led him up out of Scyros in my good hollow ship, in the wake of the goodly-greaved Achaeans. Now oft as we took counsel around Troy town, he was ever the first to speak, and no word missed the mark; the godlike Nestor and I alone surpassed him. But whensoever we Achaeans did battle on the plain of Troy, he never tarried behind in the throng or the press of men, but ran out far before us all, yielding to none in that might of his. And many men he slew in warfare dread; but I could not tell of all or name their names, even all the host he slew in succouring the Argives; but, ah, how he smote with the sword that son of Telephus, the hero Eurypylus, and many Ceteians of his company were slain around him, by reason of a woman's bribe. He truly was the comeliest man that ever I saw, next to goodly Memnon. And again when we, the best of the Argives, were about to go down into the horse which Epeus wrought, and the charge of all was laid on me, both to open the door of our good ambush and to shut the same, then did the other princes and counsellors of the Danaans wipe away the tears, and the limbs of each one trembled beneath him, but never once did I see thy son's fair face wax pale, nor did he wipe the tears from his cheeks: but he besought me often to let him go forth from the horse, and kept handling his sword-hilt, and his heavy bronze-shod spear, and he was set on mischief against the Trojans. But after we had sacked the steep city of Priam, he embarked unscathed with his share of the spoil, and with a noble prize; he was not smitten with the sharp spear, and got no wound in close fight: and many such chances there be in war, for Ares rageth confusedly.'

"So I spake, and the spirit of Achilles, fleet of foot, passed with great strides along the mead of asphodel, rejoicing in that I had told him of his son's renown.

"But lo, other spirits of the dead that be departed stood sorrowing, and each one asked of those that were dear to them. The soul of Aias son of Telamon, alone stood apart being still angry for the victory wherein I prevailed against him, when defending my claim by the ships concerning the arms of Achilles, that his lady mother had set for a prize; and the sons of the Trojans made award and Pallas Athene. Would that I had never prevailed and won such a prize! So goodly a head hath the earth closed over, for the sake of those arms, even over Aias, who in beauty and in feats of war was of a mould above all the other Danaans, next to the noble son of Peleus. To him then I spake softly, saying:

" 'Aias, son of noble Telamon, so art thou not even in death to forget thy wrath against me, by reason of those arms accursed, which the gods set to be the bane of the Argives? What a tower of strength fell in thy fall, and we Achaeans cease not to sorrow for thee, even as for the life of Achilles, son of Peleus! Nay, there is none other to blame, but Zeus, who hath borne wondrous hate to the army of the Danaan spearsmen, and laid on thee thy doom. Nay, come hither, my lord, that thou mayest hear my word and my speech; master thy wrath and thy proud spirit.'

"So I spake, but he answered me not a word and passed to Hades after the other spirits of the dead that be departed. Even then, despite his anger, would he have spoken to me or I to him, but my heart within me was minded to see the spirits of those others that were departed.

"There then I saw Minos, glorious son of Zeus, wielding a

golden sceptre, giving sentence from his throne to the dead, while they sat and stood around the prince, asking his dooms through the wide-gated house of Hades.

"And after him I marked the mighty Orion driving the wild beasts together over the mead of asphodel, the very beasts that himself had slain on the lonely hills, with a strong mace all of bronze in his hands, that is ever unbroken.

"And I saw Tityos, son of renowned Earth, lying on a levelled ground, and he covered nine roods as he lay, and vultures twain beset him one on either side, and gnawed at his liver, piercing even to the caul, but he drave them not away with his hands. For he had dealt violently with Leto, the famous bed-fellow of Zeus, as she went up to Pytho through the fair lawns of Paponeus.

"Moreover I beheld Tantalus [1] in grievous torment, standing in a mere and the water came nigh unto his chin. And he stood straining as one athirst, but he might not attain to the water to drink of it. For often as that old man stooped down in his eagerness to drink, so often the water was swallowed up and it vanished away, and the black earth still showed at his feet, for some god parched it evermore. And tall trees flowering shed their fruit overhead, pears and pomegranates and apple trees with bright fruit, and sweet figs and olives in their bloom, whereat when that old man reached out his hands to clutch them, the wind would toss them to the shadowy clouds.

"Yea and I beheld Sisyphus [2] in strong torment, grasping a monstrous stone with both his hands. He was pressing thereat with hands and feet, and trying to roll the stone upward toward the brow of the hill. But oft as he was about to hurl it over the top, the weight would drive him back, so once again to the plain rolled the stone, the shameless

---

[1] There are various accounts of the sin for which he was punished; either he served his son's flesh to the gods, or stole their nectar, or revealed their secrets.

[2] A legendary king of Corinth, reputed the most cunning of mankind. He is being punished for various misdeeds, including chaining up Death when Death came to take him.

thing. And he once more kept heaving and straining, and the sweat the while was pouring down his limbs, and the dust rose upwards from his head.

"And after him I descried the mighty Heracles,[3] his phantom, I say; but as for himself he hath joy at the banquet among the deathless gods, and hath to wife Hebe of the fair ankles, child of great Zeus, and of Here of the golden sandals. And all about him there was a clamour of the dead, as it were fowls flying every way in fear, and he like black Night, with bow uncased, and shaft upon the string, fiercely glancing around, like one in the act to shoot. And about his breast was an awful belt, a baldric of gold, whereon wondrous things were wrought, bears and wild boars and lions with flashing eyes, and strife and battles and slaughters and murders of men. Nay, now that he hath fashioned this, never another may he fashion, whoso stored in his craft the device of that belt! And anon he knew me when his eyes beheld me, and making lament he spake unto me winged words:

" 'Son of Laertes, of the seed of Zeus, Odysseus of many devices: ah! wretched one, dost thou too lead such a life of evil doom, as I endured beneath the rays of the sun? I was the son of Zeus Cronion, yet had I trouble beyond measure, for I was subdued unto a man far worse than I. And he enjoined on me hard adventures, yea and on a time he sent me hither to bring back the hound of hell; for he devised no harder task for me than this. I lifted the hound and brought him forth from out of the house of Hades; and Hermes sped me on my way and the grey-eyed Athene.'

"Therewith he departed again into the house of Hades, but I abode there still, if perchance some one of the hero folk besides might come, who died in old time. Yea and I should have seen the men of old, whom I was fain to look on, Theseus and Peirithous, renowned children of the gods. But ere that might be the myriad tribes of the dead

---

[3] One of the greatest of Greek heroes, the subject of innumerable stories.

thronged up together with wondrous clamour: and pale fear gat hold of me, lest the high goddess Persephone should send me the head of the Gorgon, that dread monster, from out of Hades.

"Straightway then I went to the ship, and bade my men mount the vessel, and loose the hawsers. So speedily they went on board, and sat upon the benches. And the wave of the flood bore the barque down the stream of Oceanus, we rowing first, and afterwards the fair wind was our convoy."

XII

Scylla and Charybdis

Now after the ship had left the stream of the river Oceanus, and was come to the wave of the wide sea, and the isle Aeaean, where is the dwelling place of early Dawn and her dancing grounds, and the land of sunrising, upon our coming thither we beached the ship in the sand, and ourselves too stept ashore on the sea-beach. There we fell on sound sleep and awaited the bright Dawn.

"So soon as early Dawn shone forth, the rosy-fingered, I sent forth my fellows to the house of Circe to fetch the body of the dead Elpenor. And speedily we cut billets of wood and sadly we buried him, where the furthest headland runs out into the sea, shedding big tears. But when the dead man was burned and the arms of the dead, we piled a barrow and dragged up thereon a pillar, and on the topmost mound we set the shapen oar.

"Now all that task we finished, and our coming from out of Hades was not unknown to Circe, but she arrayed herself and speedily drew nigh, and her handmaids with her bare flesh and bread in plenty and dark red wine. And the fair goddess stood in the midst and spake in our ears, saying:

" 'Men overbold, who have gone alive into the house of Hades, to know death twice, while all men else die once for all. Nay come, eat ye meat and drink wine here all day long; and with the breaking of the day ye shall set sail, and myself I will show you the path and declare each thing, that ye may

not suffer pain or hurt through any grievous ill-contrivance
by sea or on the land.'

"So spake she, and our lordly souls consented thereto.
Thus for that time we sat the livelong day, until the going
down of the sun, feasting on abundant flesh and on sweet
wine. Now when the sun sank and darkness came on, my

The Sun, Gladdener of the World.

PAINTING FROM AN APULIAN CRATER.
(BRITISH MUSEUM)

company laid them to rest by the hawsers of the ship. Then
she took me by the hand and led me apart from my dear
company, and made me to sit down and laid herself at my
feet, and asked all my tale. And I told her all in order duly.
Then at the last the lady Circe spake unto me, saying:

" 'Even so, now all these things have an end; do thou
then hearken even as I tell thee, and the god himself shall
bring it back to thy mind. To the Sirens first shalt thou
come, who bewitch all men, whosoever shall come to them.
Whoso draws nigh them unwittingly and hears the sound

of the Sirens' voice, never doth he see wife or babes stand
by him on his return, nor have they joy at his coming; but
the Sirens enchant him with their clear song, sitting in the
meadow, and all about is a great heap of bones of men,
corrupt in death, and round the bones the skin is wasting.
But do thou drive thy ship past, and knead honey-sweet
wax, and anoint therewith the ears of thy company, lest
any of the rest hear the song; but if thou thyself art minded
to hear, let them bind thee in the swift ship hand and foot,
upright in the mast-stead, and from the mast let rope-ends
be tied, that with delight thou mayest hear the voice of the
Sirens. And if thou shalt beseech thy company and bid
them to loose thee, then let them bind thee with yet more
bonds. But when thy friends have driven thy ship past these,
I will not tell thee fully which path shall thenceforth be
thine, but do thou thyself consider it, and I will speak to
thee of either way. On the one side there are beetling rocks,
and against them the great wave roars of dark-eyed Amphitrite.[1] These, ye must know, are they the blessed gods call the
Rocks Wandering. By this way even winged things may
never pass, nay, not even the cowering doves that bear ambrosia to Father Zeus, but the sheer rock evermore takes
away one even of these, and the Father sends in another to
make up the tale. Thereby no ship of men ever escapes that
comes thither, but the planks of ships and the bodies of men
confusedly are tossed by the waves of the sea and the storms
of ruinous fire. One ship only of all that fare by sea hath
passed that way, even Argo, that is in all men's minds, on
her voyage from Aeëtes. And even her the wave would
lightly have cast there upon the mighty rocks, but Here sent
her by for love of Iason.

" 'On the other part are two rocks, whereof the one
reaches with sharp peak to the wide heaven, and a dark
cloud encompasses it; this never streams away, and there is
no clear air about the peak neither in summer nor in harvest tide. No mortal man may scale it or set foot thereon,

one
route—
whole
he
does
not
take

---

[1] Wife of Poseidon.

The other route—
shorter—but
dangerous

not though he had twenty hands and feet. For the rock is smooth, and sheer, as it were polished. And in the midst of the cliff is a dim cave turned to Hades, towards the place of darkness, whereby ye shall even steer your hollow ship, noble Odysseus. Not with an arrow from a bow might a man in his strength reach from his hollow ship into that deep cave. And therein dwelleth Scylla, yelping terribly. Her voice indeed is no greater than the voice of a new-born whelp, but a dreadful monster is she, nor would any look on her gladly, not if it were a god that met her. Verily she hath twelve feet all dangling down, and six necks exceeding long, and on each a hideous head, and therein three rows of teeth set thick and close, full of black death. Up to her middle is she sunk far down in the hollow cave, but forth she holds her heads from the dreadful gulf, and there she fishes, swooping round the rock, for dolphins or sea-dogs, or whatso greater beast she may anywhere take, whereof the deep-voiced Amphitrite feeds countless flocks. Thereby no sailors boast that they had fled scatheless ever with their ship, for with each head she carries off a man, whom she hath snatched from out the dark-prowed ship.

"'But that other cliff, Odysseus, thou shalt note, lying lower, hard by the first: thou couldest send an arrow across. And thereon is a great fig-tree growing, in fullest leaf, and beneath it mighty Charybdis sucks down black water, for thrice a day she spouts it forth, and thrice a day she sucks it down in terrible wise. Never mayest thou be there when she sucks the water, for none might save thee then from thy bane, not even the Earth-shaker! But take heed and swiftly drawing nigh to Scylla's rock drive the ship past, since of a truth it is far better to mourn six of thy company in the ship, than all in the selfsame hour.'

"So spake she, but I answered, and said unto her: 'Come I pray thee herein, goddess, tell me true, if there be any means whereby I might escape from the deadly Charybdis and avenge me on that other, when she would prey upon my company.'

"So spake I, and that fair goddess answered me: 'Man

overbold, lo, now again the deeds of war are in thy mind and the travail thereof. Wilt thou not yield thee even to the deathless gods? As for her, she is no mortal, but an immortal plague, dread, grievous, and fierce, and not to be fought with; and against her there is no defence; flight is the bravest way. For if thou tarry to do on thine armour by the cliff, I fear lest once again she sally forth and catch at thee with so many heads, and seize as many men as before. So drive past with all thy force, and call on Cratais, mother of Scylla, which bore her for a bane to mortals. And she will then prevent her from darting forth thereafter.

" 'Then thou shalt come unto the isle Thrinacia; there are the many kine of Helios and his brave flocks feeding, seven herds of kine and as many goodly flocks of sheep, and fifty in each flock. They have no part in birth or in corruption, and there are goddesses to shepherd them, nymphs with fair tresses, Phaethusa and Lampetie whom bright Neaera bare to Helios Hyperion. Now when the lady their mother had borne and nursed them, she carried them to the isle Thrinacia to dwell afar, that they should guard their father's flocks and his kine with shambling gait. If thou doest these no hurt, being heedful of thy return, truly ye may even yet reach Ithaca, albeit in evil case. But if thou hurtest them, I foreshow ruin for thy ship and for thy men, and even though thou shouldest thyself escape, late shalt thou return in evil plight with the loss of all thy company.'

"So spake she, and anon came the golden-throned Dawn. Then the fair goddess took her way up the island. But I departed to my ship and roused my men themselves to mount the vessel and loose the hawsers. And speedily they went aboard and sat upon the benches, and sitting orderly smote the grey sea water with their oars. And in the wake of our dark-prowed ship she sent a favouring wind that filled the sails, a kindly escort,—even Circe of the braided tresses, a dread goddess of human speech. And straightway we set in order the gear throughout the ship and sat us down, and the wind and the helmsman guided our barque.

"Then I spake among my company with a heavy heart:

'Friends, forasmuch as it is not well that one or two alone should know of the oracles that Circe, the fair goddess, spake unto me, therefore will I declare them, that with foreknowledge we may die, or haply shunning death and destiny escape. First she bade us avoid the sound of the voice of the wondrous Sirens, and their field of flowers, and me only she bade listen to their voices. So bind ye me in a hard bond, that I may abide unmoved in my place, upright in the maststead, and from the mast let rope-ends be tied, and if I beseech and bid you to set me free, then do ye straiten me with yet more bonds.'

"Thus I rehearsed these things one and all, and declared them to my company. Meanwhile our good ship quickly came to the island of the Sirens twain, for a gentle breeze sped her on her way. Then straightway the wind ceased, and lo, there was a windless calm, and some god lulled the waves. Then my company rose up and drew in the ship's sails, and stowed them in the hold of the ship, while they sat at the oars and whitened the water with their polished pine blades. But I with my sharp sword cleft in pieces a great circle of wax, and with my strong hands kneaded it. And soon the wax grew warm, for that my great might constrained it, and the beam of the lord Helios, son of Hyperion. And I anointed therewith the ears of all my men in their order, and in the ship they bound me hand and foot upright in the mast-stead, and from the mast they fastened rope-ends and themselves sat down, and smote the grey sea water with their oars. But when the ship was within the sound of a man's shout from the land, we fleeing swiftly on our way, the Sirens espied the swift ship speeding toward them, and they raised their clear-toned song:

" 'Hither, come hither, renowned Odysseus, great glory of the Achaeans, here stay thy barque, that thou mayest listen to the voice of us twain. For none hath ever driven by this way in his black ship, till he hath heard from our lips the voice sweet as the honeycomb, and hath had joy thereof and gone on his way the wiser. For lo, we know all things, all the travail that in wide Troy-land the Argives and Trojans bare by the gods' designs, yea, and we know all that shall hereafter be upon the fruitful earth.'

"So spake they uttering a sweet voice, and my heart was fain to listen, and I bade my company unbind me, nodding at them with a frown, but they bent to their oars and rowed on. Then straight uprose Perimedes and Eurylochus and bound me with more cords and straitened me yet the more. Now when we had driven past them, nor heard we any longer the sound of the Sirens or their song, forthwith my dear company took away the wax wherewith I had anointed their ears and loosed me from my bonds.

"But so soon as we left that isle, thereafter presently I saw smoke and a great wave, and heard the sea roaring. Then for very fear the oars flew from their hands, and down the stream they all splashed, and the ship was holden there, for my company no longer plied with their hands the tapering oars. But I paced the ship and cheered on my men, as I stood by each one and spake smooth words:

" 'Friends, forasmuch as in sorrow we are not all unlearned, truly this is no greater woe that is upon us, than when the Cyclops penned us by main might in his hollow cave; yet even thence we made escape by my manfulness, even by my counsel and my wit, and some day I think that this adventure too we shall remember. Come now, therefore, let us all give ear to do according to my word. Do ye smite the deep surf of the sea with your oars, as ye sit on the benches, if peradventure Zeus may grant us to escape from and shun this death. And as for thee, helmsman, thus I charge thee, and ponder it in thine heart seeing that thou wieldest the helm of the hollow ship. Keep the ship well away from this smoke and from the wave and hug the rocks, lest the ship, ere thou art aware, start from her course to the other side, and so thou hurl us into ruin.'

"So I spake, and quickly they hearkened to my words. But of Scylla I told them nothing more, a bane none might deal with, lest haply my company should cease from rowing for fear, and hide them in the hold. In that same hour I suffered myself to forget the hard behest of Circe in that she bade me in no wise be armed; but I did on my glorious harness and caught up two long lances in my hands, and went on to the decking of the prow, for thence methought that Scylla of the rock would first be seen, who was to bring woe on my company. Yet could I not spy her anywhere, and my eyes waxed weary for gazing all about toward the darkness of the rock.

"Next we began to sail up the narrow strait lamenting. For on the one hand lay Scylla, and on the other mighty Charybdis in terrible wise sucked down the salt sea water. As often as she belched it forth, like a caldron on a great fire she would seethe up through all her troubled deeps, and overhead the spray fell on the tops of either cliff. But oft as she gulped down the salt sea water, within she was all plain to see through her troubled deeps, and the rock around roared horribly and beneath the earth was manifest black with sand, and pale fear gat hold on my men. Toward her, then, we looked fearing destruction; but Scylla meanwhile caught from out my hollow ship six of my company, the hardiest of their hands and the chief in might. And looking into the swift ship to find my men, even then I marked their feet and hands as they were lifted on high, and they cried aloud in their agony, and called me by my name for that last time of all. Even as when a fisher on some headland lets down with a long rod his baits for a snare to the little fishes below, casting into the deep the horn of an ox of the homestead, and as he catches each flings it writhing ashore, so writhing were they borne upward to the cliff. And there she devoured them shrieking in her gates, they stretching forth their hands to me in the dread death-struggle. And the most pitiful thing was this that mine eyes have seen of all my travail in searching out the paths of the sea.

"Now when we had escaped the Rocks and dread Charybdis and Scylla, thereafter we soon came to the fair island of the god; where were the goodly kine, broad of brow, and the many brave flocks of Helios Hyperion. Then while as yet I was in my black ship upon the deep, I heard the lowing of the cattle being stalled and the bleating of the sheep, and on my mind there fell the saying of the blind seer, Theban Teiresias, and of Circe of Aia, who charged me very straitly to shun the isle of Helios, the gladdener of the world. Then I spake out among my company in sorrow of heart:

"'Hear my words, my men, albeit in evil plight, that I may declare unto you the oracles of Teiresias and of Circe of Aia, who very straitly charged me to shun the isle of Helios, the gladdener of the world. For there she said the

The Ship of Odysseus and the Song of the Sirens.
PAINTING FROM A CRATER FOUND AT VULCI. (BRITISH MUSEUM)

most dreadful mischief would befall us. Nay, drive ye then the black ship beyond and past that isle.'

"So spake I, and their heart was broken within them. And Eurylochus straightway answered me sadly, saying:

"'Hardy art thou, Odysseus, of might beyond measure, and thy limbs are never weary; verily thou art fashioned all of iron, that sufferest not thy fellows, foredone with toil and drowsiness, to set foot on shore, where we might presently prepare us a good supper in this sea-girt island. But even as we are thou biddest us fare blindly through the sudden night, and from the isle go wandering on the misty deep. And strong winds, the bane of ships, are born of the night. How could a man escape from utter doom, if there chanced to come a sudden blast of the South Wind, or of the boisterous West, which mainly wreck ships, beyond the will of the gods, the lords of all? Howbeit for this present let us yield to the black night, and we will make ready our supper abiding by the swift ship, and in the morning we will climb on board, and put out into the broad deep.'

"So spake Eurylochus, and the rest of my company consented thereto. Then at the last I knew that some god was indeed imagining evil, and I uttered my voice and spake unto him winged words:

" 'Eurylochus, verily ye put force upon me, being but one among you all. But come, swear me now a mighty oath, one and all, to the intent that if we light on a herd of kine or a great flock of sheep, none in the evil folly of his heart may slay any sheep or ox; but in quiet eat ye the meat which the deathless Circe gave.'

"So I spake, and straightway they swore to refrain as I commanded them. Now after they had sworn and done that oath, we stayed our well-built ship in the hollow harbour near to a well of sweet water, and my company went forth from out the ship and deftly got ready supper. But when they had put from them the desire of meat and drink, thereafter they fell a weeping as they thought upon their dear companions whom Scylla had snatched from out the hollow ship and so devoured. And deep sleep came upon them amid their weeping. And when it was the third watch of the night, and the stars had crossed the zenith, Zeus the cloudgatherer roused against them an angry wind with wondrous tempest, and shrouded in clouds land and sea alike, and from heaven sped down the night. Now when early Dawn shone forth, the rosy-fingered, we beached the ship, and dragged it up within a hollow cave, where were the fair dancing grounds of the nymphs and the places of their session. Thereupon I ordered a gathering of my men and spake in their midst, saying:

" 'Friends, forasmuch as there is yet meat and drink in the swift ship, let us keep our hands off those kine, lest some evil thing befall us. For these are the kine and the brave flocks of a dread god, even of Helios, who overseeth all and over-heareth all things.'

"So I spake, and their lordly spirit hearkened thereto. Then for a whole month the South Wind blew without ceasing, and no other wind arose, save only the East and the South.

"Now so long as my company still had corn and red wine, they refrained them from the kine, for they were fain of life. But when the corn was now all spent from out the ship, and they went wandering with barbed hooks in quest of game, as needs they must, fishes and fowls, whatsoever might come to their hand, for hunger gnawed at their belly, then at last I departed up the isle, that I might pray to the gods, if perchance some one of them might show me a way of returning. And now when I had avoided my company on my way through the island, I laved my hands where was a shelter from the wind, and prayed to all the gods that hold Olympus. But they shed sweet sleep upon my eyelids. And Eurylochus the while set forth an evil counsel to my company:

"'Hear my words, my friends, though ye be in evil case. Truly every shape of death is hateful to wretched mortals, but to die of hunger and so meet doom is most pitiful of all. Nay come, we will drive off the best of the kine of Helios and will do sacrifice to the deathless gods who keep wide heaven. And if we may yet reach Ithaca, our own country, forthwith will we rear a rich shrine to Helios Hyperion, and therein would we set many a choice offering. But if he be somewhat wroth for his cattle with straight horns, and is fain to wreck our ship, and the other gods follow his desire, rather with one gulp at the wave would I cast my life away, than be slowly pinched to death in a desert isle.'

"So spake Eurylochus, and the rest of the company consented thereto. Forthwith they drave off the best of the kine of Helios that were nigh at hand, for the fair kine of shambling gait and broad of brow were feeding no great way from the dark-prowed ship. Then they stood around the cattle and prayed to the gods, plucking the fresh leaves from an oak of

Eurylochus tells them [ ] killing the cattle

lofty boughs, for they had no white barley on board the decked ship. Now after they had prayed and cut the throats of the kine and flayed them, they cut out slices of the thighs and wrapped them in the fat, making a double fold, and thereon they laid raw flesh. Yet had they no pure wine to pour over the flaming sacrifices, but they made libation with water and roasted the entrails over the fire. Now after the thighs were quite consumed and they had tasted the inner parts, they cut the rest up small and spitted it on spits. In the same hour deep sleep sped from my eyelids and I sallied forth to the swift ship and the sea-banks. But on my way as I drew near to the curved ship, the sweet savour of the fat came all about me; and I groaned and spake out before the deathless gods:

" 'Father Zeus, and all ye other blessed gods that live for ever, verily to my undoing ye have lulled me with a ruthless sleep, and my company abiding behind have imagined a monstrous deed.'

"Then swiftly to Helios Hyperion came Lampetie of the long robes, with the tidings that we had slain his kine. And straight he spake with angry heart amid the Immortals:

" 'Father Zeus, and all ye other blessed gods that live for ever, take vengeance I pray you on the company of Odysseus, son of Laertes, that have insolently slain my cattle, wherein I was wont to be glad as I went toward the starry heaven, and when I again turned earthward from the firmament. And if they pay me not full atonement for the cattle, I will go down to Hades and shine among the dead.'

"And Zeus the cloud-gatherer answered him, saying: 'Helios, do thou, I say, shine on amidst the deathless gods, and amid mortal men upon the earth, the grain-giver. But as for me, I will soon smite their swift ship with my white bolt, and cleave it in pieces in the midst of the wine-dark deep.'

"This I heard from Calypso of the fair hair; and she said that she herself had heard it from Hermes the Messenger.

"But when I had come down to the ship and to the sea, I went up to my companions and rebuked them one by one;

but we could find no remedy, the cattle were dead and gone. And soon thereafter the gods showed forth signs and wonders to my company. The skins were creeping, and the flesh bellowing upon the spits, both the roast and raw, and there was a sound as the voice of kine.

"Then for six days my dear company feasted on the best of the kine of Helios which they had driven off. But when Zeus, son of Cronos, had added the seventh day thereto, thereafter the wind ceased to blow with a rushing storm, and at once we climbed the ship and launched into the broad deep, when we had set up the mast and hoisted the white sails.

"But now when we left that isle nor any other land appeared, but sky and sea only, even then the son of Cronos stayed a dark cloud above the hollow ship, and beneath it the deep darkened. And the ship ran on her way for no long while, for of a sudden came the shrilling West, with the rushing of a great tempest, and the blast of wind snapped the two forestays of the mast, and the mast fell backward and all the gear dropped into the bilge. And behold, on the hind part of the ship the mast struck the head of the pilot and brake all the bones of his skull together, and like a diver he dropt down from the deck, and his brave spirit left his bones. In that same hour Zeus thundered and cast his bolt upon the ship, and she reeled all over being stricken by the bolt of Zeus, and was filled with sulphur, and lo, my company fell from out the vessel. Like sea-gulls they were borne round the black ship upon the billows, and the god reft them of returning.

"But I kept pacing through my ship, till the surge loosened the sides from the keel, and the wave swept her along stript of her tackling, and brake her mast clean off at the keel. Now the backstay fashioned of an oxhide had been flung thereon; therewith I lashed together both keel and mast and sitting thereon I was borne by the ruinous winds.

"Then verily the West Wind ceased to blow with a rushing storm, and swiftly withal the South Wind came, bringing sorrow to my soul, that so I might again measure back that space of sea, the way to deadly Charybdis. All the night was I borne, but with the rising of the sun I came to the rock of Scylla, and to dread Charybdis. Now she had sucked down her salt sea water, when I was swung up on high to the tall fig tree whereto I clung like a bat, and could find no sure rest for my feet nor place to stand, for the roots spread far below and the branches hung aloft out of reach, long and large, and overshadowed Charybdis. Steadfast I clung till she should spew forth mast and keel again; and late they came to my desire. At the hour when a man rises up from the assembly and goes to supper, one who judges the many quarrels of the young men that seek to him for law, at that same hour those timbers came forth to view from out Charybdis. And I let myself drop down hands and feet, and plunged heavily in the midst of the waters beyond the long timbers, and sitting on these I rowed hard with my hands. But the father of gods and of men suffered me no more to behold Scylla, else I should never have escaped from utter doom.

"Thence for nine days was I borne, and on the tenth night the gods brought me nigh to the isle of Ogygia, where dwells Calypso of the braided tresses, an awful goddess of mortal speech, who took me in and treated me kindly. But why rehearse all this tale? For even yesterday I told it to thee and to thy noble wife in thy house; and it liketh me not twice to tell a plain-told tale."

XIII

Athena came in the guise of a young shepherd boy.
PAINTING FROM AN AMPHORA.
(VATICAN MUSEUM)

Odysseus Reaches Ithaca

❲ The story so pleases Alcinous that he orders further gifts given to Odysseus. The next day he himself directs the loading of the ship and speeds Odysseus on his way. As the ship sets sail Odysseus falls asleep; he is still asleep in the morning as the sailors lay him and his gifts on the shore of Ithaca. The returning ship, fulfilling a prophecy, is turned into a rock by Poseidon as it nears its harbor. *still to be seen*

Odysseus, protected by a mist, does not recognize his surroundings when he awakens and laments until told where he is by Athene, in the guise of a young man. Fearful for himself and his goods, Odysseus spins a tale of lies about his adventures which amuses Athene, who reveals herself to him in her true shape.

After Odysseus has hidden his gifts in the cave of the Naiads, he and Athene take counsel together. She changes his appearance to that of a poor old man so that he will not be recognized, and then sends him to the home of his loyal swineherd while she calls Telemachus home from Sparta.

she appears also as Mentes, Mentor

XIV

Odysseus, King of Ithaca, Attacking.
PAINTING FROM AN ARCHAIC TYRRHENIAN AMPHORA WITH BLACK FIGURES.
(BASSEGGIO COLL., ROME)

Odysseus and Eumaeus

❡ Odysseus seeks the home of Eumaeus, master of his swine, who cares for the property of Odysseus as though it were his own. Because all strangers and beggars come from Zeus, Eumaeus greets him with the rites of hospitality, accompanying them with continual mourning for his absent master, whom he supposes dead: "Never again shall I find a lord so gentle." Odysseus swears an oath that in this same year his master will surely return to take vengeance on the suitors. Unbelieving, Eumaeus turns the conversation to his guest, who tells his story —another interesting fabrication quite different from the one told to Athene and much more complicated. He pretends that during his adventures, he has had word of the safety of Odysseus, but the old swineherd still cannot be persuaded, having been fooled by other travellers. Afterwards, while Odysseus sleeps in comfort by the fire, Eumaeus sleeps near the boars, ever watchful of his master's possessions.

XV

"Beautiful Helen" Speaking to Telemachus.
PAINTING FROM AN AMPHORA.
(COLL. OF DUKE OF MARLBOROUGH)

Telemachus Comes Home

❦ In Sparta, Telemachus is bidden by Athene to return home lest his mother marry again; she also warns him of the threat offered by the suitors waiting in their ship.

When Telemachus and Peisistratus reach Pylos on their return journey, Telemachus goes to his ship instead of to Nestor's house, so eager is he to be gone. He takes aboard with him a stranger, Theoclymenus, the seer, who has slain a man of his own blood and who is fleeing the avengers.

Meanwhile Odysseus asks Eumaeus for a guide to the city, so that he may bear tidings to Penelope and perhaps find service among the suitors. Eumaeus warns him of the cruelty of the suitors. He also gives Odysseus news of old Laertes, his father, and of his mother. Eumaeus then tells the story of how he, the son of a king, was sold into slavery as a child.

With the dawn, Telemachus arrives safely on the shore of Ithaca. He sends Theoclymenus home with his faithful companion Piraeus and goes himself to the home of Eumaeus, as Athene had bidden him.

*to avoid the
suitors*

XVI

Telemachus: What a transformation, oh my guest! Art thou one of the Gods. Odysseus: No God am I! Nay, I am thy father.

PAINTING FROM A KELEBE.
(WURTZBURG MUSEUM)

Odysseus and Telemachus Meet

⟨ *Telemachus is greeted with joy by Eumaeus, whom he sends to Penelope with the news of his return. Odysseus, on the advice of Athene, who restores his normal appearance, reveals himself to his son. Together they plan the downfall of the suitors. Telemachus counts them: one hundred and eight, and ten servants. Meanwhile the suitors have learned of the safe return of Telemachus and angrily plot to slay him. Athene makes Odysseus an old man again so that the returning Eumaeus will not recognize him at this time.*

XVII

Penelope Talking to Telemachus.

PAINTING FROM AN HYDRIA.
(BERLIN MUSEUM)

Odysseus Returns to His Palace

a famous detail

❦ Telemachus goes to his mother and reveals what he has learned on his travels. She is further reassured by the prophecy of Theoclymenus, whom Telemachus brings into his own home, that Odysseus is even now in his own country. Following the command of Telemachus, Eumaeus takes the disguised Odysseus into the city to beg. At the door of Odysseus' house his hound Argus wags his tail, recognizing his master, and then dies.

Telemachus welcomes the "beggar" into the house, and all the wooers give him food save Antinous, who, after the exchange of angry words, hits him with a stool. Hearing of this act, Penelope is grieved and sends for the stranger to learn whether he has news of her lord. He promises to speak with her after the going down of the sun, so that then he may be less noticed by the suitors.

the one who defied Telemachus in the council

XVIII

Young Wooer Bringing his Present to Penelope.
PAINTING FROM AN AMPHORA FOUND AT VULCI.
(CAMPANARI COLL., ROME)

Odysseus and the Beggar

⟨ Odysseus is accosted by Irus, a common beggar, jealous of another beggar in the house. Hearing them exchange threats the suitors hasten to match them against each other in a contest. With one blow Odysseus crushes the bones of Irus' neck; he is rewarded with food by the suitors.

Penelope is moved to show herself to the suitors. As she sleeps, her beauty is enhanced by Athene, and when she goes to the great hall, the hearts of the suitors are enchanted. When Eurymachus praises her, she reproves the men who waste her substance, saying that in the old days, wooers brought gifts for the bride. So each man gives her a beautiful gift.

When she retires, the suitors turn to their evening pleasures of singing and dancing. Melantho, one of the maids, reviles Odysseus for his poverty. When Eurymachus, one of the suitors, likewise taunts him, he replies so boldly that Eurymachus hurls a stool at him, narrowly missing him. Such a hubbub ensues that Telemachus sends his "guests" home.

XIX

they first remove the suitors' weapons (108 suitors!)

Odysseus and Eurycleia

Now the goodly Odysseus was left behind in the hall, devising with Athene's aid the slaying of the wooers, and straightway he spake winged words to Telemachus:

"Telemachus, we must needs lay by the weapons of war within, every one; and when the wooers miss them and ask thee concerning them, thou shalt beguile them with soft words, saying:

"Out of the smoke I laid them by, since they were no longer like those that Odysseus left behind him of old, when he went to Troy, but they are wholly marred, so mightily hath passed upon them the vapour of fire. Moreover some god hath put into my heart this other and greater care, that perchance when ye are heated with wine, ye set a quarrel between you and wound one the other, and thereby shame the feast and the wooing; for iron of itself draws a man thereto."

Thus he spake, and Telemachus hearkened to his dear father, and called forth to him the nurse Eurycleia and spake to her, saying:

"Nurse, come now I pray thee, shut up the women in their chambers till I shall have laid by in the armoury the goodly weapons of my father, which all uncared for the smoke dims in the hall, since my father went hence, and I was still but a child. Now I wish to lay them by where the vapour of the fire will not reach them."

Then the good nurse Eurycleia answered him, saying:

"Ah, my child, if ever thou wouldest but take careful thought in such wise as to mind the house, and guard all this wealth! But come, who shall fetch the light and bear it, if thou hast thy way, since thou wouldest not that the maidens, who might have given light, should go before thee?"

Then wise Telemachus made answer to her: "This stranger here, for I will keep no man in idleness who eats of my bread, even if he have come from afar."

Thus he spake, and wingless her speech remained, and she closed the doors of the fair-lying chambers. Then they twain sprang up, Odysseus and his renowned son, and set to carry within the helmets and the bossy shields, and the sharp-pointed spears; and before them Pallas Athene bare a golden cresset and cast a most lovely light. Thereon Telemachus spake to his father suddenly:

"Father, surely a great marvel is this that I behold with mine eyes; meseems, at least, that the walls of the hall and the fair main-beams of the roof and the cross-beams of pine, and the pillars that run aloft, are bright as it were with flaming fire. Verily some god is within, of those that hold the wide heaven."

And Odysseus of many counsels answered him and said: "Hold thy peace and keep thy thoughts in check and ask not hereof. Lo, this is the wont of the gods that hold Olympus. But do thou go and lay thee down, and I will abide here, that I may yet further provoke the maids and thy mother to answer; and she in her sorrow will ask me concerning each thing, one by one."

So he spake, and Telemachus passed out through the hall to his chamber to lie down, by the light of the flaming torches, even to the chamber where of old he took his rest, when sweet sleep came over him. There now too he lay down and awaited the bright Dawn. But goodly Odysseus was left behind in the hall, devising with Athene's aid the slaying of the wooers.

Now forth from her chamber came the wise Penelope, like Artemis or golden Aphrodite, and they set a chair for her hard by before the fire, where she was wont to sit, a chair well-wrought and inlaid with ivory and silver, which on a time the craftsman Icmalius had fashioned, and had joined thereto a footstool, that was part of the chair, whereon a great fleece was used to be laid. Here, then, the wise Penelope sat her down, and next came white-armed handmaids from the women's chamber, and began to take away the many fragments of food, and the tables and the cups whence the proud lords had been drinking, and they raked out the fire from the braziers on to the floor, and piled many fresh logs upon them, to give light and warmth.

Then Melantho began to revile Odysseus yet a second time, saying: "Stranger, wilt thou still be a plague to us here, circling round the house in the night, and spying the women? Nay, get thee forth, thou wretched thing, and be thankful for thy supper, or straightway shalt thou even be smitten with a torch and so fare out of the doors."

Then Odysseus of many counsels looked fiercely on her, and said: "Good woman, what possesses thee to assail me thus out of an angry heart? Is it because I go filthy and am clothed about in sorry raiment, and beg through the land, for necessity is laid on me? This is the manner of beggars and of wandering men. For I too once had a house of mine own among men, a rich man with a wealthy house, and many a time would I give to a wanderer, what manner of man soever he might be, and in whatsoever need he came. And I had countless thralls, and all else in plenty, whereby folk live well and have a name for riches. But Zeus, the son of Cronos, made me desolate of all, for surely it was his will. Wherefore, woman, see lest some day thou too lose all thy fine show wherein thou now excellest among the handmaids, as well may chance, if thy mistress be provoked to anger with thee, or if Odysseus come home, for there is yet a place for hope. And even if he hath perished as ye deem, and is never more to return, yet by Apollo's grace he hath a son like him, Telemachus, and none of the women works wantonness in his halls without his knowledge, for he is no longer of an age not to mark it."

Thus he spake, and the wise Penelope heard him, and rebuked the handmaid, and spake and hailed her:

"Thou reckless thing and unabashed, be sure thy great sin

is not hidden from me, and thy blood shall be on thine own head for the same! For thou knewest right well, in that thou hadst heard it from my lips, how that I was minded to ask the stranger in my halls for tidings of my lord; for I am grievously afflicted."

Therewith she spake likewise to the housedame, Eurynome, saying:

"Eurynome, bring hither a settle with a fleece thereon, that the stranger may sit and speak with me and hear my words, for I would ask him all his story."

So she spake, and the nurse made haste and brought a polished settle, and cast a fleece thereon; and then the steadfast goodly Odysseus sat him down there, and the wise Penelope spake first, saying:

"Stranger, I will make bold first to ask thee this: who art thou of the sons of men, and whence? Where is thy city, and where are they that begat thee?"

And Odysseus of many counsels answered her and said: "Lady, no one of mortal men in the wide world could find fault with thee, for lo, thy fame goes up to the wide heaven, as doth the fame of a blameless king, one that fears the gods and reigns among many men and mighty, maintaining right, and the black earth bears wheat and barley, and the trees are laden with fruit, and the sheep bring forth and fail not, and the sea gives store of fish, and all out of his good guidance, and the people prosper under him. Wherefore do thou ask me now in thy house all else that thou wilt, but inquire not concerning my race and mine own country, lest as I think thereupon thou fill my heart the more with pains, for I am a man of many sorrows. Moreover it beseems me not to sit weeping and wailing in another's house, for it is little good to mourn always without ceasing, lest perchance one of the maidens, or even thyself, be angry with me and say that I swim in tears, as one that is heavy with wine."

Then wise Penelope answered him, and said: "Stranger, surely my excellence, both of face and form, the gods destroyed in the day when the Argives embarked for Illium,

Explains the meaning - a shroud for his father

and with them went my lord Odysseus. If but he might come and watch over this my life, greater and fairer thus would be my fame! But now am I in sorrow, such a host of ills some god has sent against me. For all the noblest that are princes in the isles, in Dulichium and Same and wooded Zacynthus, and they that dwell around even in clear-seen Ithaca, these are wooing me against my will, and devouring the house. Wherefore I take no heed of strangers, nor suppliants, nor at all of heralds, the craftsmen of the people. But I waste my heart away in longing for Odysseus; so they speed on my marriage and I weave a web of wiles. First some god put it into my heart to set up a great web in the halls, and thereat to weave a robe fine of woof and very wide; and anon I spake among them, saying: 'Ye princely youths, my wooers, now that goodly Odysseus is dead, do ye abide patiently, how eager soever to speed on this marriage of mine, till I finish the robe. I would not that the threads perish to no avail, even this shroud for the hero Laertes, against the day when the ruinous doom shall bring him low, of death that lays men at their length. So shall none of the Achaean women in the land count it blame in me, as well might be, were he to lie without a winding sheet, a man that had gotten great possessions.'

"So spake I, and their high hearts consented thereto. So then in the daytime I would weave the mighty web, and in the night unravel the same, when I had let place the torches by me. Thus for the space of three years I hid the thing by craft and beguiled the minds of the Achaeans. But when the fourth year arrived, and the seasons came round as the months waned, and many days were accomplished, then it was that by help of the handmaids, shameless things and reckless, the wooers came and trapped me, and chid me loudly. Thus did I finish the web by no will of mine, for so I must. And now I can neither escape the marriage nor devise any further counsel, and my parents are instant with me to marry, and my son chafes that these men devour his livelihood, as he takes note of all; for by this time he has come to man's estate, and is full able to care for a household, for one to which Zeus vouchsafes honour. But even so tell me of thine own stock, whence thou art, for thou art not sprung of oak or rock, whereof old tales tell."

And Odysseus of many counsels answered her and said:

"O wife revered of Odysseus, son of Laertes, wilt thou never have done asking me about mine own race? Nay, but I will tell thee: yet surely thou wilt give me over to sorrows yet more than those wherein I am holden, for so it ever is when a man has been afar from his own country, so long as now I am, wandering in sore pain to many cities of mortals. Yet even so I will tell thee what thou askest and inquirest. There is a land called Crete in the midst of the wine-dark sea, a fair land and a rich, begirt with water, and therein are many men innumerable, and ninety cities. And all have not the same speech, but there is confusion of tongues; there dwell Achaeans and there too Cretans of Crete, high of heart, and Cydonians there and Dorians of waving plumes and goodly Pelasgians. And among these cities is the mighty city Cnosus, wherein Minos when he was nine years old began to rule, he who held converse with great Zeus, and was the father of my father, even of Deucalion, high of heart. Now Deucalion begat me and Idomeneus the prince. Howbeit, he had gone in his beaked ships up into Ilium, with the sons of Atreus; but my famed name is Aethon, being the younger of the twain and he was the first born and the better man. There I saw Odysseus, and gave him guest-gifts, for the might of the wind bare him too to Crete, as he was making for Troy-land, and had driven him wandering past Malea. So he stayed his ships in Amnisus, whereby is the cave of Eilithyia, in havens hard to win, and scarce he escaped the tempest. Anon he came up to the city and asked for Idomeneus, saying that he was his friend and held by him in love and honour. But it was now the tenth or the eleventh dawn since Idomeneus had gone in his beaked ships up into Ilium. Then I led him to the house, and gave him good entertainment with all loving-kindness out of the plenty in my house, and for him and for the rest of his company, that went with him, I gathered and gave barleymeal and dark wine out of the public store, and oxen to sacrifice to his heart's desire. There the goodly Achaeans abode twelve days, for the strong North Wind penned them there, and suffered them not to stay upon the coast, for some angry god had roused it. On the thirteenth day the wind fell, and then they lifted anchor."

So he told many a false tale in the likeness of truth, and her tears flowed as she listened, and her flesh melted. And even as the snow melts in the high places of the hills, the snow that the South-East wind has thawed, when the West has scattered it abroad, and as it wastes the river streams run full, even so her fair cheeks melted beneath her tears, as she wept her own lord, who even then was sitting by her. Now Odysseus had compassion of heart upon his wife in her lamenting, but his eyes kept steadfast between his eyelids as it were horn or iron, and craftily he hid his tears. But she, when she had taken her fill of tearful lamentation, answered him in turn and spake, saying:

"Friend as thou art, even now I think to make trial of thee, and learn whether in very truth thou didst entertain my lord there in thy halls with his godlike company, as thou sayest. Tell me what manner of raiment he was clothed in about his body, and what manner of man he was himself, and tell me of his fellows that went with him."

Then Odysseus of many counsels answered her saying: "Lady, it is hard for one so long parted from him to tell thee all this, for it is now the twentieth year since he went thither and left my country. Yet even so I will tell thee as I see him in spirit. Goodly Odysseus wore a thick purple mantle, twofold, which had a brooch fashioned in gold, with two sheaths for the pins, and on the face of it was a curious device: a hound in his forepaws held a dappled fawn and gazed on it as it writhed. And all men marvelled at the workmanship, how, wrought as they were in gold, the hound was gazing on the fawn and strangling it, and the fawn was writhing with his feet and striving to flee. Moreover, I marked the shining doublet about his body, like the gleam over the skin of a dried onion, so smooth it was, and glistening as the sun;

truly many women looked thereon and wondered. Yet another thing will I tell thee, and do thou ponder it in thy heart. I know not if Odysseus was thus clothed upon at home, or if one of his fellows gave him the raiment as he went on board the swift ship, or even it may be some stranger, seeing that to many men was Odysseus dear, for few of the Achaeans were his peers. I, too, gave him a sword of bronze, and a fair purple mantle with double fold, and a tasselled doublet, and I sent him away with all honour on his decked ship. Moreover, a henchman bare him company, somewhat older than he, and I will tell thee of him too, what manner of man he was. He was round-shouldered, black-skinned, and curly-headed, his name Eurybates; and Odysseus honoured him above all his company, because in all things he was like-minded with himself."

So he spake, and in her heart he stirred yet more the desire of weeping, as she knew the certain tokens that Odysseus showed her. So when she had taken her fill of tearful lament, then she answered him, and spake saying:

"Now verily, stranger, thou that even before wert held in pity, shalt be dear and honourable in my halls, for it was I who gave him these garments, as judging from thy words, and folded them myself, and brought them from the chamber, and added besides the shining brooch to be his jewel. But him I shall never welcome back, returned home to his own dear country. Wherefore with an evil fate it was that Odysseus went hence in the hollow ship to see that evil Ilium, never to be named!"

And Odysseus of many counsels answered her saying: "Wife revered of Odysseus, son of Laertes, destroy not now thy fair flesh any more, nor waste thy heart with weeping for thy lord;—not that I count it any blame in thee, for many a woman weeps that has lost her wedded lord, to whom she has borne children in her love,—albeit a far other man than Odysseus, who, they say, is like the gods. Nay, cease from thy lamenting, and lay up my word in thy heart; for I will tell thee without fail, and will hide nought, how but lately I heard tell of the return of Odysseus, that he is nigh at hand, and yet alive in the fat land of the men of Thesprotia, and is bringing with him many choice treasures, as he begs through the land. But he has lost his dear companions and his hollow ship on the wine-dark sea, on his way from the isle Thrinacia: for Zeus and Helios had a grudge against him, because his company had slain the kine of Helios. They for their part all perished in the wash of the sea, but the wave cast him on the keel of the ship out upon the coast, on the land of the Phaeacians that are near of kin to the gods, and they did him all honour heartily as unto a god, and gave him many gifts, and themselves would fain have sent him scatheless home. Yea and Odysseus would have been here long since, but he thought it more profitable to gather wealth, as he journeyed over wide lands; so truly is Odysseus skilled in gainful arts above all men upon earth, nor may any mortal men contend with him. So Pheidon king of the Thesprotians told me. Moreover he sware, in mine own presence, as he poured the drink-offering in his house, that the ship was drawn down to the sea and his company were ready, who were to convey him to his own dear country. But me he first sent off, for it chanced that a ship of the Thesprotians was on her way to Dulichium, a land rich in grain. And he showed me all the wealth that Odysseus had gathered, yea, it would suffice for his children after him, even to the tenth generation, so great were the treasures he had stored in the chambers of the king. As for him he had gone, he said, to Dodona to hear the counsel of Zeus, from the high leafy oak tree of the god, how he should return to his own dear country, having now been long afar, whether openly or by stealth.

"In this wise, as I tell thee, he is safe and will come shortly, and very near he is and will not much longer be far from his friends and his own country; yet withal I will give thee my oath on it. Zeus be my witness first, of gods the highest and best, and the hearth of noble Odysseus whereunto I am come, that all these things shall surely be accomplished even as I tell thee. In this same year Odysseus shall come hither, as the old moon wanes and the new is born."

Then wise Penelope answered him: "Ah! stranger, would that this word may be accomplished. Soon shouldst thou be aware of kindness and many a gift at my hands, so that whoso met with thee would call thee blessed. But on this wise my heart has a boding, and so it shall be. Neither shall Odysseus come home any more, nor shalt thou gain an escort hence, since there are not now such masters in the house as Odysseus was among men,—if ever such an one there was,—to welcome guests revered and speed them on their way. But do ye, my handmaids, wash this man's feet and strew a couch for him, bedding and mantles and shining blankets, that well and warmly he may come to the time of golden throned Dawn. And very early in the morning bathe him and anoint him, that within the house beside Telemachus he may eat meat, sitting quietly in the hall. And it shall be the worse for any hurtful man of the wooers, that vexes the stranger, yea, he shall not henceforth profit himself here, for all his sore anger. For how shalt thou learn concerning me, stranger, whether indeed I excel all women in wit and thrifty device, if all unkempt and evil clad thou sittest at supper in my halls? Man's life is brief enough! And if any be a hard man and hard at heart, all men cry evil on him for the time to come, while yet he lives, and all men mock him when he is dead. But if any be a blameless man and blameless of heart, his guests spread abroad his fame over the whole earth, and many people call him noble."

Then Odysseus of many counsels answered her and said: "O wife revered of Odysseus, son of Laertes, mantles verily and shining blankets are hateful to me, since first I left behind me the snowy hills of Crete, voyaging in the long-oared galley; nay, I will lie as in time past I was used to rest through the sleepless nights. For full many a night I have lain on an unsightly bed, and awaited the bright throned Dawn. And baths for the feet are no longer my delight, nor shall any women of those who are serving maidens in thy house touch my foot, unless there chance to be some old wife, true of heart, one that has borne as much trouble as myself; I would not grudge such an one to touch my feet."

Then wise Penelope answered him: "Dear stranger, for never yet has there come to my house, of strangers from afar, a dearer man or so discreet as thou, uttering so heedfully the words of wisdom. I have an ancient woman of an understanding heart, that diligently nursed and tended that hapless man my lord, she took him in her arms in the hour when his mother bare him. She will wash thy feet, albeit her strength is frail. Up now, wise Eurycleia, and wash this man, whose years are the same as thy master's. Yea and perchance such even now are the feet of Odysseus, and such too his hands, for quickly men age in misery."

So she spake, and the old woman covered her face with her hands and shed hot tears, and spake a word of lamentation, saying:

"Ah, woe is me, child, for thy sake, all helpless that I am! Surely Zeus hated thee above all men, though thou hadst a god-fearing spirit! For never yet did any mortal burn so many fat pieces of the thigh and so many choice hecatombs to Zeus, whose joy is in the thunder, as thou didst give to him, praying that so thou mightest grow to a smooth old age and near thy renowned son. But now from thee alone hath Zeus wholly cut off the day of thy returning. Haply at him too did the women mock in a strange land afar, whensoever he came to the famous palace of any lord, even as here these shameless ones all mock at thee. To shun their insults and many taunts it is that thou sufferest them not to wash thy feet, but the daughter of Icarius, wise Penelope, hath bidden me that am right willing to this task. Wherefore I will wash thy feet, both for Penelope's sake and for thine own, for that my heart within me is moved and troubled. But come, mark the word that I shall speak. Many strangers travel-worn have ere now come hither, but I say that I have never seen any so like another, as thou art like Odysseus, in fashion in voice and in feet."

Then Odysseus of many counsels answered her saying: "Old wife, even so all men declare, that have beheld us twain, that we favour each other exceedingly, even as thou dost mark and say."

Thereupon the crone took the shining caldron, where-from she set to wash his feet, and poured in much cold water and next mingled therewith the warm. Now Odysseus sat aloof from the hearth, and of a sudden he turned his face to the darkness, for anon he had a misgiving of heart lest when she handled him she might know the scar again, and all should be revealed. Now she drew near her lord to wash him, and straightway she knew the scar of the wound, that the boar had dealt him with his white tusk long ago, when Odysseus went to Parnassus to see Autolycus, and the son of Autolycus, his mother's noble father, who outdid all men in thievery and skill in swearing. This skill was the gift of the god himself, even Hermes, for that he burned to him the well-pleasing sacrifice of the thighs of lambs and kids; where-fore Hermes abetted him gladly. Now Autolycus once had gone to the rich land of Ithaca, and found his daughter's son a child new-born, and when he was making an end of supper, behold, Eurycleia set the babe on his knees, and spake and hailed him: "Autolycus, find now a name thyself to give thy child's own son; for lo, he is a child of many prayers."

Then Autolycus made answer and spake: "My daughter and my daughter's lord, give ye him whatsoever name I tell you. Forasmuch as I am come hither in wrath against many a one, both man and woman, over the fruitful earth, where-fore let the child's name be 'a man of wrath,' Odysseus. But when the child reaches his full growth, and comes to the great house of his mother's kin at Parnassus, whereby are my possessions, I will give him a gift out of these and send him on his way rejoicing."

Therefore it was that Odysseus went to receive the splen-did gifts. And Autolycus and the sons of Autolycus grasped his hands and greeted him with gentle words, and Amphi-thea, his mother's mother, clasped him in her arms and kissed his face and both his fair eyes. Then Autolycus called to his renowned sons to get ready the meal, and they hearkened to the call. So presently they led in a five-year-old bull, which they flayed and busily prepared, and cut up all the limbs and deftly chopped them small, and pierced them with spits and roasted them cunningly, dividing the portions. So for that livelong day they feasted till the going down of the sun, and their soul lacked not ought of the equal banquet. But when the sun sank and darkness came on, then they laid them to rest and took the boon of sleep.

Now so soon as early Dawn shone forth, the rosy-fingered, they all went forth to the chase, the hounds and the sons of Autolycus, and with them went the goodly Odysseus. So they fared up the steep hill of wood-clad Parnassus, and quickly they came to the windy hollows. Now the sun was but just striking on the fields, and was come forth from the soft flowing stream of deep Oceanus. Then the beaters reached a glade of the woodland, and before them went the hounds tracking a scent, but behind came the sons of Autolycus, and among them goodly Odysseus followed close on the hounds, swaying a long spear. Thereby in a thick lair was a great boar lying, and through the coppice the force of the wet winds blew never, neither did the bright sun light on it with his rays, nor could the rain pierce through, so thick it was, and of fallen leaves there was great plenty therein. Then the tramp of the men's feet and of the dogs' came upon the boar, as they pressed on in the chase, and forth from his lair he sprang towards them with crest well bristled and fire shining in his eyes, and stood at bay before them all. Then Odysseus was the first to rush in, holding his spear aloft in his strong hand, most eager to stab him; but the boar was too quick and drave a gash above the knee, ripping deep into the flesh with his tusk as he charged sideways, but he reached not to the bone of the man. Then Odysseus aimed well and smote him on his right shoulder, so that the point of the bright spear went clean through, and the boar fell in the dust with a cry, and his life passed from him. Then the dear sons of Autolycus began to busy them with the carcase, and as for the wound of the noble godlike Odysseus, they bound it up skilfully, and stayed the black blood with a song of healing, and straightway returned to the house of their dear father. Then Autolycus and the sons of Autolycus got him well healed of his hurt, and gave him splendid gifts, and

Odysseus Leaving for the Hunt.
PAINTING FROM AN ARCHAIC ATTIC AMPHORA WITH BLACK FIGURES.
(LOUVRE MUSEUM)

Another recognition
scene — common in this
kind of story
XIX · Odysseus and Eurycleia 361

quickly sent him with all love to Ithaca, gladly speeding a glad guest. There his father and lady mother were glad of his returning, and asked him of all his adventures, and of his wound how he came by it, and duly he told them all, namely, how the boar gashed him with his white tusk in the chase, when he had gone to Parnassus with the sons of Autolycus.

Now the old woman took the scarred limb and passed her hands down it, and knew it by the touch and let the foot drop suddenly, so that the knee fell into the bath, and the brazen vessel rang, being turned over on the other side, and behold, the water was spilled on the ground. Then joy and anguish came on her in one moment, and both her eyes filled up with tears, and the voice of her utterance was stayed, and touching the chin of Odysseus she spake to him, saying:

"Yea verily, thou art Odysseus my dear child, and I knew thee not before, till I had handled all the body of my lord."

Therewithal she looked towards Penelope, as minded to make a sign that her husband was now home. But Penelope could not meet her eyes nor take note of her, for Athene had bent her thoughts to other things. But Odysseus feeling for the old woman's throat gript it with his right hand and with the other drew her closer to him and spake saying:

"Woman, why wouldest thou indeed destroy me? It was thou that didst nurse me there at thine own breast, and now after travail and much pain I am come in the twentieth year to mine own country. But since thou art ware of me, and the god has put this in thy heart, be silent, lest another learn the matter in the halls. For on this wise I will declare it, and it shall surely be accomplished:—if the gods subdue the lordly wooers unto me, I will not hold my hand from thee, my nurse though thou art, when I slay the other handmaids in my halls."

Then wise Eurycleia answered, saying: "My child, what word hath escaped the door of thy lips? Thou knowest how firm is my spirit and unyielding, and I will keep me fast as stubborn stone or iron. Yet another thing will I tell thee,

He swears her to silence

and do thou ponder it in thine heart. If the gods subdue the lordly wooers to thy hand, then will I tell thee all the tale of the women in the halls, which of them dishonour thee and which be guiltless."

Then Odysseus of many counsels answered her saying: "Nurse, wherefore I pray thee wilt thou speak of these? Thou needest not, for even I myself will mark them well and take knowledge of each. Nay, do thou keep thy saying to thyself, and leave the rest to the gods."

Even so he spake, and the old woman passed forth from the hall to bring water for his feet, for the first water was all spilled. So when she had washed him and anointed him well with olive-oil, Odysseus again drew up his settle nearer to the fire to warm himself, and covered up the scar with his rags. Then the wise Penelope spake first, saying:

"Stranger, there is yet a little thing I will make bold to ask thee, for soon will it be the hour for pleasant rest, for him on whomsoever sweet sleep falls, though he be heavy with care. But to me has the god given sorrow, yea sorrow measureless, for all the day I have my fill of wailing and lamenting, as I look to mine own housewiferies and to the tasks of the maidens in the house. But when night comes and sleep takes hold of all, I lie on my couch, and shrewd cares, thick thronging about my inmost heart, disquiet me in my sorrowing. Even as when the daughter of Pandareus, the nightingale of the greenwood, sings sweet in the first season of the spring, from her place in the thick leafage of the trees, and with many a turn and trill she pours forth her full-voiced music bewailing her child, dear Itylus, whom on a time she slew with the sword unwitting, Itylus the son of Zethus the prince; even as her song, my troubled soul sways to and fro. Shall I abide with my son, and keep all secure, all the things of my getting, my thralls and great high-roofed home, having respect unto the bed of my lord and the voice of the people, or even now follow with the best of the Achaeans that woos me in the halls, and gives a bride-price beyond reckoning? Now my son, so long as he was a child and light of heart, suffered me not to marry and leave the house of my husband;

but now that he is great of growth, and is come to the full measure of manhood, lo now he prays me to go back home from these walls, being vexed for his possessions that the Achaeans devour before his eyes. But come now, hear a dream of mine and tell me the interpretation thereof. Twenty geese I have in the house, that eat wheat, coming forth from the water, and I am gladdened at the sight. Now a great eagle of crooked beak swooped from the mountain, and brake all their necks and slew them; and they lay strewn in a heap in the halls, while he was borne aloft to the bright air. Thereupon I wept and wailed, in a dream though it was, and around me were gathered the fair-tressed Achaean women as I made piteous lament, for that the eagle had slain my geese. But he came back and sat him down on a jutting point of the roof-beam, and with the voice of a man he spake, and stayed my weeping:

" 'Take heart, O daughter of renowned Icarius; this is no dream but a true vision, that shall be accomplished for thee. The geese are the wooers, and I that before was the eagle am now thy husband come again, who will let slip unsightly death upon all the wooers.' With that word sweet slumber let me go, and I looked about, and beheld the geese in the court pecking their wheat at the trough, where they were wont before."

Then Odysseus of many counsels answered her and said: "Lady, none may turn aside the dream to interpret it otherwise, seeing that Odysseus himself hath showed thee how he will fulfil it. For the wooers destruction is clearly boded, for all and every one; not a man shall avoid death and the fates."

Then wise Penelope answered him: "Stranger, verily dreams are awkward and confusing things; nor are all things therein fulfilled for men. Twain are the gates of shadowy dreams, the one is fashioned of horn and one of ivory. Such dreams as pass through the portals of sawn ivory are deceitful, and bear tidings that are unfulfilled. But the dreams that come forth through the gates of polished horn bring a true issue, whosoever of mortals beholds them. Yet methinks my strange dream came not thence; of a truth that would be most welcome to me and to my son. But another thing will I tell thee, and do thou ponder it in thy heart. Lo, even now draws nigh the morn of evil name, that is to sever me from the house of Odysseus, for now I am about to ordain for a trial those axes that he would set up in a row in his halls, like stays of oak in ship-building, twelve in all, and he would stand far apart and shoot his arrow through them all. And now I will offer this contest to the wooers: whoso shall most easily string the bow in his hands, and shoot through all twelve axes, with him will I go and forsake this house, this house of my wedlock, so fair and filled with all livelihood, which methinks I shall yet remember, aye, in a dream."

Then Odysseus of many counsels answered her and said: "Wife revered of Odysseus, son of Laertes, no longer delay this contest in thy halls; for, lo, Odysseus of many counsels will be here, before these men, for all their handling of this polished bow, shall have strung it, and shot the arrow through the iron."

Then the wise Penelope answered him: "Stranger, if only thou wert willing still to sit beside me in the halls and to delight me, not upon my eyelids would sleep be shed. But men may in no wise abide sleepless ever, for the immortals have made a time for all things for mortals on the grain-giving earth. Howbeit I will go aloft to my upper chamber, and lay me on my bed, the place of my groanings, that is ever watered by my tears, since the day that Odysseus went to see that evil Ilium, never to be named. There will I lay me down, but do thou lie in this house; either strew thee somewhat on the floor, or let them lay bedding for thee."

Therewith she ascended to her shining upper chamber, not alone, for with her likewise went her handmaids. So she went aloft to her upper chamber with the women her handmaids, and there was bewailing Odysseus, her dear lord, till grey-eyed Athene cast sweet sleep upon her eyelids.

XX

The Wooers Are Revelling.

Bad Omens for the Suitors

❬ When Odysseus lies down to sleep in the portico, his anger is aroused by a group of women, the mistresses of the suitors, who come out of the house on their way to their lovers. As he lies angry and sleepless, considering how he may slay the wooers, Athene brings him promise of aid. Praying to Zeus in the dawn, he is further cheered by favorable omens. Likewise he gains comfort from Eumaeus the swineherd and Philoetius the neatherd, who come bringing swine and goats for the suitors, although he is angered by the taunts of Melanthius the goatherd.

On this last day of their lives the suitors outdo themselves in insolence and insults against Odysseus in his beggar's disguise. Pallas Athene drives them on to words and acts of infatuation. Theoclymenus the seer prophesies evil, and in their frolicking they laugh at his words and at Telemachus' guests.

XXI

an inspiration – from cause!
a divine source, of

Odysseus Strings the Great Bow

Now the goddess, grey-eyed Athene, put it into the heart of the daughter of Icarius, wise Penelope, to set the bow and the axes of grey iron, for the wooers in the halls of Odysseus, to be the weapons of the contest, and the beginning of death. So she descended the tall staircase of her chamber, and took the well-bent key in her strong hand, a goodly key of bronze, whereon was a handle of ivory. And she betook her, with her handmaidens, to the treasure-chamber in the uttermost part of the house, where lay the treasures of her lord, bronze and gold and well-wrought iron. And there lay the back-bent bow and the quiver for the arrows, and many shafts were therein, winged for death, gifts of a friend of Odysseus, that met with him in Lacedaemon, Iphitus son of Eurytus, a man like to the gods. These twain fell in with one another in Messene, in the house of wise Ortilochus. Now Odysseus had gone thither to recover somewhat that was owing to him from all the people, for the men of Messene had lifted three hundred sheep in benched ships from out of Ithaca, with the shepherds of the flock. In quest of these it was that Odysseus went on a far embassy, being yet a lad; for his father and the other elders sent him forth. Moreover, Iphitus came thither in his search for twelve brood mares, which he had lost, with sturdy mules at the teat. These same it was that brought him death and destiny in the latter end, when he came to the child of Zeus, hardy of heart, the man Heracles, that had knowledge of great adventures, who smote Iphitus though his guest in his house, in his frowardness, and had no regard for the vengeance of the gods, nor for the table which he spread before him; for after the meal he slew him, his guest though he was, and kept for himself in the halls the horses strong of hoof. After these was Iphitus asking, when he met with Odysseus, and he gave him the bow, which of old great Eurytus bare and had left at his death to his son in his lofty house. And Odysseus gave Iphitus a sharp sword and a mighty spear, for the beginning of a loving friendship; but never had they acquaintance one of another at the board; ere that might be, the son of Zeus slew Iphitus son of Eurytus, a man like to the immortals, the same that gave Odysseus the bow. But goodly Odysseus would never take it with him on the black ships, as he went to the wars, but the bow was laid by at home in the halls as a memorial of a dear guest, and he carried it on his own land.

Now when the fair lady had come even to the treasure-chamber, and had stept upon the threshold of oak, which the carpenter had on a time planed cunningly, and over it had made straight the line,—doorposts also had he fitted thereby, whereon he set shining doors,—anon she quickly loosed the strap from the handle of the door, and thrust in the key, and with a straight aim shot back the bolts. And even as a bull roars that is grazing in a meadow, so mightily roared the fair doors smitten by the key; and speedily they flew open before her. Then she stept on to the high floor, where the coffers stood, wherein the fragrant raiment was stored. Thence she stretched forth her hand, and took the bow from off the peg, all in the bright case which sheathed it around. And there she sat down, and set the case upon her knees, and cried aloud and wept, and took out the bow of her lord. Now when she had her fill of tearful lament, she set forth to go to the hall to the company of the proud wooers, with the back-bent bow in her hands, and the quiver for the arrows, and many shafts were therein winged for death. And her maidens along with her bare a chest, wherein lay much store of iron and bronze, the gear of combat of their lord. Now when the fair lady had come unto the wooers, she stood by the pillar of the well-built roof, holding up a fold of her bright headdress before her face; and a faithful maiden stood on either side of her, and straightway she spake out among the wooers and declared her word, saying:

"Hear me, ye lordly wooers, who have vexed this house, that ye might eat and drink here evermore, forasmuch as the master is long gone, nor could ye find any other pretext for your conduct, but all your desire was to wed me and take me to wife. Nay come now, ye wooers, seeing that this is the prize that is put before you. I will set forth for you the great bow of divine Odysseus, and whoso shall most easily string the bow in his hands, and shoot through all twelve axes, with him will I go and forsake this house, this house of my wedlock, so fair and filled with all livelihood, which methinks I shall yet remember, aye, in a dream."

So spake she, and commanded Eumaeus, the goodly swineherd, to set the bow for the wooers and the axes of grey iron. And Eumaeus took them with tears, and laid them down; and otherwhere the neatherd wept, when he beheld the bow of his lord. Then Antinous rebuked them, and spake and hailed them:

"Foolish boors, whose thoughts look not beyond the day, ah, wretched pair, wherefore now do ye shed tears, and stir the soul of the lady within her, when her heart already lies low in pain, for that she has lost her dear lord? Nay sit, and feast in silence, or else get ye forth and weep, and leave the bow here behind, to be a terrible contest for the wooers, for methinks that this polished bow does not lightly yield itself to be strung. For there is no man among all these present such as Odysseus was, and I myself saw him, yea I remember it well, though I was still but a child."

So spake he, but his heart within him hoped that he would string the bow, and shoot through the iron. Yet verily, he was to be the first that should taste the arrow at the hands of the noble Odysseus, whom but late he was dishonouring as he sat in the halls, and was inciting all his fellows to do like-wise.

Then the mighty prince Telemachus spake among them, saying: "Lo now, in very truth, Zeus has robbed me of my wits! My dear mother, wise as she is, declares that she will go with a stranger and forsake this house; yet I laugh and in my silly heart I am glad. Nay come now, ye wooers, seeing that this is the prize which is set before you, a lady, the like of whom there is not now in the Achaean land, neither in sacred Pylos, nor in Argos, nor in Mycenae, nor yet in Ithaca, nor in the dark mainland. Nay but ye know all this yourselves,—why need I praise my mother? Come therefore, delay not the issue with excuses, nor hold much longer aloof from the drawing of the bow, that we may see the thing that is to be. Yea and I myself would make trial of this bow. If I shall string it, and shoot through the iron, then should I not sorrow if my lady mother were to quit these halls and go with a stranger, seeing that I should be left behind, well able now to lift my father's goodly gear of combat."

Therewith he cast from off his neck his cloak of scarlet, and sprang to his full height, and put away the sword from his shoulders. First he dug a good trench and set up the axes, one long trench for them all, and over it he made straight the line and round about stamped in the earth. And amazement fell on all that beheld how orderly he set the axes, though never before had he seen it so. Then he went and stood by the threshold and began to prove the bow. Thrice he made it to tremble in his great desire to draw it, and thrice he rested from his effort, though still he hoped in his heart to string the bow, and shoot through the iron. And now at last he might have strung it, mightily straining thereat for the fourth time, but Odysseus nodded frowning and stayed him, for all his eagerness. Then the strong prince Telemachus spake among them again:

"Lo you now, even to the end of my days I shall be a coward and a weakling, or it may be I am too young, and have as yet no trust in my hands to defend me from such an one as does violence without a cause. But come now, ye who are mightier men than I, essay the bow and let us make an end of the contest."

Therewith he put the bow from him on the ground, leaning it against the smooth and well-compacted doors, and the swift shaft he propped hard by against the fair bow-tip, and then he sat down once more on the high seat, whence he had risen.

Then Antinous, son of Eupeithes, spake among them, saying: "Rise up in order, all my friends, beginning from the left, even from the place whence the wine is poured."

So spake Antinous, and the saying pleased them well. Then first stood up Leiodes, son of Oenops, who was their soothsayer and ever sat by the fair mixing bowl at the extremity of the hall; he alone hated their infatuate deeds and was indignant with all the wooers. He now first took the bow and the swift shaft, and he went and stood by the threshold, and began to prove the bow; but he could not bend it; or ever that might be, his hands grew weary with the straining, his unworn, delicate hands; so he spake among the wooers, saying:

"Friends, of a truth I cannot bend it, let some other take it. Ah, many of our bravest shall this bow rob of spirit and of life, since truly it is far better for us to die, than to live on and to fail of that for which we assemble evermore in this place, day by day expecting the prize. Many there be even now that hope in their hearts and desire to wed Penelope, the bed-fellow of Odysseus: but when such an one shall make trial of the bow and see the issue, thereafter let him woo some other fair-robed Achaean woman with his bridal gifts and seek to win her. So may our lady wed the man that gives most gifts, and comes as the chosen of fate."

So he spake, and put from him the bow leaning it against the smooth and well-compacted doors, and the swift shaft he propped hard by against the fair bow-tip, and then he sat down once more on the high seat, whence he had risen.

But Antinous rebuked him, and spake and hailed him: "Leiodes, what word hath escaped the door of thy lips; a hard word, and a grievous? Nay, it angers me to hear it, and to think that a bow such as this shall rob our bravest of spirit and of life, and all because thou canst not draw it. For I tell thee that thy lady mother bare thee not of such might as to draw a bow and shoot arrows: but there be others of the proud wooers that shall draw it soon."

So he spake, and commanded Melanthius, the goatherd, saying: "Up now, light a fire in the halls, Melanthius; and place a great settle by the fire and a fleece thereon, and bring forth a great ball of lard that is within, that we young men may warm and anoint the bow therewith and prove it, and make an end of the contest."

So he spake, and Melanthius soon kindled the never-resting fire, and drew up a settle and placed it near, and put a fleece thereon, and he brought forth a great ball of lard that was within. Therewith the young men warmed the bow, and made essay, but could not string it, for they were greatly lacking of such might. And Antinous still held to the task and godlike Eurymachus, chief men among the wooers, who were far the most excellent of all.

But those other twain went forth both together from the house, the neatherd and the swineherd of godlike Odysseus; and Odysseus passed out after them. But when they were now gotten without the gates and the courtyard, he uttered his voice and spake to them in gentle words:

"Neatherd and thou swineherd, shall I say somewhat or keep it to myself? Nay, my spirit bids me declare it. What manner of men would ye be to help Odysseus, if he should come thus suddenly, I know not whence, and some god were to bring him? Would ye stand on the side of the wooers or of Odysseus? Tell me even as your heart and spirit bid you."

Then the neatherd answered him, saying: "Father Zeus, if but thou wouldst fulfil this wish:—oh, that that man might come, and some god lead him hither! So shouldest thou know what my might is, and how my hands follow to obey."

In like manner Eumaeus prayed to all the gods that wise Odysseus might return to his own home.

Now when he knew for a surety what spirit they were of, once more he answered and spake to them, saying:

"Behold, home am I come, even I; after much travail and sore am I come in the twentieth year to mine own country. And I know how that my coming is desired by you alone of all my thralls, for from none besides have I heard a prayer that I might return once more to my home. And now I will tell you all the truth, even as it shall come to pass. If the god shall subdue the proud wooers to my hands, I will bring you each one a wife, and will give you a heritage of your own and a house builded near to me, and ye twain shall be thereafter in mine eyes as the brethren and companions of Telemachus. But behold, I will likewise show you a most manifest token, that ye may know me well and be certified in heart, even the wound that the boar dealt me with his white tusk long ago, when I went to Parnassus with the sons of Autolycus."

Therewith he drew aside the rags from the great scar. And when the twain had beheld it and marked it well, they cast their arms about the wise Odysseus, and fell a weeping; and kissed him lovingly on head and shoulders. And in like manner Odysseus too kissed their heads and hands. And now would the sunlight have gone down upon their sorrowing, had not Odysseus himself stayed them saying:

"Cease ye from weeping and lamentation, lest some one come forth from the hall and see us, and tell it likewise in the house. Nay, go ye within one by one and not both together, I first and you following, and let this be the token between us. All the rest, as many as are proud wooers, will not suffer that I should be given the bow and quiver; do thou then, goodly Eumaeus, as thou bearest the bow through the hall, set it in my hands and speak to the women that they bar the well-fitting doors of their chamber. And if any of them hear the sound of groaning or the din of men within our walls, let them not run forth but abide where they are in silence at their work. But on thee, goodly Philoetius, I lay this charge, to bolt and bar the outer gate of the court and swiftly to tie the knot."

Therewith he passed within the fair-lying halls, and went and sat upon the settle whence he had risen. And likewise the two thralls of divine Odysseus went within.

And now Eurymachus was handling the bow, warming it on this side and on that at the light of the fire; yet even so he could not string it, and in his great heart he groaned mightily; and in heaviness of spirit he spake and called aloud, saying:

"Lo you now, truly am I grieved for myself and for you all! Not for the marriage do I mourn so greatly, afflicted though I be; there are many Achaean women besides, some in sea-begirt Ithaca itself and some in other cities. Nay, but I grieve, if indeed we are so far worse than godlike Odysseus in might, seeing that we cannot bend the bow. It will be a shame even for men unborn to hear thereof."

Then Antinous, son of Eupeithes, answered him: "Eurymachus, this shall not be so, and thou thyself too knowest it. For to-day the feast of the archer god is held in the land a holy feast. Who at such a time would be bending bows? Nay, set it quietly by; what and if we should let the axes all stand as they are? None methinks will come to the hall of Odysseus, son of Laertes, and carry them away. Go to now, let the wine-bearer pour for libation into each cup in turn, that after the drink-offering we may set down the curved bow. And in the morning bid Melanthius, the goatherd, to lead hither the very best goats in all his herds, that we may lay pieces of the thighs on the altar of Apollo the archer, and essay the bow and make an end of the contest."

So spake Antinous, and the saying pleased them well. Then the henchmen poured water on their hands, and pages crowned the mixing-bowls with drink, and served out the wine to all, when they had poured for libation into each cup in turn. But when they had poured forth and had drunken to their hearts' desire, Odysseus of many counsels spake among them out of a crafty heart, saying:

"Hear me, ye wooers of the renowned queen, that I may say that which my heart within me bids. And mainly to Eurymachus I make my prayer and to the godlike Antinous, forasmuch as he has spoken even this word aright, namely, that for this present ye cease from your archery and leave the issue to the gods; and in the morning the god will give the victory to whomsoever he will. Come therefore, give me the polished bow, that in your presence I may prove my hands and strength, whether I have yet any force such as once was in my supple limbs, or whether my wanderings and needy fare have even now destroyed it."

So spake he and they all were exceeding wroth, for fear lest he should string the polished bow. And Antinous rebuked him, and spake and hailed him:

"Wretched stranger, thou hast no wit, nay never so little. Art thou not content to feast at ease in our high company, and to lack not thy share of the banquet, but to listen to our speech and our discourse, while no guest and beggar beside thee hears our speech? Wine it is that wounds thee, honeysweet wine, that is the bane of others too, even of all who take great draughts and drink out of measure. Wine it was that darkened the mind even of the Centaur, renowned Eurytion, in the hall of high-hearted Peirithous, when he went to the Lapithae; and after that his heart was darkened with wine, he wrought foul deeds in his frenzy, in the house of Peirithous. Then wrath fell on all the heroes, and they leaped up and dragged him forth through the porch, when they had shorn off his ears and nostrils with the pitiless sword, and then with darkened mind he bare about with him the burden of his sin in foolishness of heart. Thence was the feud begun between the Centaurs and mankind; but first for himself gat he hurt, being heavy with wine. And even so I declare great mischief unto thee if thou shalt string the bow, for thou shalt find no courtesy at the hand of any one in our land, and anon we will send thee in a black ship to Echetus, the maimer of all men, and thence thou shalt not be saved alive. Nay then, drink at thine ease, and strive not still with men that are younger than thou."

Then wise Penelope answered him: "Antinous, truly it is not fair nor just to rob the guests of Telemachus of their due, whosoever he may be that comes to this house. Dost thou think if yonder stranger strings the great bow of Odysseus, in the pride of his might and of his strength of arm, that he will lead me to his home and make me his wife? Nay he himself, methinks, has no such hope in his breast; so, as for that, let not any of you fret himself while feasting in this place; that were indeed unmeet."

Then Eurymachus, son of Polybus, answered her, saying: "Daughter of Icarius, wise Penelope, it is not that we deem that he will lead thee to his home,—far be such a thought from us,—but we dread the speech of men and women, lest some day one of the baser sort among the Achaeans say: 'Truly men far too mean are wooing the wife of one that is noble, nor can they string the polished bow. But a stranger and a beggar came in his wanderings, and lightly strung the bow, and shot through the iron.' Thus will they speak, and this will turn to our reproach."

Then wise Penelope answered him: "Eurymachus, never can there be fair fame in the land for those that devour and dishonour the house of a prince, but why make ye this thing into a reproach? But, behold, our guest is great of growth and well-knit, and avows him to be born the son of a good father. Come then, give ye him the polished bow, that we may see that which is to be. For thus will I declare my saying, and it shall surely come to pass. If he shall string the bow and Apollo grant him renown, I will clothe him in a mantle and a doublet, goodly raiment, and I will give him a sharp javelin to defend him against dogs and men, and a two-edged sword and sandals to bind beneath his feet, and I will send him whithersoever his heart and spirit bid him go."

Then wise Telemachus answered her, saying: "My mother, as for the bow, no Achaean is mightier than I to give or to deny it to whomso I will, neither as many as are lords in rocky Ithaca nor in the isles on the side of Elis, the pasture-land of horses. Not one of these shall force me in mine own despite, if I choose to give this bow, yea once and for all, to the stranger to bear away with him. But do thou go to thine own chamber and mind thine own housewiferies, the loom and distaff, and bid thine handmaids ply their tasks. But the bow shall be for men, for all, but for me in chief, for mine is the lordship in the house."

Then in amaze she went back to her chamber, for she laid up the wise saying of her son in her heart. She ascended to her upper chamber with the women her handmaids, and then was bewailing Odysseus, her dear lord, till grey-eyed Athene cast sweet sleep upon her eyelids.

Now the goodly swineherd had taken the curved bow, and was bearing it, when the wooers all cried out upon him in the halls. And thus some one of the haughty youths would speak: "Whither now art thou bearing the curved bow, thou wretched swineherd, crazed in thy wits? Lo, soon shall the swift hounds of thine own breeding eat thee hard by thy swine, alone and away from men, if Apollo will be gracious to us and the other deathless gods."

Even so they spake, and he took and set down the bow in that very place, being affrighted because many cried out on him in the halls. Then Telemachus from the other side spake threateningly, and called aloud:

"Father, bring hither the bow, soon shalt thou rue it that thou servest many masters. Take heed, lest I that am younger than thou pursue thee to the field, and pelt thee with stones, for in might I am the better. If only I were so much mightier in strength of arm than all the wooers that are in the halls, soon would I send many an one forth on a woeful way from out our house, for they imagine mischief against us."

So he spake, and all the wooers roared with laughter at him, and ceased now from their cruel anger toward Telemachus. Then the swineherd bare the bow through the hall, and went up to wise Odysseus, and set it in his hands. And he called forth the nurse Eurycleia from the chamber and spake to her:

"Wise Eurycleia, Telemachus bids thee bar the well-fitting doors of thy chamber, and if any of the women hear the sound of groaning or the din of men within our walls, let them not go forth, but abide where they are in silence at their work."

So he spake, and wingless her speech remained, and she barred the doors of the fair-lying chambers.

Then Philoetius hasted forth silently from the house, and barred the outer gates of the fenced court. Now there lay beneath the gallery the cable of a curved ship, fashioned of the papyrus plant, wherewith he made fast the gates, and then himself passed within. Then he went and sat on the settle whence he had risen, and gazed upon Odysseus. He already was handling the bow, turning it every way about, and proving it on this side and on that, lest the worms might have eaten the horns when the lord of the bow was away. And thus men spake looking each one to his neighbour:

"Verily he has a good eye, and a shrewd turn for a bow! Either, methinks, he himself has such a bow lying by at home or else he is set on making one, in such wise does he turn it hither and thither in his hands, this evil-witted beggar."

And another again of the haughty youths would say: "Would that the fellow may have profit thereof, just so surely as he shall ever prevail to bend this bow!"

So spake the wooers, but Odysseus of many counsels had lifted the great bow and viewed it on every side, and even as when a man that is skilled in the lyre and in minstrelsy easily stretches a cord about a new peg, after tying at either end the twisted sheep-gut, even so Odysseus straightway bent the great bow, all without effort, and took it in his right hand and proved the bow-string, which rang sweetly at the touch, in tone like a swallow. Then great grief came upon the wooers, and the colour of their countenance was changed, and Zeus thundered loud showing forth his tokens. And the steadfast goodly Odysseus was glad thereat, in that the son of deep-counselling Cronos had sent him a sign. Then he caught up a swift arrow which lay by his table, bare, but the other shafts were stored within the hollow quiver, those whereof the Achaeans were soon to taste. He took and laid it on the bridge of the bow, and held the notch and drew the string, even from the settle whereon he sat, and with straight aim shot the shaft and missed not one of the axes, beginning from the first axe-handle, and the bronze-weighted shaft passed clean through and out at the last. Then he spake to Telemachus, saying:

"Telemachus, thy guest that sits in the halls does thee no shame. In no wise did I miss my mark, nor was I wearied with long bending of the bow. Still is my might steadfast—not as the wooers say scornfully to slight me. But now is it time that supper too be got ready for the Achaeans, while it is yet light, and thereafter must we make other sport with the dance and the lyre, for these are the crown of the feast."

Therewith he nodded with bent brows, and Telemachus, the dear son of divine Odysseus, girt his sharp sword about him and took the spear in his grasp, and stood by his high seat at his father's side, armed with the gleaming bronze.

XXII

The Killing of the Wooers

THEN Odysseus of many counsels stripped him of his rags and leaped on to the great threshold with his bow and quiver full of arrows, and poured forth all the swift shafts there before his feet, and spake among the wooers:

"Lo, now is this terrible trial ended at last; and now will I know of another mark, which never yet man has smitten, if perchance I may hit it and Apollo grant me renown."

With that he pointed the bitter arrow at Antinous. Now he was about raising to his lips a fair two-handled chalice of gold, and behold, he was handling it to drink of the wine, and death was far from his thoughts. For who among men at feast would deem that one man amongst so many, how hardy soever he were, would bring on him foul death and black fate? But Odysseus aimed and smote him with the arrow in the throat, and the point passed clean out through his delicate neck, and he fell sidelong and the cup dropped from his hand as he was smitten, and at once through his nostrils there came up a thick jet of slain man's blood, and quickly he spurned the table from him with his foot, and spilt the food on the ground, and the bread and the roast flesh were defiled. Then the wooers raised a clamour through the halls when they saw the man fallen, and they leaped from their high seats, as men stirred by fear, all through the hall, peering everywhere along the well-builded walls, and nowhere was there a shield or mighty spear to lay hold on. Then they reviled Odysseus with angry words:

"Stranger, thou shootest at men to thy hurt. Never again shalt thou enter other lists, now is utter doom assured thee. Yea, for now hast thou slain the man that was far the best of all the noble youths in Ithaca; wherefore vultures shall devour thee here."

So each one spake, for indeed they thought that Odysseus had not slain him wilfully; but they knew not in their folly that on their own heads, each and all of them, the bands of death had been made fast. Then Odysseus of many counsels looked fiercely on them, and spake:

"Ye dogs, ye said in your hearts that I should never more

The Slaughter of the Wooers.
PAINTING FROM A CRATER FOUND AT CORNETO (RESTITUTION).
(BERLIN MUSEUM)

come home from the land of the Trojans, in that ye wasted my house, and lay with the maidservants by force, and traitorously wooed my wife while I was yet alive, and ye had no fear of the gods, that hold the wide heaven, nor of the indignation of men hereafter. But now the bands of death have been made fast upon you one and all."

Even so he spake, and pale fear gat hold on the limbs of all, and each man looked about, where he might shun utter doom. And Eurymachus alone answered him, and spake: "If thou art indeed Odysseus of Ithaca, come home again, with right thou speakest thus, of all that the Achaeans have wrought, many infatuate deeds in thy halls and many in the field. Howbeit, he now lies dead that is to blame for all, Antinous; for he brought all these things upon us, not as longing very greatly for the marriage nor needing it sore,

[handwritten marginalia: "seems reasonable, but they must pay with their lives"]

but with another purpose, that Zeus has not fulfilled for him, namely, that he might himself be king over all the land of stablished Ithaca, and he was to have lain in wait for thy son and killed him. But now he is slain after his deserving, and do thou spare thy people, even thine own; and we will hereafter go about the township and yield thee amends for all that has been eaten and drunken in thy halls, each for himself bringing atonement of twenty oxen worth, and requiting thee in gold and bronze till thy heart is softened, but till then none may blame thee that thou art angry."

Then Odysseus of many counsels looked fiercely on him, and said: "Eurymachus, not even if ye gave me all your heritage, all that ye now have, and whatsoever else ye might in any wise add thereto, not even so would I henceforth hold my hands from slaying, ere the wooers had paid for all their transgressions. And now the choice lies before you, whether to fight in fair battle or to fly, if any may avoid death and the fates. But there be some, methinks, that shall not escape from utter doom."

He spake, and their knees were straightway loosened and their hearts melted within them. And Eurymachus spake among them yet again:

"Friends, it is plain that this man will not hold his unconquerable hands, but now that he has caught up the polished bow and quiver, he will shoot from the smooth threshold, till he has slain us all; wherefore let us take thought for the delight of battle. Draw your blades, and hold up the tables to ward off the arrows of swift death, and let us all have at him with one accord, and drive him, if it may be, from the threshold and the doorway and then go through the city, and quickly would the cry be raised. Thereby should this man soon have shot his latest bolt."

Therewith he drew his sharp two-edged sword of bronze, and leapt on Odysseus with a terrible cry, but in the same moment goodly Odysseus shot the arrow forth and struck him on the breast by the pap, and drave the swift shaft into his liver. So he let the sword fall from his hand, and grovelling over the table he bowed and fell, and spilt the food and the two-handled cup on the floor. And in his agony he smote the ground with his brow, and spurning with both his feet he overthrew the high seat, and the mist of death was shed upon his eyes.

Then Amphinomus made at renowned Odysseus, setting straight at him, and drew his sharp sword, if perchance he might make him give ground from the door. But Telemachus was beforehand with him, and cast and smote him from behind with a bronze-shod spear between the shoulders, and drave it out through the breast, and he fell with a crash and struck the ground full with his forehead. Then Telemachus sprang away, leaving the long spear fixed in Amphinomus, for he greatly dreaded lest one of the Achaeans might run upon him with his blade, and stab him as he drew forth the spear, or smite him with a down stroke of the sword. So he started and ran and came quickly to his father, and stood by him, and spake winged words:

"Father, lo, now I will bring thee a shield and two spears and a helmet all of bronze, close fitting on the temples, and when I return I will arm myself, and likewise give arms to the swineherd and to the neatherd yonder: for it is better to be clad in full armour."

And Odysseus of many counsels answered him saying: "Run and bring them while I have arrows to defend me, lest they thrust me from the doorway, one man against them all."

So he spake, and Telemachus obeyed his dear father, and went forth to the chamber, where his famous weapons were lying. Thence he took out four shields and eight spears, and four helmets of bronze, with thick plumes of horse hair, and he started to bring them and came quickly to his father. Now he girded the gear of bronze about his own body first, and in like manner the two thralls did on the goodly armour, and stood beside the wise and crafty Odysseus. Now he, so long as he had arrows to defend him, kept aiming and smote the wooers one by one in his house, and they fell thick one upon another. But when the arrows failed the prince in his archery, he leaned his bow against the doorpost of the stablished hall, against the shining faces of the entrance. As for him he girt his fourfold shield about his shoulders and bound on his mighty head a well-wrought helmet, with horse hair crest, and terribly the plume waved aloft. And he grasped two mighty spears tipped with bronze.

Now there was in the well-built wall a certain postern raised above the floor, and there by the topmost level of the threshold of the stablished hall, was a way into an open passage, closed by well-fitted folding doors. So Odysseus bade the goodly swineherd stand near thereto and watch the way, for thither was there but one approach. Then Agelaus spake among them, and declared his word to all:

"Friends, will not some man climb up to the postern, and give word to the people, and a cry would be raised straightway; so should this man soon have shot his latest bolt?"

Then Melanthius, the goatherd, answered him, saying: "It may in no wise be, prince Agelaus; for the fair gate of the courtyard is terribly nigh, and perilous is the entrance to the passage, and one man, if he were valiant, might keep back a host. But come, let me bring you armour from the inner chamber, that ye may be clad in hauberks, for, methinks, within that room and not elsewhere did Odysseus and his renowned son lay by the arms."

Therewith Melanthius, the goatherd, climbed up by the clerestory of the hall to the inner chambers of Odysseus, whence he took twelve shields and as many spears, and as many helmets of bronze with thick plumes of horse hair, and he came forth and brought them speedily, and gave them to the wooers. Then the knees of Odysseus were loosened and his heart melted within him, when he saw them girding on the armour and brandishing the long spears in their hands, and great, he saw, was the adventure. Quickly he spake to Telemachus winged words:

"Telemachus, sure I am that one of the women in the halls is stirring up an evil battle against us, or perchance it is Melanthius."

Then wise Telemachus answered him: "My father, it is I that have erred herein and none other is to blame, for I left the well-fitted door of the chamber open, and there has been one of them but too quick to spy it. Go now, goodly Eumaeus, and close the door of the chamber, and mark if it be indeed one of the women that does this mischief, or Melanthius, son of Dolius, as methinks it is."

Even so they spake one to the other. And Melanthius, the goatherd, went yet again to the chamber to bring the fair armour. But the goodly swineherd was ware thereof, and quickly he spake to Odysseus who stood nigh him:

"Son of Laertes, of the seed of Zeus, Odysseus, of many devices, lo, there again is that baleful man, whom we ourselves suspect, going to the chamber; do thou tell me truly, shall I slay him if I prove the better man, or bring him hither to thee, that he may pay for the many transgressions that he has devised in thy house?"

Then Odysseus of many counsels answered saying: "Verily, I and Telemachus will keep the proud wooers within the halls, for all their fury, but do ye twain tie his feet and arms behind his back and cast him into the chamber, and close the doors after you, and make fast to his body a twisted rope, and drag him up the lofty pillar till he be near the roof-beams, that he may hang there and live for long, and suffer grievous torment."

So he spake, and they gave good heed and hearkened. So they went forth to the chamber, but the goatherd who was within knew not of their coming. Now he was seeking for the armour in the secret place of the chamber, but they twain stood in waiting on either side the doorposts. And when Melanthius, the goatherd, was crossing the threshold with a goodly helm in one hand, and in the other a wide shield and an old, stained with rust, the shield of the hero Laertes that he bare when he was young—but at that time it was laid by, and the seams of the straps were loosened,—then the twain rushed on him and caught him, and dragged him in by the hair, and cast him on the floor in sorrowful plight, and bound him hand and foot in a bitter bond, tightly winding each limb behind his back, even as the son of Laertes bade them, the steadfast goodly Odysseus. And they made fast to his body a twisted rope, and dragged him up the lofty pillar till he came near the roof-beams. Then didst thou speak to him and gird at him, swineherd Eumaeus:

"Now in good truth, Melanthius, shalt thou watch all night, lying in a soft bed as beseems thee, nor shall the early-born Dawn escape thy ken, when she comes forth from the streams of Oceanus, on her golden throne, in the hour when thou art wont to drive the goats to make a meal for the wooers in the halls."

So he was left there, stretched tight in the deadly bond. But they twain got into their harness, and closed the shining door, and went to Odysseus, wise and crafty chief. There they stood breathing fury, four men by the threshold, while those others within the halls were many and good warriors. Then Athene, daughter of Zeus, drew nigh them, like Mentor in fashion and in voice, and Odysseus was glad when he saw her and spake, saying:

"Mentor, ward from us hurt, and remember me thy dear companion, that befriended thee often, and thou art of like age with me."

So he spake, deeming the while that it was Athene, summoner of the host. But the wooers on the other side shouted in the halls, and first Agelaus son of Damastor rebuked Athene, saying:

"Mentor, let not the speech of Odysseus beguile thee to fight against the wooers, and to succour him. For methinks that on this wise we shall work our will. When we shall have slain these men, father and son, thereafter shalt thou perish with them, such deeds thou art set on doing in these halls; nay, with thine own head shalt thou pay the price. But when with the sword we shall have overcome your violence, we will mingle all thy possessions, all that thou hast at home or in the field, with the wealth of Odysseus, and we will not suffer thy sons nor thy daughters to dwell in the halls, nor thy good wife to gad about in the town of Ithaca."

So spake he, and Athene was mightily angered at heart, and chid Odysseus in wrathful words: "Odysseus, thou hast no more steadfast might nor any prowess, as when for nine whole years continually thou didst battle with the Trojans for high born Helen, of the white arms, and many men thou slewest in terrible warfare, and by thy device the wide-wayed city of Priam was taken. How then, now that thou art come to thy house and thine own possessions, dost thou bewail thee and art of feeble courage to stand before the wooers? Nay, come hither, friend, and stand by me, and I will show thee a thing, that thou mayest know what manner of man is Mentor, son of Alcimus, to repay good deeds in the ranks of foemen."

She spake, and gave him not yet clear victory in full, but still for a while made trial of the might and prowess of Odysseus and his renowned son. As for her she flew up to the roof timber of the murky hall, in such fashion as a swallow flies, and there sat down.

Now Agelaus, son of Damastor, urged on the wooers, and likewise Eurynomus and Amphimedon and Demoptolemus and Peisandrus son of Polyctor, and wise Polybus, for these were in valiancy far the best men of the wooers, that still lived and fought for their lives; for the rest had fallen already beneath the bow and the thick rain of arrows. Then Agelaus spake among them, and made known his word to all:

"Friends, now at last will this man hold his unconquerable hands. Lo, now has Mentor left him and spoken but vain boasts, and these remain alone at the entrance of the doors. Wherefore now, throw not your long spears all together, but come, do ye six cast first, if perchance Zeus may grant us to smite Odysseus and win renown. Of the rest will we take no heed, so soon as that man shall have fallen."

So he spake and they all cast their javelins, as he bade them, eagerly; but behold, Athene so wrought that they were all in vain. One man smote the doorpost of the stablished hall, and another the well-fastened door, and the ashen spear of yet another wooer, heavy with bronze, stuck fast in the wall. So when they had avoided all the spears of the wooers, the steadfast goodly Odysseus began first to speak among them:

"Friends, now my word is that we too cast and hurl into the press of the wooers, that are mad to slay and strip us beyond the measure of their former iniquities."

So he spake, and they all took good aim and threw their sharp spears, and Odysseus smote Demoptolemus, and Telemachus Euryades, and the swineherd slew Elatus, and the neatherd Peisandrus. Thus they all bit the wide floor with their teeth, and the wooers fell back into the inmost part of the hall. But the others dashed upon them, and drew forth the shafts from the bodies of the dead.

Then once more the wooers threw their sharp spears eagerly; but behold, Athene so wrought that many of them were in vain. One man smote the doorpost of the stablished hall, and another the well-fastened door, and the ashen spear of another wooer, heavy with bronze, stuck in the wall. Yet Amphimedon hit Telemachus on the hand by the wrist lightly, and the shaft of bronze wounded the surface of the skin. And Ctesippus grazed the shoulder of Eumaeus with a long spear high above the shield, and the spear flew over and fell to the ground. Then again Odysseus, the wise and crafty, he and his men cast their swift spears into the press of the wooers, and now once more Odysseus, waster of cities, smote Eurydamas, and Telemachus Amphimedon, and the swineherd slew Polybus, and last, the neatherd struck Ctesippus in the breast and boasted over him, saying:

"O son of Polytherses, thou lover of jeering, never give place at all to folly to speak so big, but leave thy case to the gods, since in truth they are far mightier than thou. This gift is thy recompense for the ox-foot that thou gavest of late to the divine Odysseus, when he went begging through the house."

So spake the keeper of the shambling kine. Next Odysseus wounded the son of Damastor in close fight with his long spear, and Telemachus wounded Leocritus son of Euenor, right in the flank with his lance, and drave the bronze point clean through, that he fell prone and struck the ground full with his forehead. Then Athene held up her destroying aegis on high from the roof, and their minds were scared, and they fled through the hall, like a drove of kine that the flitting gadfly falls upon and scatters hither and thither in spring time, when the long days begin. But the others set on like vultures of crooked claws and curved beak, that come forth from the mountains and dash upon smaller birds, and these scour low in the plain, stooping in terror from the clouds, while the vultures pounce on them and slay them, and there is no help nor way of flight, and men are glad at the sport; even so did the company of Odysseus set upon the wooers and smite them right and left through the hall; and there rose a hideous moaning as their heads were smitten, and the floor all ran with blood.

Now Leiodes took hold of the knees of Odysseus eagerly, and besought him and spake winged words: "I entreat thee by thy knees, Odysseus, and do thou show mercy on me and have pity. For never yet, I say, have I wronged a maiden in thy halls by froward word or deed, nay I bade the other wooers refrain, whoso of them wrought thus. But they hearkened not unto me to keep their hands from evil. Wherefore they have met a shameful death through their own infatuate deeds. Yet I, the soothsayer among them, that have wrought no evil, shall fall even as they, for no grace abides for good deeds done."

Then Odysseus of many counsels looked askance at him, and said: "If indeed thou dost avow thee to be the soothsayer of these men, thou art like to have often prayed in the halls that the issue of a glad return might be far from me, and that my dear wife should follow thee and bear thee children; wherefore thou shalt not escape the bitterness of death."

Therewith he caught up a sword in his strong hand, that lay where Agelaus had let it fall to the ground when he was slain, and drave it clean through his neck, and as he yet spake his head fell even to the dust.

But the son of Terpes, the minstrel, still sought how he might shun black fate, Phemius, who sang among the wooers of necessity. He stood with the loud lyre in his hand hard by the postern gate, and his heart was divided within him, whether he should slip forth from the hall and sit down by the well-wrought altar of great Zeus of the household court, whereon Laertes and Odysseus had burnt many pieces of the thighs of oxen, or should spring forward and beseech Odysseus by his knees. And as he thought thereupon this seemed to him the better way, to embrace the knees of Odysseus, son of Laertes. So he laid the hollow lyre on the ground between the mixing-bowl and the high seat inlaid with silver, and himself sprang forward and seized Odysseus by the knees, and besought him and spake winged words:

"I entreat thee by thy knees, Odysseus, and do thou show mercy on me and have pity. It will be a sorrow to thyself in the aftertime if thou slayest me who am a minstrel, and sing before gods and men. Yea none has taught me but myself, and the god has put into my heart all manner of lays, and methinks I sing to thee as to a god, wherefore be not eager to cut off my head. And Telemachus will testify of this, thine own dear son, that not by mine own will or desire did I resort to thy house to sing to the wooers at their feasts; but being so many and stronger than I they led me by constraint."

So he spake, and the mighty prince Telemachus heard him and quickly spake to his father at his side: "Hold thy hand, and wound not this blameless man with the sword; and let us save also the henchman Medon, that ever had charge of me in our house when I was a child, unless perchance Philoetius or the swineherd have already slain him, or he hath met thee in thy raging through the house."

So he spake, and Medon, wise of heart, heard him. For he lay crouching beneath a high seat, clad about in the new-flayed hide of an ox and shunned black fate. So he rose up quickly from under the seat, and cast off the oxhide, and sprang forth and caught Telemachus by the knees, and besought him and spake winged words:

"Friend, here am I; prithee stay thy hand and speak to thy father, lest he harm me with the sharp sword in the greatness of his strength, out of his anger for the wooers that wasted his possessions in the halls, and in their folly held thee in no honour."

And Odysseus of many counsels smiled on him and said: "Take courage, for lo, he has saved thee and delivered thee, that thou mayst know in thy heart, and tell it even to another, how far more excellent are good deeds than evil. But go forth from the halls and sit down in the court apart from the slaughter, thou and the full-voiced minstrel, till I have accomplished all that I must needs do in the house."

Therewith the two went forth and gat them from the hall. So they sat down by the altar of great Zeus, peering about on every side, still expecting death. And Odysseus peered all through the house, to see if any man was yet alive and hiding away to shun black fate. But he found all the sort of them fallen in their blood in the dust, like fishes that the fishermen have drawn forth in the meshes of the net into a hollow of the beach from out the grey sea, and all the fish, sore longing for the salt sea waves, are heaped upon the sand, and the sun shines forth and takes their life away; so now the wooers lay heaped upon each other. Then Odysseus of many counsels spake to Telemachus:

"Telemachus, go, call me the nurse Eurycleia, that I may tell her a word that is on my mind."

So he spake, and Telemachus obeyed his dear father, and smote at the door, and spake to the nurse Eurycleia: "Up now, aged wife, that overlookest all the women servants in our halls, come hither, my father calls thee and has somewhat to say to thee."

Even so he spake, and wingless her speech remained, and she opened the doors of the fair-lying halls, and came forth, and Telemachus led the way before her. So she found Odysseus among the bodies of the dead, stained with blood and soil of battle, like a lion that has eaten of an ox of the homestead and goes on his way, and all his breast and his cheeks on either side are flecked with blood, and he is terrible to behold; even so was Odysseus stained, both hands and feet.

always religious

Now the nurse, when she saw the bodies of the dead and the great gore of blood, made ready to cry aloud for joy, beholding so great an adventure. But Odysseus checked and held her in her eagerness, and uttering his voice spake to her winged words:

"Within thine own heart rejoice, old nurse, and be still, and cry not aloud; for it is an unholy thing to boast over slain men. Now these hath the destiny of the gods overcome, and their own cruel deeds, for they honoured none of earthly men, neither the bad nor yet the good, that came among them. Wherefore they have met a shameful death through their own infatuate deeds. But come, tell me the tale of the women in my halls, which of them dishonour me, and which be guiltless."

Then the good nurse Eurycleia answered him: "Yea now, my child, I will tell thee all the truth. Thou hast fifty women-servants in thy halls, that we have taught the ways of house-wifery, how to card wool and to bear bondage. Of these twelve in all have gone the way of shame, and honour not me, nor their lady Penelope. And Telemachus hath but newly come to his strength, and his mother suffered him not to take command over the women in this house. But now, let me go aloft to the shining upper chamber, and tell all to thy wife, on whom some god hath sent a sleep."

And Odysseus of many counsels answered her, saying: "Wake her not yet, but bid the women come hither, who in time past behaved themselves unseemly."

So he spake, and the old wife passed through the hall, to tell the women and to hasten their coming. Then Odysseus called to him Telemachus, and the neatherd, and the swineherd, and spake to them winged words:

"Begin ye now to carry out the dead, and bid the women help you, and thereafter cleanse the fair high seats and the tables with water and porous sponges. And when ye have set all the house in order, lead the maidens without the stablished hall, between the vaulted room and the goodly fence of the court, and there slay them with your long blades, till

they shall have all given up the ghost and forgotten the love
that of old they had at the bidding of the wooers, in secret
dalliance."

Even so he spake, and the women came all in a crowd together, making a terrible lament and shedding big tears.
So first they carried forth the bodies of the slain, and set
them beneath the gallery of the fenced court, and propped
them one on another; and Odysseus himself hasted the
women and directed them, and they carried forth the dead
perforce. Thereafter they cleansed the fair high seats and the
tables with water and porous sponges. And Telemachus, and
the neatherd, and the swineherd, scraped with spades the
floor of the well-builded house, and, behold, the maidens
carried the scrapings forth and laid them without the doors.

Now when they had made an end of setting the hall in
order, they led the maidens forth from the stablished hall,
and drove them up in a narrow space between the vaulted
room and the goodly fence of the court, whence none might
avoid; and wise Telemachus began to speak to his fellows,
saying:

"God forbid that I should take these women's lives by a
clean death, these that have poured dishonour on my head
and on my mother, and have lain with the wooers."

With that word he tied the cable of a dark-prowed ship
to a great pillar and flung it round the vaulted room, and
fastened it aloft, that none might touch the ground with her
feet. And even as when thrushes, long of wing, or doves fall
into a net that is set in a thicket, as they seek to their
roosting-place, and a loathly bed harbours them, even so the
women held their heads all in a row, and about all their
necks nooses were cast, that they might die by the most pitiful death. And they writhed with their feet for a little space,
but for no long while.

Then they led out Melanthius through the doorway and
the court, and cut off his nostrils and his ears with the pitiless sword, and drew forth his vitals for the dogs to devour
raw, and cut off his hands and feet in their cruel anger.

Thereafter they washed their hands and feet, and went

into the house to Odysseus, and all the adventure was over. So Odysseus called to the good nurse Eurycleia: "Bring sulphur, old nurse, that cleanses all pollution and bring me fire, that I may purify the house with sulphur, and do thou bid Penelope come here with her handmaidens, and tell all the women to hasten into the hall."

Then the good nurse Eurycleia made answer: "Yea, my child, herein thou hast spoken aright. But go to, let me bring thee a mantle and a doublet for raiment, and stand not thus in the halls with thy broad shoulders wrapped in rags; it were blame in thee so to do."

And Odysseus of many counsels answered her saying: "First let a fire now be made me in the hall."

So he spake, and the good nurse Eurycleia was not slow to obey, but brought fire and brimstone; and Odysseus thoroughly purged the women's chamber and the great hall and the court.

Then the old wife went through the fair halls of Odysseus to tell the women, and to hasten their coming. So they came forth from their chamber with torches in their hands, and fell about Odysseus, and embraced him and kissed and clasped his head and shoulders and his hands lovingly, and a sweet longing came on him to weep and moan, for he remembered them every one.

XXIII

Odysseus Reveals Himself to Penelope

THEN the ancient woman went up into the upper chamber laughing aloud, to tell her mistress how her dear lord was within, and her knees moved fast for joy, and her feet stumbled one over the other; and she stood above the lady's head and spake to her, saying:

"Awake, Penelope, dear child, that thou mayest see with thine own eyes that which thou desirest day by day. Odysseus hath come, and hath got him to his own house, though late hath he come, and hath slain the proud wooers that troubled his house, and devoured his substance and oppressed his child."

Then wise Penelope answered her: "Dear nurse, the gods have made thee distraught, the gods that can make foolish even the wisdom of the wise, and that stablish the simple in understanding. They it is that have marred thy reason, though heretofore thou hadst a prudent heart. Why dost thou mock me, who have a spirit full of sorrow, to speak these wild words, and rousest me out of sweet slumber, that had bound me and overshadowed mine eyelids? Never yet have I slept so sound since the day that Odysseus went forth to see that evil Ilium, never to be named. Go to now, get thee down and back to the women's chamber, for if any other of the maids of my house had come and brought me such tidings, and wakened me from sleep, straightway would I have sent her back woefully to return within the women's chamber; but this time thine old age shall stand thee in good stead."

Then the good nurse Eurycleia answered her: "I mock thee not, dear child, but in very deed Odysseus is here, and hath come home, even as I tell thee. He is that guest on whom all men wrought such dishonour in the halls. But long ago Telemachus was ware of him, that he was within the house, yet in his prudence he hid the counsels of his father, that he might take vengeance on the violence of the haughty wooers."

Thus she spake, and then was Penelope glad, and leaping from her bed she fell on the old woman's neck, and let fall the tears from her eyelids, and uttering her voice spake to her winged words: "Come, dear nurse, I pray thee, tell me all truly—if indeed he hath come home as thou sayest—how he hath laid his hands on the shameless wooers, he being but one man, while they abode ever in their companies within the house."

Then the good nurse Eurycleia answered her: "I saw not, I wist not, only I heard the groaning of men slain. And we in an inmost place of the well-builded chambers sat all amazed, and the close-fitted doors shut in the room, till thy son called me from the chamber, for his father sent him out to that end. Then I found Odysseus standing among the slain, who around him, stretched on the hard floor, lay one upon the other; it would have comforted thy heart to see him, all stained like a lion with blood and soil of battle. And now are all the wooers gathered in an heap by the gates of the court, while he is purifying his fair house with brimstone, and hath kindled a great fire, and hath sent me forth to call thee. So come with me, that ye may both enter into your hearts' delight, for ye have suffered much affliction. And even now hath this thy long desire been fulfilled; thy lord hath come alive to his own hearth, and hath found both thee and his son in the halls; and the wooers that wrought him evil he hath slain, every man of them in his house."

Then wise Penelope answered her: "Dear nurse, boast

not yet over them with laughter. Thou knowest how welcome the sight of him would be in the halls to all, and to me in chief, and to his son that we got between us. But this is no true tale, as thou declarest it, nay but it is one of the deathless gods that hath slain the proud wooers, in wrath at their bitter insolence and evil deeds. For they honoured none of earthly men, neither the good nor yet the bad, that came among them. Wherefore they have suffered an evil doom through their own infatuate deeds. But Odysseus, far away hath lost his homeward path to the Achaean land, and himself is lost."

Then the good nurse Eurycleia made answer to her: "My child, what word hath escaped the door of thy lips, in that thou saidest that thy lord, who is even now within, and by his own hearthstone, would return no more? Nay, thy heart is ever hard of belief. Go to now, and I will tell thee besides a most manifest token, even the scar of the wound that the boar on a time dealt him with his white tusk. This I spied while washing his feet, and fain I would have told it even to thee, but he laid his hand on my mouth, and in the fulness of his wisdom suffered me not to speak. But come with me and I will stake my life on it; and, if I play thee false, do thou slay me by a death most pitiful."

Then wise Penelope made answer to her: "Dear nurse, it is hard for thee, how wise soever, to observe the purposes of the everlasting gods. None the less let us go to my child, that I may see the wooers dead, and him that slew them."

With that word she went down from the upper chamber, and much her heart debated, whether she should stand apart, and question her dear lord or draw nigh, and clasp and kiss his head and hands. But when she had come within and had crossed the threshold of stone, she sat down over against Odysseus, in the light of the fire, by the further wall. Now he was sitting by the tall pillar, looking down and waiting to know if perchance his noble wife would speak to him, when her eyes beheld him. But she sat long in silence, and amazement came upon her soul, and now she would look upon him steadfastly with her eyes, and now again she knew him not, for that he was clad in vile raiment. And Telemachus rebuked her, and spake and hailed her:

"Mother mine, ill mother, of an ungentle heart, why turnest thou thus away from my father, and dost not sit by him and question him and ask him all? No other woman in the world would harden her heart to stand thus aloof from her lord, who after much travail and sore had come to her in the twentieth year to his own country. But thy heart is ever harder than stone."

Then wise Penelope answered him, saying: "Child, my mind is amazed within me, and I have no strength to speak, nor to ask him aught, nay nor to look on him face to face. But if in truth this be Odysseus, and he hath indeed come home, verily we shall be ware of each other the more surely, for we have tokens that we twain know, even we, secret from all others."

So she spake, and the steadfast goodly Odysseus smiled, and quickly he spake to Telemachus winged words: "Telemachus, leave now thy mother to make trial of me within the chambers; so shall she soon come to a better knowledge than heretofore. But now I go filthy, and am clad in vile raiment, wherefore she has me in dishonour, and as yet will not allow that I am he. Let us then advise us how all may be for the very best. For whoso has slain but one man in a land, even one that leaves not many behind him to take up the feud for him, turns outlaw and leaves his kindred and his own country; but we have slain the very stay of the city, the men who were far the best of all the noble youths in Ithaca. So this I bid thee consider."

Then wise Telemachus answered him, saying: "Father, see thou to this, for they say that thy counsel is far the best among men, nor might any other of mortal men contend with thee. But right eagerly will we go with thee now, and I think we shall not lack prowess, so far as might is ours."

And Odysseus of many counsels answered him saying: "Yea now, I will tell on what wise methinks it is best. First, go ye to the bath and array you in your doublets, and bid the maidens in the chambers to put on their garments. Then

Better to be nury torin when the news get dry!

The gods well advise him

let the divine minstrel, with his loud lyre in hand, lead off for us the measure of the mirthful dance. So shall any man that hears the sound from without, whether a wayfarer or one of those that dwell around, say that it is a wedding feast. And thus the slaughter of the wooers shall not be noised abroad through the town before we go forth to our well-wooded farm-land. Thereafter shall we consider what gainful counsel the Olympian may vouchsafe us."

So he spake, and they gave good ear and hearkened to him. So first they went to the bath, and arrayed them in doublets, and the women were apparelled, and the divine minstrel took the hollow harp, and aroused in them the desire of sweet song and of the happy dance. Then the great hall rang round them with the sound of the feet of dancing men and of fair-girdled women. And whoso heard it from without would say:

"Surely some one has wedded the queen of many wooers. Hard of heart was she, nor had she courage to keep the great house of her wedded lord continually till his coming."

Even so men spake, and knew not how these things were ordained. Meanwhile, the house-dame Eurynome had bathed the great-hearted Odysseus within his house, and anointed him with olive-oil, and cast about him a goodly mantle and a doublet. Moreover, Athene shed great beauty from his head downwards, and made him greater and more mighty to behold, and from his head caused deep curling locks to flow, like the hyacinth flower. And as when some skilful man overlays gold upon silver, one that Hephaestus and Pallas Athene have taught all manner of craft, and full of grace is his handiwork, even so did Athene shed grace about his head and shoulders, and forth from the bath he came, in form like to the Immortals. Then he sat down again on the high seat, whence he had arisen, over against his wife, and spake to her, saying:

"Strange lady, surely to thee above all womankind the Olympians have given a heart that cannot be softened. No other woman in the world would harden her heart to stand thus aloof from her husband, who after much travail and

sore had come to her, in the twentieth year, to his own country. Nay come, nurse, strew a bed for me to lie all alone, for
assuredly her spirit within her is as iron."

Then wise Penelope answered him again: "Strange man,
I have no proud thoughts nor do I think scorn of thee, nor
am I too greatly astonied, but I know right well what manner of man thou wert, when thou wentest forth out of
Ithaca, on the long-oared galley. But come, Eurycleia, spread
for him the good bedstead outside the stablished bridal
chamber that he built himself. Thither bring ye forth the
good bedstead and cast bedding thereon, even fleeces and
rugs and shining blankets."

So she spake and made trial of her lord, but Odysseus in
sore displeasure spake to his true wife, saying: "Verily a bitter word is this, lady, that thou hast spoken. Who has set my
bed otherwhere? Hard it would be for one, howsoever skilled,
unless a god were to come that might easily set it in another
place, if so he would. But of men there is none living, howsoever strong in his youth, that could lightly upheave it, for
a great token is wrought in the fashioning of the bed, and it
was I that made it and none other. There was growing a
bush of olive, long of leaf, and most goodly of growth,
within the inner court, and the stem as large as a pillar.
Round about this I built the chamber, till I had finished it,
with stones close set, and I roofed it over well and added
thereto compacted doors fitting well. Next I sheared off all
the light wood of the long-leaved olive, and rough-hewed
the trunk upwards from the root, and smoothed it around
with the adze, well and skilfully, and made straight the line
thereto and so fashioned it into the bed-post, and I bored it
all with the auger. Beginning from this bed-post, I wrought
at the bedstead till I had finished it, and made it fair with
inlaid work of gold and of silver and of ivory. Then I made
fast therein a bright purple band of oxhide. Even so I declare to thee this token, and I know not, lady, if the bedstead be yet fast in his place, or if some man has cut away
the stem of the olive tree, and set the bedstead otherwhere."

So he spake, and at once her knees were loosened, and

her heart melted within her, as she knew the sure tokens that Odysseus showed her. Then she fell a weeping, and ran straight toward him and cast her hands about his neck, and kissed his head and spake, saying:

"Be not angry with me, Odysseus, for thou wert ever at other times the wisest of men. It is the gods that gave us sorrow, the gods who begrudged us that we should abide together and have joy of our youth, and come to the threshold of old age. So now be not wroth with me hereat nor full of indignation, because at the first, when I saw thee, I did not welcome thee straightway. For always my heart within my breast shuddered, for fear lest some man should come and deceive me with his words, for many they be that devise gainful schemes and evil. Nay even Argive Helen, daughter of Zeus, would not have lain with a stranger, and taken him for a lover, had she known that the warlike sons of the Achaeans would bring her home again to her own dear country. Howsoever, it was the god that set her upon this shameful deed; nor ever, ere that, did she lay up in her heart the thought of this folly, a bitter folly, whence on us too first came sorrow. But now that thou hast told all the sure tokens of our bed, which never was seen by mortal man, save by thee and me and one maiden only, the daughter of Actor, that my father gave me ere yet I had come hither, she who kept the doors of our strong bridal chamber, even now dost thou bend my soul, all ungentle as it is."

Thus she spake, and in his heart she stirred yet a greater longing to lament, and he wept as he embraced his beloved wife and true. And even as when the sight of land is welcome to swimmers, whose well-wrought ship Poseidon hath smitten on the deep, all driven with the wind and swelling waves, and but a remnant hath escaped the grey sea-water and swum to the shore, and their bodies are all crusted with the brine, and gladly have they set foot on land and escaped an evil end; so welcome to her was the sight of her lord, and her white arms she would never quite let go from his neck. And now would the rosy-fingered Dawn have risen upon their weeping, but the goddess, grey-eyed Athene, had other thoughts. The night she held long in the utmost West, and on the other side she stayed the golden throned Dawn by the stream Oceanus, and suffered her not to harness the swift-footed steeds that bear light to men, Lampus and Phaethon, the steeds ever young, that bring the morning.

Then at the last, Odysseus of many counsels spake to his wife, saying: "Lady, we have not yet come to the issue of all our labours; but still there will be toil unmeasured, long and difficult, that I must needs bring to a full end. Even so the spirit of Teiresias foretold to me, on that day when I went down into the house of Hades, to inquire after a returning for myself and my company. Wherefore come, lady, let us to bed, that forthwith we may take our joy of rest beneath the spell of sweet sleep."

Then wise Penelope answered him: "Thy bed verily shall be ready whensoever thy soul desires it, forasmuch as the gods have indeed caused thee to come back to thy stablished home and thine own country. But now that thou hast noted it and the god has put it into thy heart, come, tell me of this ordeal, for methinks the day will come when I must learn it, and timely knowledge is no hurt."

And Odysseus of many counsels answered her saying: "Ah, why now art thou so instant with me to declare it? Yet I will tell thee all and hide nought. Howbeit thy heart shall have no joy of it, as even I myself have no pleasure therein. For Teiresias bade me fare to many cities of men, carrying a shapen oar in my hands, till I should come to such men as know not the sea, neither eat meat savoured with salt, nor have they knowledge of ships of purple cheek nor of shapen oars, which serve for wings to ships. And he told me this with manifest token, which I will not hide from thee. In the day when another wayfarer should meet me and say that I had a winnowing fan on my stout shoulder, even then he bade me make fast my shapen oar in the earth, and do goodly sacrifice to the lord Poseidon, even with a ram and a bull and a boar, the mate of swine, and depart for home, and offer holy hecatombs to the deathless gods, that keep the wide heaven, to each in order due. And from the sea shall mine own death come, the gentlest death that may be, which shall end me, foredone with smooth old age, and the folk shall dwell happily around. All this, he said, was to be fulfilled."

Then wise Penelope answered him saying: "If indeed the gods will bring about for thee a happier old age at the last, then is there hope that thou mayest yet have an escape from evil."

Thus they spake one to the other. Meanwhile, Eurynome and the nurse spread the bed with soft coverlets, by the light of the torches burning. But when they had busied them and spread the good bed, the ancient nurse went back to her chamber to lie down, and Eurynome, the bower-maiden, guided them on their way to the couch, with torches in her hands, and when she had led them to the bridal-chamber she departed. And so they came gladly to the rites of their bed, as of old. But Telemachus, and the neatherd, and the swineherd stayed their feet from dancing, and made the women to cease, and themselves gat them to rest through the shadowy halls.

Now when the twain had taken their fill of sweet love, they had delight in the tales, which they told one to the other. The fair lady spoke of all that she had endured in the halls at the sight of the ruinous throng of wooers, who for her sake slew many cattle, kine and goodly sheep; and many a cask of wine was broached. And in turn, Odysseus, of the seed of Zeus, recounted all the griefs he had wrought on men, and all his own travail and sorrow and she was delighted with the story, and sweet sleep fell not upon her eyelids till the tale was ended.

⁋ With the dawn, Odysseus goes to see his father, accompanied by Telemachus, the neatherd and the swineherd. They are hidden in night by Athene as they go out of town.

XXIV

Peace Comes to Ithaca

❡ *Summoning the souls of the wooers from the hall, Hermes leads them down to Hades, where they find many noble Achaeans. There Agamemnon speaks of the evil manner of his own death, and tells Achilles of the glory of his funeral before Troy, and how Achilles' goddess mother and the maidens of the sea mourned for him, and how the funeral games were held and the mound was built high above his bones and those of Patroclus.*

Among the souls of the suitors Agamemnon sees Amphimedon, a guest-friend of his, who tells him all the tale of the wooers; whereupon Agamemnon praises the wisdom of Penelope, contrasting his own wife with her.

Meanwhile Odysseus and his friends make their way to the farm of Laertes. Odysseus hunts out his aged, withered father and strings him a tale of false adventure. Finally he reveals himself but is accepted only after he has shown his knowledge of the kinds of trees in the orchard, a gift from his father long ago.

While Odysseus, Laertes, and their friends eat together, Rumor goes around the city telling the fate of the wooers. The people claim and bury their dead, and then plan vengeance on Odysseus. In spite of the warning of Medon and the minstrel, many of the people put on their mail and assemble before the town.

Now Athene spake to Zeus, the son of Cronos, saying: "O Father, our father Cronides, throned in the highest, answer and tell me what is now the hidden counsel of thy heart? Wilt thou yet further rouse up evil war and the terrible din of battle, or art thou minded to set them at one again in friendship?"

Then Zeus, the gatherer of the clouds, answered her saying: "My child, why dost thou thus straitly question me, and ask me this? Nay, didst not thou thyself devise this very thought, namely, that Odysseus should indeed take vengeance on these men at his coming? Do as thou wilt, but I will tell thee of the better way. Now that goodly Odysseus hath wreaked vengeance on the wooers, let them make a

People from Ithaca Talking about the Slaughter
of the Wooers.
PAINTING FROM A KYLIX.
(BRUSCHI COLL., CORNETO)

firm covenant together with sacrifice, and let him be king all his days, and let us bring about oblivion of the slaying of their children and their brethren; so may both sides love one another as of old, and let peace and wealth abundant be their portion."

Therewith he roused Athene to yet greater eagerness, and from the peaks of Olympus she came glancing down.

Now when they had put from them the desire of honeysweet food, the steadfast goodly Odysseus began to speak among them, saying:

"Let one go forth and see, lest the people be already drawing near against us."

So he spake, and the son of Dolius went forth at his bidding, and stood on the outer threshold and saw them all close at hand. Then straightway he spake to Odysseus winged words:

"Here they be, close upon us! Quick, let us to arms!"

Thereon they rose up and arrayed them in their harness, Odysseus and his men being four, and the six sons of Dolius, and likewise Laertes and Dolius did on their armour, grey-headed as they were, warriors through stress of need. Now when they had clad them in shining mail, they opened the gates and went forth and Odysseus led them.

Then Athene, daughter of Zeus, drew near them in the likeness of Mentor, in fashion and in voice. And the steadfast goodly Odysseus beheld her and was glad, and straightway he spake to Telemachus his dear son:

"Telemachus, soon shalt thou learn this, when thou thyself art got to the place of the battle where the best men try the issue,—namely, not to bring shame on thy father's house, on us who in time past have been eminent for might and hardihood over all the world."

Then wise Telemachus answered him, saying: "Thou shalt see me, if thou wilt, dear father, in this my mood no whit disgracing thy line, according to thy word."

So spake he, and Laertes was glad and spake, saying: "What a day has dawned for me, kind gods; yea, a glad man am I! My son and my son's son are vying with one another in valour."

Then grey-eyed Athene stood beside Laertes, and spake to him: "O son of Arceisius that art far the dearest of all my friends, pray first to the grey-eyed maid and to father Zeus, then swing thy long spear aloft and hurl it straightway."

Therewith Pallas Athene breathed into him great strength. Then he prayed to the daughter of mighty Zeus, and straightway swung his long spear aloft and hurled it, and smote Eupeithes through his casque with the cheekpiece of bronze. The armour kept not out the spear that went clean through, and he fell with a crash, and his arms rattled about his body. Then Odysseus and his renowned son fell on the fore-fighters, and smote them with swords and two-headed spears. And now would they have slain them all and cut off their return, had not Athene called aloud, the daughter of Zeus lord of the aegis, and stayed all the host of the enemy, saying:

"Hold your hands from fierce fighting, ye men of Ithaca, that so ye may be parted quickly, without bloodshed."

So spake Athene, and pale fear gat hold of them all. The arms flew from their hands in their terror and fell all upon the ground, as the goddess uttered her voice. To the city they turned their steps, as men fain of life, and the steadfast goodly Odysseus with a terrible cry gathered himself together and hurled in on them, like an eagle of lofty flight. Then in that hour the son of Cronos cast forth a flaming bolt, and it fell at the feet of the grey-eyed goddess, the daughter of the mighty Sire. Then grey-eyed Athene spake to Odysseus, saying:

"Son of Laertes, of the seed of Zeus, Odysseus of many devices, refrain thee now and stay the strike of even-handed war, lest perchance the son of Cronos be angry with thee, even Zeus of the far-borne voice."

So spake Athene, and he obeyed and was glad at heart. And thereafter Pallas Athene set a covenant between them with sacrifice, she, the daughter of Zeus lord of the aegis, in the likeness of Mentor, both in fashion and in voice.

PRONOUNCING INDEX

Accented syllables are in capitals.

a = add   ā = āle   à = whàt   ä = ärt   e = end   ē = ēve   i = ill
ī = īce   o = odd   ō = ōld   ōō = fōōd   u = up   ū = cūbe

Argus	ÄR-gus
Artemis	ÄR-te-mis
Athene (Pallas Athene)	à-THE-nē (PAL-las)
Atreus	Ā-trē-us
Briseis	brī-SĒ-is
Calchas	KAL-kas
Calypso	ka-LIP-sō
Charybdis	ka-RIB-dis
Chronos	KRŌ-nos
Chryseis	krī-SĒ-is
Chryses	KRĪ-sēs
Cicones	si-KŌ-nēs
Cimmerians	sim-MER-i-ans
Circe	SIR-sē
Clytemnestra	klī-tem-NES-tra
Cocytus	ko-SĪ-tus
Cyclops	SĪ-klops
Danaans	DAN-ā-ans
Dardanians	dar-DĀ-ni-ans
Deiphobus	de-IF-o-bus
Demodocus	de-MOD-o-kus
Diomedes	dī-o-MĒ-dēs
Elpenor	el-PĒ-nōr
Eumaeus	ū-MĒ-us
Euryalus	ū-RĪ-à-lus
Eurycleia	ū-ri-KLĪ-à
Eurylocus	ū-RIL-o-kus
Eurymachus	ū-RIM-à-kus
Eurynome	ū-RIN-ō-mē
Hades	HĀ-dēs
Hector	HEK-ter
Hecuba	HEK-ū-bà
Helios Hyperion	HĒ-li-os hī-PĒ-ri-on
Hephaestus	he-FES-tus
Hera	HĒ-rà
Heracles	HER-à-klēz
Hermes	HER-mēz
Idomeneus	ī-DOM-e-nōōs